COLORANTS AND AUXILIARIES
ORGANIC CHEMISTRY AND APPLICATION PROPERTIES

Volume 2 – Auxiliaries

Colorants and auxiliaries

Organic chemistry and application properties

Volume 2 – Auxiliaries

Edited by John Shore

BTTG–Shirley, Manchester, England

1990

Society of Dyers and Colourists

Published by the Society of Dyers and Colourists, PO Box 244, Perkin House, 82 Grattan Road, Bradford, West Yorkshire BD1 2JB, England, on behalf of the Dyers' Company Publications Trust.

Typeset by the Society of Dyers and Colourists and printed by Staples Printers Rochester Ltd

ISBN 0 901956 52 X

Dyers' Company Publications Trust

The Dyers' Company Publications Trust was instituted by the Worshipful Company of Dyers of the City of London in 1971 to encourage the publication of textbooks and other aids to learning in the science and technology of colour and coloration and related fields. The Society of Dyers and Colourists acts as trustee to the fund, its Textbooks Committee being the Trust's technical subcommittee.

Contributors

Terence M Baldwinson
Colours Division, Yorkshire Chemicals plc, Leeds

Alec V Mercer
Department of Colour Chemistry and Dyeing, University of Leeds

Preface to Volume 2

This textbook is a further addition to the series on colour and coloration technology initiated by the Textbooks Committee of the Society of Dyers and Colourists under the aegis of the Dyers' Company Publications Trust Management Committee, which administers the trust fund generously provided by the Worshipful Company of Dyers.

The major objective of this series of books, produced at irregular intervals over the last fifteen years, has been to establish a coherent body of explanatory information on the principles and application technology of relevance for students preparing to take the Associateship examinations of the Society. This particular book is directed specifically to the subject areas covered by Section A of Paper B: the organic chemistry and application of dyes and pigments and of the auxiliaries used with them in textile coloration processes. It is hoped that qualified chemists and colourists interested in the properties of colorants and their auxiliaries will also find this useful as a work of reference. For several reasons it is convenient to publish the material in two separate volumes: 1. Colorants, 2. Auxiliaries.

This second volume of the book collects together a remarkable quantity and variety of factual information linking the application properties of auxiliary products in textile coloration and related processes to as much as is known of the chemical structure of these agents. In contrast to the first volume, there is (alas) no universally accepted comprehensive auxiliaries index, analogous to the *Colour Index International*, that could be used as a framework for this theme. Other textbooks and reviews can be cited in the subject areas of Chapter 9 (surfactants) and Chapter 11 (fluorescent brightening agents), but the bulk of the material for this volume has been amassed from a scattered range of primary sources.

With the invaluable help of constructive comments and suggestions from referees and co-authors, the authors of this volume and I feel that we have put together a unique survey of this particular subject area. We hope that students and qualified chemists with interest in these topics will help us to disseminate this information and work for a more rational and systematic approach to this somewhat neglected area of coloration technology. We are particularly grateful to Paul Dinsdale, the Society's editor, and to Dr Jean Macqueen, the latter for distilling the essentials from the more flamboyant sections of our original scripts, producing in this published form a more economical style that now does full justice to our technological message. We also thank Elaine Naylor and Jane Roberts for their very diligent work in keying the text and preparing the illustrations for publication from our original typescripts.

JOHN SHORE

Contents

Chapters in Volume 1

CHAPTER 8

Functions and properties of dyeing and printing auxiliaries

Terence M Baldwinson

8.1 THE NEED FOR AUXILIARIES

There is hardly a dyeing or printing process of commercial importance that can be adequately operated by the use of dyes and water alone. Practically every colorant–substrate system requires the use of additional products, known as auxiliaries, to ensure its reliable functioning and control. This was the case even centuries ago, when the use of natural vat and mordant dyes depended entirely on the proper, albeit rule of thumb, use of additives. These controlled pH, reduction, oxidation and mordanting to enable the dyes to be applied to the natural fibres of those days. Many of the auxiliaries, like the dyes and fibres, were of natural origin. Dung and urine [1] were among the agents used, and soap was clearly the first surfactant to be employed. Indeed, from the standpoint of today, one can only wonder at the degree of purely empirical expertise so successfully developed and applied by the ancient dyers and printers.

Our current level of understanding is clearly a phenomenal advance on the ancient arts, yet our need for auxiliaries remains. For example, even before dyeing or printing the substrate must be cleaned and wetted. Products are needed to convert non-substantive vat and sulphur dyes to substantive forms, to help stabilise the conditions that bring about the substantivity, and then to reconvert the dyes to their insoluble non-substantive forms (see sections 1.6.1 and 1.6.2). Mordant dyes still require the appropriate chelating agents, as well as other agents to create and maintain the optimum chelating conditions. Printers still need thickening agents to facilitate the localised application of dye. Inevitably, however, the present-day plethora of dyes, fibres and coloration processes has created additional reasons for the use of auxiliaries, whilst the concurrent evolution of the chemical industry has satisfied these needs as they arose. Moreover, a vastly more comprehensive understanding of the physico-chemical processes involved has enabled auxiliaries to be precisely engineered for specific purposes.

Hand-in-hand with this theoretical knowledge, practical evaluation has become increasingly sophisticated. Nevertheless, it is often difficult to differentiate between auxiliaries promoted purely for commercial reasons and those that serve a definite technical need. Dye manufacturers are acutely aware of the positive part played by auxiliaries in helping to sell dyes, and dyers today are under constant pressure to use more of them. Some additives offer cost savings by improving reproducibility and minimising reprocessing; nevertheless it is all too tempting to incorporate too many products without critically evaluating their efficacy, thus inevitably and unnecessarily increasing processing costs. Consequently it is more important than ever that the dyer or printer understands the function of auxiliary products and is equipped to evaluate their use realistically and to monitor it continually.

As has already been implied, functional demands for auxiliaries continue to grow, with each dye–fibre system and dyeing or printing process having particular needs. The primary functions of auxiliaries are:

(a) to prepare or improve the substrate in readiness for coloration by
    – scouring, bleaching and desizing
    – wetting
    – enhancing the whiteness by a fluorescent brightening effect
(b) to modify the sorption characteristics of colorants by
    – acceleration
    – retardation
    – creating a blocking or resist effect
    – providing sorption sites
    – unifying otherwise divergent sorption rates
    – improving or resisting the migration of dyes
(c) to stabilise the application media by
    – improving dye solubility
    – stabilising a dispersion or solution
    – thickening a print paste or pad liquor
    – inhibiting or promoting foaming
    – forming an emulsion
    – scavenging or minimising the effects of impurities
    – preventing or promoting oxidation and reduction
(d) to protect or modify the substrate by
    – creating or resisting dyeability
    – lubricating the substrate
    – protecting against the effects of temperature and other processing conditions
(e) to improve the fastness of dyes, as in
    – the aftertreatment of direct and reactive dyes
    – the aftertreatment of acid dyes on nylon
    – the chroming of acid dyes on wool and nylon

    – giving protection against atmospheric influences as in u.v. absorbers
      or inhibitors of gas fume fading
    – back-scouring or reduction-clearing

(f) to enhance the properties of laundering formulations (fluorescent
    brightening agents).

Some auxiliaries fulfil more than one of the above functions. For example, an auxiliary to improve dye solubility may also accelerate (or retard) a coloration process, or an emulsifying agent may also act as a thickening agent; pH-control agents may both stabilise a system and also affect the rate of sorption.

8.2 THE GENERAL TYPES AND CHARACTERISTICS OF AUXILIARIES

An auxiliary has been defined [2] as 'a chemical or formulated chemical product which enables a processing operation in preparation, dyeing, printing or finishing to be carried out more effectively or which is essential if a given effect is to obtained'. It is much harder to devise a classification system for auxiliaries than it is for dyes. This is undoubtedly one of the main reasons why, as mentioned in section 1.3, there has been considerable reluctance to produce an auxiliaries index comparable with the *Colour Index*. It is difficult enough to put together a comprehensive yet manageable list of general application types; it becomes even more difficult to classify them chemically, especially as many of them are more or less complex mixtures, are of imprecisely known structure or are the subject of a good deal of trade confidentiality. Although the Society of Dyers and Colourists has shown reluctance to be involved in this area, a very useful biennial trade publication [3] has made considerable progress in the ordered listing of currently available commercial products. This first appeared in 1967. The eleventh edition (1988) lists over 6000 currently available products and is arranged in three sections:

(a) textile auxiliaries arranged alphabetically by trade name (248 pages)
(b) textile auxiliaries arranged according to use (59 pages)
(c) names and addresses of textile auxiliary suppliers (7 pages).

Unfortunately this publication does not include a listing by chemical type; although the first section does give whatever chemical descriptions the manufacturers are prepared to divulge, these tend to be bland broadly based descriptions such as 'non-ionic aqueous emulsion of modified wax' or 'quaternary ammonium compound, cationic'. In spite of these shortcomings it remains an indispensible guide to the vast range of products on the market today.

    The broadest classification of auxiliaries is achieved simply by dividing them into non-surfactants and surfactants, as detailed below.

Non-surfactants include simple electrolytes, acids and bases, both inorganic and organic. Examples include sodium chloride, sodium acetate, sulphuric acid, acetic acid and sodium carbonate, together with complexing agents (such as sodium dichromate, copper(II) sulphate, ethylenediamine-tetra-acetic acid, sodium hexametaphosphate), oxidising agents (hydrogen peroxide, sodium chlorite) and reducing agents (sodium dithionite, sodium sulphide). Anionic polyelectrolytes such as sodium alginate or carboxy-methylcellulose, used mainly as thickening agents and migration inhib-itors, also fall within the class of non-surfactants; so too do sorption accelerants such as o-phenylphenol, butanol and methylnaphthalene, although they normally require an emulsifier to stabilise them in aqueous media. Fluorescent brightening agents (FBAs) form another large class of non-surfactant auxiliaries (see Chapter 11).

Surfactants are, in general, substantially organic in nature and struc-turally more complex than most non-surfactants. Schwartz and Perry [4] in their classic book on the chemistry and technology of surfactants emphasise the difficulty of defining surfactants in a manner sufficiently precise to satisfy everyone. However, for the purposes of this book an adequate definition of a surfactant is given by the Society's Terms and Definitions Committee [2]: 'an agent, soluble or dispersible in a liquid, which reduces the surface tension of the liquid'. In coloration processes this reduction in surface tension usually takes place at a liquid/liquid or liquid/solid interface, although liquid/gas interfaces are also occasionally impor-tant. In general, a dramatic lowering of surface tension can be brought about by a relatively small amount of surfactant: as little as 0.2 g/l of a soap such as sodium oleate will more than halve the surface tension of water. This physical effect in solution is attributed to the molecular orientation potential of a relatively small hydrophilic moiety (a hydrophile) having strong polar forces, juxtaposed with a relatively large (usually linear) hydrophobic moiety (a hydrophobe) having relatively weak electrostatic forces (Figure 8.1). In aqueous solution or dispersion the polar hydrophile tends to be oriented into the body of an aqueous solute, whilst the hydrophobe, by nature subjected to forces of rejection by the solute, is oriented towards (or at) the interfacial boundary, which may be that between the solution and air or between the solution and a fibrous (or other) substrate.

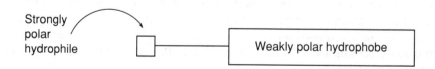

Figure 8.1 – Schematic diagram of surfactant

The surfactants used as textile auxiliaries can be divided into four major groups, depending on the type and distribution of the polar forces, an arrangement broadly resembling the ionic classification of dyes. The general scheme is shown in Table 8.1.

TABLE 8.1

General classification of surfactants

	Degree of ionic charge on the	
Class of surfactant	hydrophobe	hydrophile (associated ion)
Anionic	Weakly negative	Strongly positive
Cationic	Weakly positive	Strongly negative
Non-ionic	Uncharged	Uncharged
Amphoteric	These possess balanced negative and positive charges, one or other of which dominates in solution depending on the pH	

REFERENCES
1. H T Pratt, *Text. Chem. Colorist*, **19** (1987) 23.
2. *Colour terms and definitions* (Bradford: SDC, 1988).
3. *Index to textile auxiliaries*, 11th Edn (Bradford: World Textile Publications, 1988).
4. A M Schwartz and J W Perry, *Surface active agents* (New York: Robert E Krieger, 1949, reprinted 1978).

CHAPTER 9

The chemistry and properties of surfactants

Terence M Baldwinson

9.1 INTRODUCTION

The limitations of space do not permit a comprehensive detailed treatment of the chemistry of surfactants. The emphasis is therefore on a broad-brush discussion of the principal types of surfactant encountered in textile coloration processes and on their chemistry and properties [1–7]. More detailed treatments are available [8–15], and a useful and lucid account of the chemistry and technology of manufacturing processes is given by Davidsohn and Milwidsky [16].

9.2 HYDROPHILES

The basic purpose of the hydrophile is to confer solubility (aqueous solubility is always to be understood unless otherwise stated). The simple moieties most often employed are as follows:
(a) in anionic surfactants: sodium, potassium or ammonium cations, associated with negatively charged groups on the hydrophobe such as carboxylate, sulphonate, sulphate or phosphate
(b) in cationic surfactants: chloride, bromide or methosulphate ions, juxtaposed with, for example, positively charged quaternary nitrogen atoms
(c) in non-ionic surfactants: ethylene oxide or propylene oxide moieties.

   More complex hydrophilic moieties are sometimes encountered, however, such as mono-, di- and tri-ethanolamine and the corresponding isopropanolamines in anionic surfactants; morpholine, once employed, is now obsolete owing to its toxicity.

9.3 HYDROPHOBES

There is a much wider choice of hydrophobes. Most are based on substantially linear long-chain alkanes, either saturated or unsaturated. These were originally obtained from naturally occurring fats and oils such as castor, fish, olive, sperm, coconut and tallow oils, but these sources were later superseded by petroleum products which at that time were cheaper. More recently, not only has the price of crude oil escalated, but there has also been a growing awareness of the finite and diminishing nature of this resource. Hence there is currently an increasing return to the natural sources which, properly husbanded, are self-replenishing. The availability (and hence the prices) of both natural and synthetic raw materials varies considerably from time to time, however, thus influencing the sourcing of particular materials.

The most common hydrophobes used as the basis for surfactants are those containing eight to 18 carbon atoms, such as those listed as carboxylates in Table 9.1. Some hydrophobes are aromatic (benzene or naphthalene) moieties, often containing lower alkyl substituents; dodecylbenzene (9.1) is a common example. Alkyl-substituted toluenes, xylenes and phenols and mono- and di-alkyl-substituted naphthalenes (9.2 and 9.3) are also used.

9.1   9.2   9.3

The hydrophobes are usually, though not always, used in the form of acids, alcohols, esters or amines. Commercial products rarely contain a single pure hydrophobe, however; most are mixtures containing a range of hydrophobes, since the raw materials from which they are made are generally themselves mixtures of homologues. For example, a batch of coconut oil, a rich source of the lauric hydrophobe, may have the approximate composition shown in Table 9.2, although the proportions of the individual components may vary by 1–3% between batches. (As is the general rule in naturally occurring fats and waxes, only even-numbered carbon compounds are present; odd-numbered ones have to be made by synthesis.) Clearly, a surfactant produced from such a mixture will contain a very large, and variable, number of homologues and isomers. Hence two products with the same nominal constitution, but from different manufacturers, often differ in details of composition and properties. This is one fundamental reason why a chemical classification of auxiliaries, analogous to that for dyes in the *Colour Index*, would be extremely difficult to devise. Nevertheless, there has been a trend in recent years to produce more homogeneous fractions of the raw materials for surfactant manufacture.

Any hydrophobe can yield each of the main (i.e. anionic, cationic, nonionic or amphoteric) types of surfactant in much the same way as the same chromophore can be used in anionic, basic or non-ionic dyes. This will be demonstrated in the following sections, dealing with each class of surfactant, using the cetyl-containing ($C_{16}H_{33}$) hydrophobe.

TABLE 9.1

Examples of hydrophobes

No. of carbon atoms	Chemical name	Trivial name and formula
8	Octanoate	Caprylate $CH_3(CH_2)_6COO$
10	Decanoate	Caprate $CH_3(CH_2)_8COO$
12	Dodecanoate	Laurate $CH_3(CH_2)_{10}COO$
12	9-Dodecenoate	Lauroleate $CH_3CH_2CH=CH(CH_2)_7COO$
14	Tetradecanoate	Myristate $CH_3(CH_2)_{12}COO$
14	9-Tetradecenoate	Myristoleate $CH_3(CH_2)_3CH=CH(CH_2)_7COO$
15	Pentadecanoate	Isocetate $CH_3(CH_2)_{13}COO$
16	Hexadecanoate	Palmitate $CH_3(CH_2)_{14}COO$
16	9-Hexadecenoate	Palmitoleate $CH_3(CH_2)_5CH=CH(CH_2)_7COO$
17	Heptadecanoate	Margarate $CH_3(CH_2)_{15}COO$
18	Octadecanoate	Stearate $CH_3(CH_2)_{16}COO$
18	9-Octadecenoate	Oleate $CH_3(CH_2)_7CH=CH(CH_2)_7COO$
18	9,12-Octadecadienoate	Linoleate $CH_3(CH_2)_4(CH=CHCH_2)_2(CH_2)_6COO$
18	9,12,15-Octadecatrienoate	Linolenate $CH_3CH_2(CH=CHCH_2)_3(CH_2)_6COO$
18	12-Hydroxy-9-octadecenoate	Ricinoleate $CH_3(CH_2)_5CH(OH)CH_2CH=CH(CH_2)_7COO$

TABLE 9.2

Approximate hydrophobe composition of coconut oil

Trivial name	No. of carbon atoms	Amount /%
Caproate	6	0.5
Caprylate	8	7.0
Caprate	10	6.5
Laurate	12	49.5
Myristate	14	17.0
Palmitate	16	8.5
Stearate	18	2.5
Oleate	18	6.5
Linoleate	18	2.0

9.4 ANIONIC SURFACTANTS

This class still accounts for by far the largest number of surfactants used in coloration processes despite the very active development of non-ionic types in recent years. The essential feature of the class is a long-chain hydrophobe linked through an anionic grouping – usually carboxylate, sulphate (sulphuric ester) or sulphonate, but occasionally phosphate, carboxymethyl or other group – to a relatively small cation, generally sodium, although ammonium, potassium and other cations are also used.

Carboxylates (9.4, where R is the long-chain hydrophobe and X the cation) represent the oldest type of surfactants, since they could be obtained from naturally occurring fats and oils long before the advent of the petrochemical industry; sodium heptadecanoate (9.5), for example, incorporates the cetyl group as hydrophobe. Sodium stearate, sodium palmitate and sodium oleate are the simplest carboxylates generally used as surfactants. Alkylaryl compounds (9.6) are also known.

$$R-COO^- \ X^+ \quad 9.4 \qquad\qquad C_{16}H_{33}COO^- \ Na^+ \quad 9.5$$

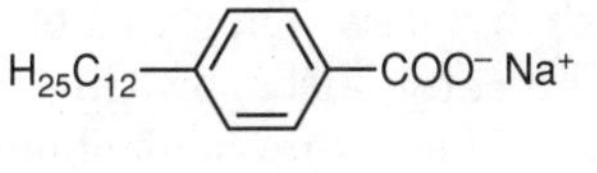

$$H_{25}C_{12}-\!\!\bigcirc\!\!-COO^- \ Na^+$$

9.6

Many carboxylates are used in the form of soaps, obtained by alkaline saponification of triglyceride fats and waxes of general formula 9.7. The three carboxylic ester groups (RCOO) may carry the same or different

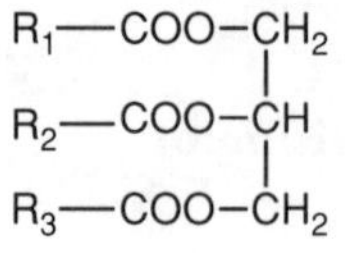

$$R_1-COO-CH_2$$
$$R_2-COO-CH$$
$$R_3-COO-CH_2 \qquad 9.7$$

hydrophobes, generally containing eight to 22 carbon atoms, the most common being laurate, palmitate and stearate among the saturated types, and oleate and linoleate among the unsaturated. At ambient temperatures the unsaturated fats tend to be liquids and the saturated ones solids.

Particularly important as wetting agents are the disodium alkenyl-succinates (9.8), in which the saturated R group may contain from three to 14 carbon atoms.

$$R-CH=CH-CHCOO^- \, Na^+$$
$$9.8 \qquad\qquad CH_2COO^- \, Na^+$$

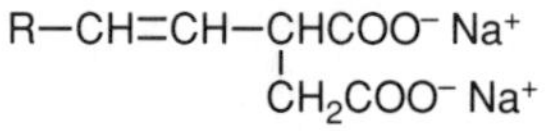

The surfactant properties of these carboxylates, as with other types of surfactant, are dependent on the number of carbon atoms in the hydro-phobe. Significant surfactant properties begin to appear in the C_8 compounds, although the C_8–C_{12} carboxylates are wetting agents rather than detergents. Better detergency and emulsifying properties become evident with C_{12}–C_{18} alkyl groups. Solubility decreases with increasing length of the alkyl group; the solubility of soaps, for example, reaches its useful limit with the C_{22} compounds. The major disadvantage of the carboxylates is that they tend to be precipitated by acids and hard water, since the free acids and the calcium and magnesium salts of the carboxylates are insoluble. This disadvantage provided the main technical reason for finding alternative products that showed tolerance to a wider range of processing conditions.

Modified carboxylates, in which the carboxylate group is converted to carboxymethylate, have recently been introduced. These are made by reaction of selected non-ionic surfactants with chloroacetic acid. The result is a useful hybrid range, lacking the sensitivity of carboxylates to calcium and magnesium whilst retaining excellent detergency; the compounds are more stable to electrolytes than are the conventional non-ionics, and more suitable for use at high temperatures as they are not susceptible to cloud point problems (see section 9.8.2).

Sulphates or sulphuric esters of the long-chain fatty acids were the first alternative to the carboxylates. They are essentially the half esters of sulphuric acid (9.9); the ester incorporating the cetyl hydrophobe (9.10) belongs to the important class of fatty alcohol sulphates. Such sulphates, using C_8–C_{18} hydrophobes, are common.

$$R-OSO_3^- \, Na^+ \qquad 9.9 \qquad\qquad C_{16}H_{33}OSO_3^- \, Na^+ \qquad 9.10$$

Just as there are mono-, di- and tri-carboxylate surfactants, the sulphates can also be prepared from mono-, di- and tri-hydrophobe-bearing products. Indeed, the first sulphates to be used were analogous to soaps in that they were the sulphation products of triglycerides. Although the chemistry of these products can be represented in simple terms, it is worth re-stating that most commercial products are highly complex mixtures. For example, a sulphated triglyceride may contain the following [17]:
– the sulphated glyceride proper
– sulphated free fatty acid
– unsulphated glyceride
– unsulphated fatty acid
– inorganic salts
– traces of glycerol.

The range of hydrophobes present may also be unexpectedly broad, since the raw materials often consist of mixtures of symmetrical and/or mixed glycerides. As little as 60% of an oil may be sulphatable; sulphation is never carried to theoretical completion and is often far below 100%. With these provisos in mind, the chemistry of the sulphated oils can be considered.

Many oils are used as starting materials; olive, castor, tallow, neatsfoot, cotton seed, rape seed and corn oils are examples. Sulphated olive oil was the first sulphated oil to be produced and was used as a mordant in dyeing as long ago as 1834. Sulphation usually occurs at the double bond of the unsaturated fatty acid in the glyceride (Scheme 9.1).

$$-CH=CH- \ + \ H_2SO_4 \longrightarrow -CH_2-\underset{\underset{OSO_3^- \ H^+}{|}}{CH}-$$

Scheme 9.1

On the other hand, in the preparation of the best-known of these products, Turkey Red Oil or sulphated (often wrongly termed 'sulphonated') castor oil, sulphation of the main component, the glyceride of ricinoleic acid (12-hydroxy-9-octadecenoic acid), takes place preferentially at the hydroxy group rather than at the double bond (Scheme 9.2). Such products possess useful wetting, emulsifying and dye-levelling properties.

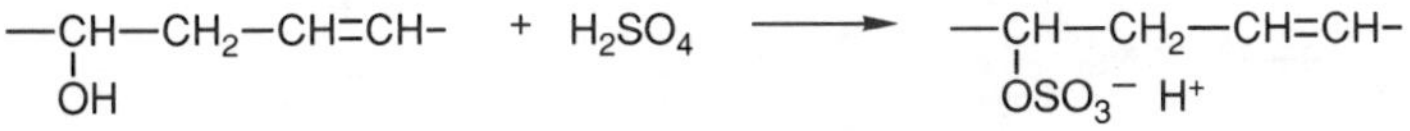

$$-\underset{\underset{OH}{|}}{CH}-CH_2-CH=CH- \ + \ H_2SO_4 \longrightarrow -\underset{\underset{OSO_3^- \ H^+}{|}}{CH}-CH_2-CH=CH-$$

Scheme 9.2

At the present time, however, the long-chain alcohol sulphates already mentioned, such as structure 9.10, and particularly the sulphated ethers are of greater importance. The stability of the sulphates to mildly acidic conditions and to hard water is much better than that of the carboxylates, and is sufficient for most purposes. Under more stringent acidic conditions, however, they can hydrolyse.

Another type of sulphated product, the ester sulphates, can be prepared by esterifying a fatty acid such as ricinoleic or oleic acid, with a short-chain (C_3-C_5) alcohol and then sulphating, such products being particularly useful foaming, wetting and emulsifying agents; an example is sulphated butyl ricinoleate (9.11).

$$CH_3(CH_2)_5CHCH_2CH=CH(CH_2)_7COO(CH_2)_3CH_3$$

9.11 $\overset{|}{O}SO_3^- \; H^+$

Currently at the forefront of developments amongst anionic surfactants are the sulphated polyethers or alcohol poly(oxyethylene) sulphates (9.12, 9.13), prepared by ethoxylating the fatty alcohol to give a polyether containing a terminal hydroxy group which is then sulphated. Aromatic hydrophobes may also be used to produce, for example, alkylphenol poly(oxyethylene) sulphates.

$$R—(OCH_2CH_2)_xOSO_3^- \; Na^+ \qquad\qquad C_{16}H_{33}—(OCH_2CH_2)_xOSO_3^- \; Na^+$$

9.12   9.13

In a general sense, a poly(oxyethylene) sulphate can be viewed as a partly anionic and partly non-ionic surfactant, although the degree of ethoxylation of these products is generally much lower than that of the purely non-ionic surfactants. Hence they are sometimes referred to as 'lightly ethoxylated alcohol sulphates'; again, their actual composition may be a good deal more complex than indicated by their nominal structural formulae.

Sulphonated anionic surfactants have the general structure 9.14, which should be compared with that of the sulphates (9.9). As well as the simple alkyl derivatives such as structure 9.15, aromatic and particularly alkylated aromatic (alkylaryl) types are technically and commercially important; indeed, sodium dodecylbenzenesulphonate (9.16) has for long been the most widely used surfactant in domestic washing powders [16].

$$R—SO_3^- \; Na^+ \qquad\qquad C_{16}H_{33}—SO_3^- \; Na^+$$

9.14   9.15

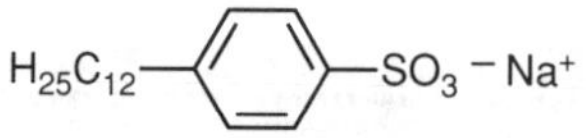

9.16

Naphthalene and other aromatic hydrophobes are also used to produce sulphonates, such as structure 9.17.

$$C_3H_7$$

9.17 [structure: naphthalene with C_3H_7 and $SO_3^- \, Na^+$ substituents]

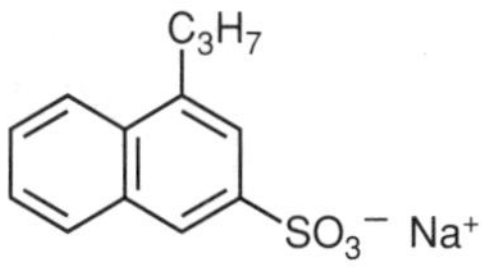

Of greater importance however, are the more complex condensation products that form the basis of many excellent dispersing, resist and aftertreating (syntan) agents. Typical examples are the condensation products of naphthalenesulphonates with formaldehyde, and the lignin-sulphonates derived from pulping processes; these are described in more detail in section 10.4.1.

Sulphosuccinates are of particular interest not only for their technical properties but also because structurally they combine the two hydrophile-characterising functions described earlier – the sulphonate and carboxylate moieties – in a single molecule (9.18). The sulphosuccinate diesters, however, are probably of greater commercial importance in textile processing than are the monoesters. The most important example is sodium dioctylsulphosuccinate (9.19), but the dinonyl, dimethylamyl and di-isobutyl analogues are also used commercially. As usual, a wide choice of hydrophobes is available and includes alcohols, lightly ethoxylated alcohols, alkanolamides and combinations of these.

9.18
$$\begin{array}{l} COOR \\ | \\ CH_2 \\ | \\ HC{-}SO_3^- \, Na^+ \\ | \\ COO^- \, Na^+ \end{array}$$

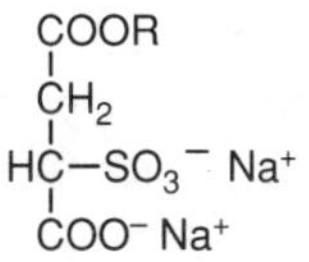

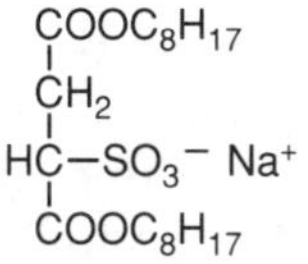

9.19
$$\begin{array}{l} COOC_8H_{17} \\ | \\ CH_2 \\ | \\ HC{-}SO_3^- \, Na^+ \\ | \\ COOC_8H_{17} \end{array}$$

Phosphate esters (9.20) represent a different class of hydrophile-characterised anionic surfactants, which are currently of growing commercial and technical importance; mono- or di-esters can be formed depending on whether one or two alkyl groups are present.

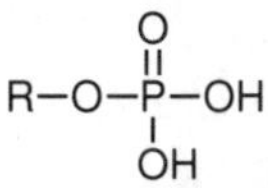

9.20
$$\begin{array}{c} O \\ \| \\ R{-}O{-}P{-}OH \\ | \\ OH \end{array} \qquad \begin{array}{c} O \\ \| \\ R{-}O{-}P{-}OH \\ | \\ R{-}O \end{array}$$

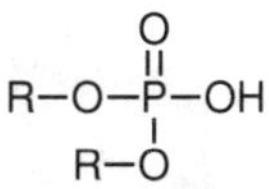

Most phosphate esters are based on alcohols and especially their ethoxylates, including aliphatic and alkylaryl types. Whereas the sulphates tend to be based on lightly ethoxylated alcohols, the phosphate esters are also made from more highly ethoxylated products. Commercial products are frequently mixtures of, for example, an alcohol phosphate and an alcohol poly(oxyethylene) phosphate.

Other anionic surfactant types include the alkylisethionates (9.21), N-acylsarcosides (9.22), N-acyltaurides (9.23) and, most recently, fluorinated alkylarylsulphonates (9.24).

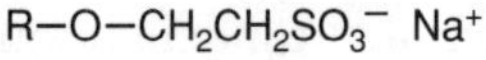

$$R-O-CH_2CH_2SO_3^- \ Na^+$$

9.21

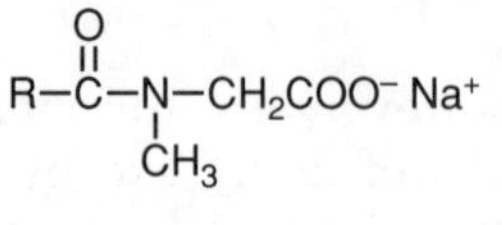

$$R-\overset{\overset{\displaystyle O}{\|}}{C}-N-CH_2COO^- \ Na^+$$
$$\qquad\quad | $$
$$\qquad\quad CH_3$$

9.22

$$R_1-\overset{\overset{\displaystyle O}{\|}}{C}-N-CH_2CH_2-SO_3^- \ Na^+$$
$$\qquad\quad | $$
$$\qquad\quad R_2$$

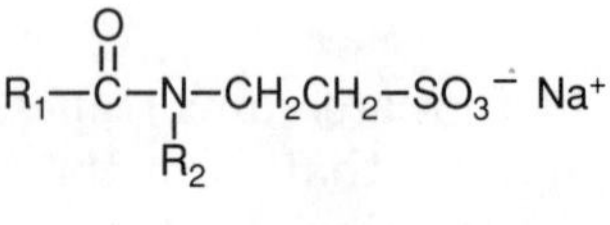

9.23

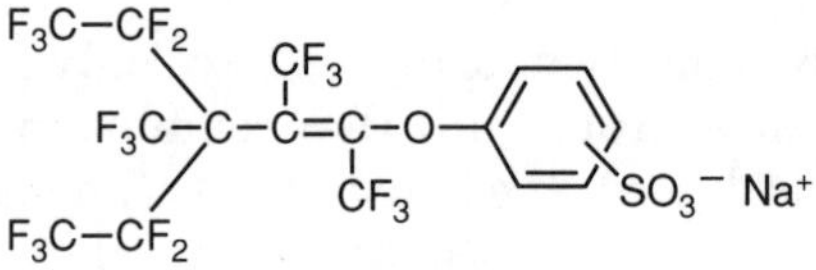

9.24

9.5 CATIONIC SURFACTANTS

By far the most important types of cationic surfactant used in textile processing are the quaternary ammonium salts (9.25, in which R is usually a long-chain hydrophobe and R_1, R_2, R_3 are lower alkyl groups). The most common anions in these and other cationic surfactants are chloride and bromide: thus cetyltrimethylammonium chloride (9.26) is typical of this class of cationic surfactants. In fact, however, all four alkyl groups on the nitrogen atom can be varied to alter the balance of properties of the products; in the alkyldimethylmethallylammonium chlorides (9.27) an unsaturated aliphatic group is used. Aromatic components are also used, as in the important alkyldimethylbenzylammonium chlorides (9.28), and both the aromatic nucleus and the alkyl groups in such products may contain substituents (9.29 and 9.30). As important as the quaternary ammonium surfactants are the pyridinium salts (9.31; R = a long-chain alkyl group), such as cetylpyridinium chloride (9.32).

9.25

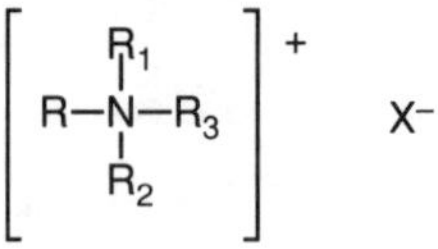

$$\left[\begin{array}{c} R_1 \\ | \\ R-N-R_3 \\ | \\ R_2 \end{array} \right]^+ \quad X^-$$

9.26

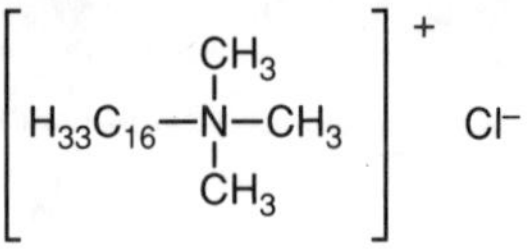

$$\left[\begin{array}{c} CH_3 \\ | \\ H_{33}C_{16}-N-CH_3 \\ | \\ CH_3 \end{array} \right]^+ \quad Cl^-$$

9.27

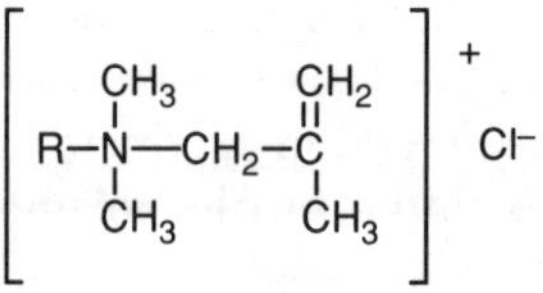

$$\left[\begin{array}{c} CH_3 \qquad CH_2 \\ | \qquad\quad \| \\ R-N-CH_2-C \\ | \qquad\quad | \\ CH_3 \qquad CH_3 \end{array} \right]^+ \quad Cl^-$$

9.28

$$\left[\begin{array}{c} CH_3 \\ | \\ R-N-CH_2- \\ | \\ CH_3 \end{array} \right]^+ \quad Cl^-$$

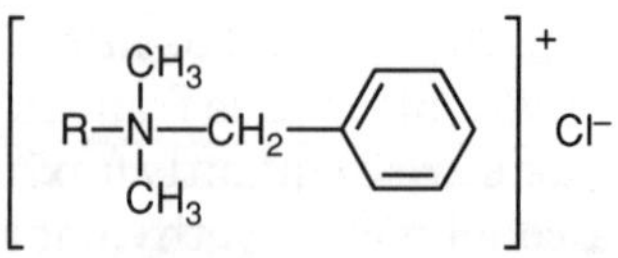

9.29

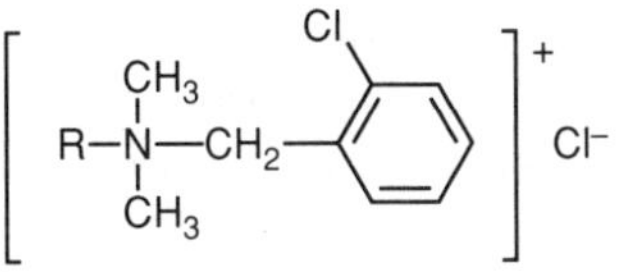

9.30

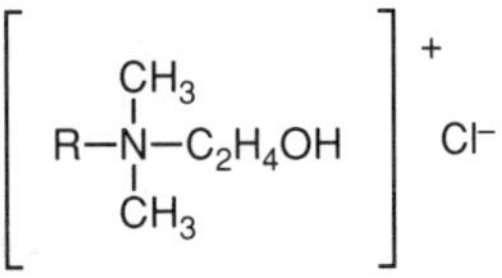

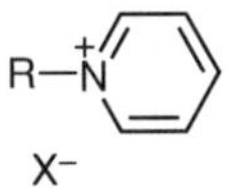

9.31

9.32

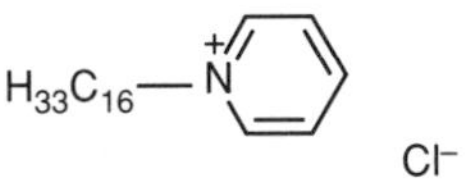

Imidazoles can be quaternised to yield cationic surfactants (such as structures 9.33 and 9.34). Long-chain alkyl primary, secondary and tertiary amines can also be used as cationic surfactants, but their use in textile processing is limited as a result of their insolubility in other than acidic aqueous media. The range of products available as cationic surfactants is truly enormous, including, for example, such complex products as alkyl mono- and di-guanidines and polyamines (9.35) which contain more than one basic nitrogen atom.

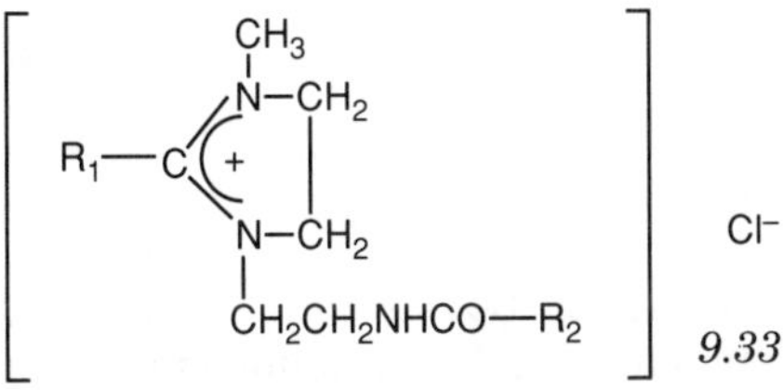

9.33

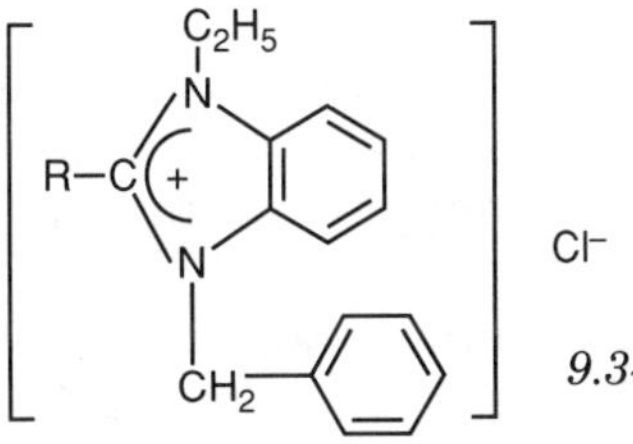

9.34

$R-(NHCH_2CH_2)_xNH_2$ 9.35

Many of these cationic products, including the quaternary amines and imidazoles, can be ethoxylated (9.36,9.37), forming cationic analogues of the ethoxysulphates and ethoxyphosphates in the anionic series. They are essentially cationic/non-ionic hybrid surfactants, variously described in manufacturers' promotional literature as 'modified cationic', 'weakly cationic' or even 'modified non-ionic'. Their value lies in the fact that the cationic nature can be controlled by varying not only the alkyl substituents but also the degree of ethoxylation. In addition the ethoxylate moiety confers useful emulsifying properties.

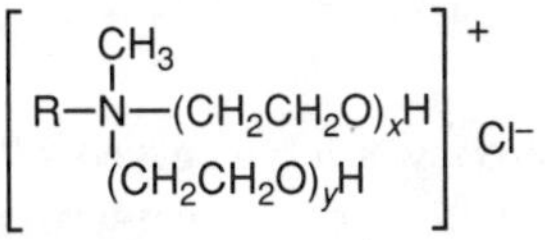

9.36

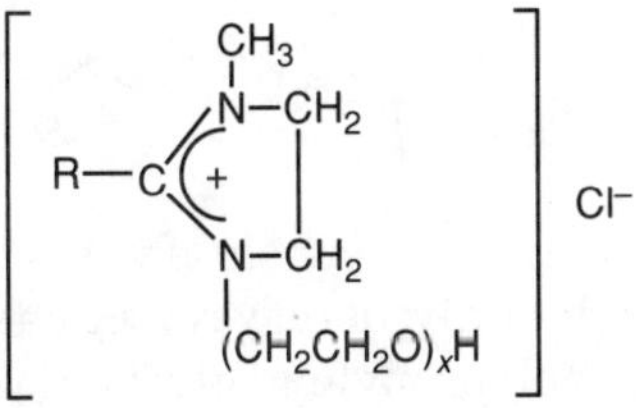

9.37

9.6 NON-IONIC SURFACTANTS

Nearly all non-ionic surfactants contain the same type of hydrophobes as do anionic and cationic surfactants, with solubilisation and surfactant properties arising from the addition of ethylene oxide to give a product having the general formula 9.38. Usually, depending on the hydrophobe, aqueous solubility and detergent properties begin to be evident when $x =$ 6, but in theory the degree of ethoxylation can be continued almost indefinitely. Optimum surfactant properties are generally found when $x =$ 10–15, although higher homologues (for example, $x = 50$) are known. The 'lightly ethoxylated' sulphates mentioned earlier usually contain only 2–4 oxyethylene units per molecule. Thus a typical non-ionic surfactant can be represented by structure 9.39.

$$R-(OCH_2CH_2)_xOH \qquad 9.38 \qquad H_{33}C_{16}-(OCH_2CH_2)_{12}OH \qquad 9.39$$

Although there are other types of non-ionic surfactant, the great majority are adducts of ethylene oxide with hydrophobes derived from three sources:
- fatty alcohols and alkylphenols
- fatty acids
- fatty amines and amides,

of which the most common are adducts with p-nonyl- and p-octyl-phenol, and to a lesser extent 2,4-dinonylphenol, p-dodecylphenol and 1-alkyl-naphthols. Since the hydrophobes used may be variable products conforming to an average nominal structure, and since the quoted degree of ethoxylation can also only be regarded as an average value, products having the same name (such as, for example, p-nonylphenol dodecaoxyethylene) may in fact differ in detailed composition and properties when obtained from different manufacturers. These provisos should be borne in mind when considering the examples below, even though there is a trend in some cases towards the manufacture of narrower fractions.

An example of an alcohol-based non-ionic (9.39) has already been given. An alkylphenol adduct (9.40) is essentially similar; both alcohols and phenols give rise to the relatively strong and stable ether link, a valuable property of this type of product. Analogues based on alkylthiols (9.41) may also be used.

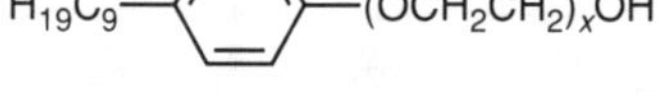

$$H_{19}C_9-\!\!\left\langle\!\!\bigcirc\!\!\right\rangle\!\!-(OCH_2CH_2)_xOH \qquad 9.40 \qquad H_{17}C_8-S-(CH_2CH_2O)_xH \qquad 9.41$$

Polyfunctional alcohols of varying complexity, such as glycols (9.42) and polypropylene glycols of varying chain length, also provide useful non-ionic agents. A polypropylene glycol molecule has a hydroxy group at each end to which ethylene oxide can add, forming random segments of poly(oxy-ethylene) and poly(oxypropylene). This results in block copolymers, which by control of starting materials and processing conditions can be engin-eered, by virtue of wide variations in segment length and degree of polymerisation, to give products specifically suited to a wide variety of pur-poses.

9.42
$$R{\overset{\displaystyle (OCH_2CH_2)_xOH}{\underset{\displaystyle (OCH_2CH_2)_xOH}{<}}}$$

$$H_{33}C_{16}CO(OCH_2CH_2)_xOH \quad 9.43$$

Whereas the alcohol and phenol derivatives are characterised by ether linkages, adducts of ethylene oxide with fatty acids give rise to both monoesters (9.43) and diesters; these are less stable than the ethers in strongly acidic or alkaline media, however, hydrolysing to the original fatty acid and polyethylene glycol.

Adducts of ethylene oxide with fatty amines can yield mono- (9.44) or di-substituted (9.45) products, as can the adducts with fatty amides (9.46, 9.47). In practice the products formed are far from being as simple or as symmetrical as represented by these formulae since, amongst other things, the ethylene oxide addition takes place randomly.

9.44 $H_{23}C_{11}NH(CH_2CH_2O)_xH$

9.45 $$H_{23}C_{11}N{\overset{\displaystyle (CH_2CH_2O)_xH}{\underset{\displaystyle (CH_2CH_2O)_xH}{<}}}$$

9.46 $$H_{23}C_{11}-\underset{\displaystyle O}{\overset{\displaystyle \|}{C}}-NH(CH_2CH_2O)_xH$$

9.47 $$H_{23}C_{11}-\underset{\displaystyle O}{\overset{\displaystyle \|}{C}}-N{\overset{\displaystyle (CH_2CH_2O)_xH}{\underset{\displaystyle (CH_2CH_2O)_xH}{<}}}$$

The non-ionic types so far discussed form the great majority used in textile processing. Of course, a great many more can be synthesised, as the possible range of permutations and combinations is truly enormous: given appropriate conditions, ethylene oxide will react with almost any proton-donating compound but the choice in practice is restricted by economic factors. Not all non-ionic surfactants are ethoxylates, however. Analogous propylene oxide adducts are known; rather more different products include sucrose and sorbitan esters, alkanolamides and fatty amine oxides. The fatty acid esters of compounds such as sucrose and sorbitol exhibit surfact-ant properties. Some, such as the sorbitan fatty esters, are insoluble in water but being oil-soluble they can be used as emulsifiers in oil-based sys-tems, or they can be ethoxylated to render them water-soluble. Mention has already been made of fatty amide poly(oxyethylene) adducts formed by condensation of a fatty acid with an alkanolamine which is then ethoxylated; some complex alkanolamides have in themselves (i.e. without ethoxylation) some surfactant properties, however. They are made by the reaction of a fatty acid (such as lauric acid or a coconut fatty acid) with a secondary alkanolamine (such as diethanolamine) to yield an amide which then further reacts with diethanolamine to yield the water-soluble alkanolamide surfactant. Typical fatty amine oxides (9.48 and 9.49) are derived, for example, from the peroxide oxidation of tertiary amines containing at least one fatty-chain group.

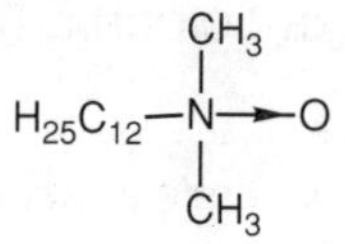

$$H_{25}C_{12}-\overset{\overset{\displaystyle CH_3}{|}}{\underset{\underset{\displaystyle CH_3}{|}}{N}}\longrightarrow O$$

9.48

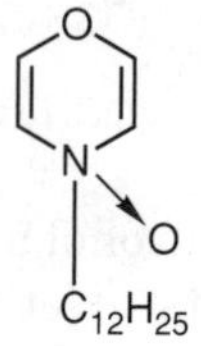

9.49 $C_{12}H_{25}$

9.7 AMPHOTERIC SURFACTANTS

As mentioned in Table 8.1, amphoteric surfactants contain both an anionic and a cationic group such that in acidic media they tend to behave as cationic agents and in alkaline media as anionic agents. Somewhere between these extremes lies what is known as the isoelectric point (which is not necessarily, or even commonly, at pH 7), at which the anionic and cationic properties are counterbalanced: at this point the molecule is said to be *zwitterionic*, and its surfactant properties and solubility tend to be at their lowest.

The 1978 reprint of Schwartz and Perry's 1949 classic book on surface-active agents [8] comments: 'None of the ampholytic surface-active agents have, to the writer's knowledge, achieved any great commercial importance.' This may have been true in 1949. The picture has changed in recent years [18–23], however, although particular surfactants and surfactant blends are sometimes incorrectly described by their suppliers as 'amphoterics' [2]. The simplest type is represented by the higher alkylaminoacids, such as compound 9.50; disubstituted amines can also be synthesised (9.51).

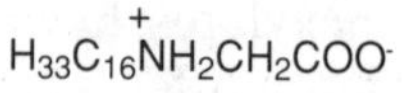

$$H_{33}C_{16}\overset{+}{N}H_2CH_2COO^-$$

9.50

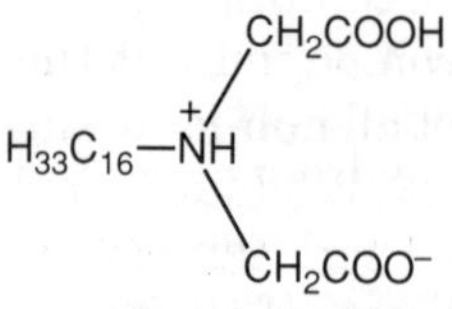

$$H_{33}C_{16}-\overset{+}{N}H\Big\langle\begin{array}{l}CH_2COOH\\[4pt]CH_2COO^-\end{array}$$

9.51

Ethoxylated products can also feature as amphoteric surfactants; an example is compound 9.52, an alkylamine poly(oxyethylene) sulphate. Of particular interest in textile processing are the tri-substituted alkylaminoacids known as betaines; *N*-alkylbetaines (9.53; R = C_8–C_{16} alkyl) and acylaminoalkylbetaines (9.54; R = C_{10}–C_{16} alkyl) are typical [18].

Sulphate and sulphonate analogues of the carboxylates, such as the sulphobetaine 9.55, can also be used as amphoteric agents.

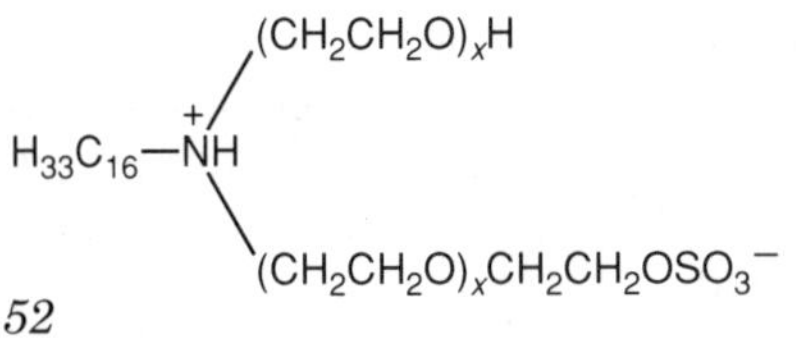

$$H_{33}C_{16}-\overset{+}{N}H\overset{\displaystyle (CH_2CH_2O)_xH}{\underset{\displaystyle (CH_2CH_2O)_xCH_2CH_2OSO_3^-}{\Big\backslash}}$$

9.52

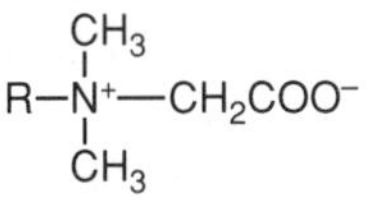

$$R-\overset{\displaystyle CH_3}{\underset{\displaystyle CH_3}{\overset{|}{\underset{|}{N^+}}}}-CH_2COO^-$$

9.53

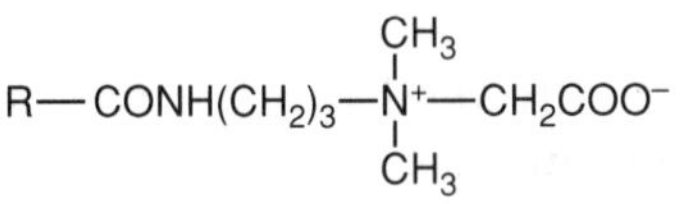

$$R-CONH(CH_2)_3-\overset{\displaystyle CH_3}{\underset{\displaystyle CH_3}{\overset{|}{\underset{|}{N^+}}}}-CH_2COO^-$$

9.54

$$R-\overset{\displaystyle CH_3}{\underset{\displaystyle CH_3}{\overset{|}{\underset{|}{^+N}}}}-(CH_2)_3SO_3^-$$

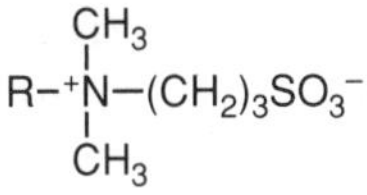

9.55

9.8 THE GENERAL PROPERTIES OF SURFACTANTS

9.8.1 Effects on the environment

The widespread use of these products focused attention on their environmental properties long ago, owing to the persistent foam-creating tendency of many surfactants when discharged. Moore et al. [24] have given a summary of the toxicity of textile surfactants to aquatic life and make reference to ten other works covering the period 1971 to 1984.

Of major importance is the broad difference between biodegradable and non-biodegradable products. It is now generally accepted that straight-chain products are adequately biodegradable to meet the requirements of present legislation, whilst branched-chain products are not. There appears to be some uncertainty regarding the biological effects of non-ionic surfactants, particularly the alkylphenol ethoxylates. In respect of aquatic toxicity Moore et al. [24] have made the following general points:

(a) biodegradability decreases with increasing hydrophobicity of surfactants and with decreasing solubility, irrespective of their ionic type
(b) increasing the degree of ethoxylation decreases toxicity
(c) anionic surfactants are generally less toxic than non-ionics because of their lesser hydrophobic character
(d) even very small quantities of surfactants in aquatic systems can damage certain food chains
(e) non-ionic surfactants are less toxic when sulphated (this decreases their hydrophobic character)
(f) anionic and cationic surfactants can react to form a complex that is readily biodegradable and much less toxic than the reactants themselves.

A further environmentally related factor is that of skin sensitisation. Although this is likely to be of less direct concern to dyers and printers than to manufacturers of domestic detergents, it does still need to be borne in mind in relation to residual surfactants, softeners and lubricants on finished fabrics. The following types are recognised as being mild to the skin: sulphosuccinate mono-esters, alkylisethionates, acylsarcosides, acyltaurides and amphoteric agents at their isoelectric points. Alkanolamides and fatty amine oxides are claimed to act as skin protectors and are used as such to counter the skin de-fatting tendency of other surfactants in some domestic products [16].

9.8.2 Application properties

Anionic and cationic products generally tend to react with each other, usually diminishing the surfactant properties of both and often resulting in precipitation of the complex formed. Amphoteric compounds can also be incompatible with anionics in acid solution but are generally compatible with cationics and non-ionics. Interaction between anionic and cationic agents can sometimes be prevented by addition of a non-ionic; in some cases, if an ethoxylated sulphate or phosphate is used as the anionic component, a cationic compound produces no obvious precipitation since the oxyethylene chain acts as dispersant for any complex that may be formed.

The main disadvantages of the carboxylates are their tendency to react with calcium and magnesium ions in hard water to give insoluble precipitates and their insolubility in acid media, although they generally have good wetting and detergent properties. The acylsarcosides are less affected by calcium and magnesium ions, however, whilst the carboxymethyl surfactants are unaffected. The sulphates were specifically developed to overcome the drawbacks of the carboxylates and, like the more recently developed phosphates, are stable towards calcium and magnesium ions. As well as being outstanding detergents, the sulphonates are also unaffected by strongly acidic and alkaline conditions, and the higher-alkyl members have useful lubricating properties. On the other hand, the sulphates can be hydrolysed by acid and sulphated monoglycerides can also be hydrolysed by alkali. Their wetting properties tend to be inferior to those of the sulphonates but they are particularly valuable as emulsifying agents, especially in combination with non-ionics. The sulphosuccinates have a high propensity to foaming and their solubility is not generally good, but the monoesters have good detergency properties and the diesters are particularly rapid wetting agents.

As a group, the phosphates have good stability to acid and alkali for most purposes, have low foaming and good detergent properties and are biodegradable. They tend to be better wetting agents than the sulphates and their solubility in organic solvents makes them useful in, for example, dry cleaning. The recently developed perfluoroalkyl anionic surfactants are currently very expensive, but are powerful surfactants at very low concentrations and are stable in chemically hostile environments; they also exhibit surface activity in organic solvents.

Cationic agents generally are less useful than anionics as detergents but they have useful properties as softeners, germicides and emulsifiers.

Non-ionic agents are generally compatible with both anionic and cationic types. They are also stable to calcium and magnesium ions. With the exception of the fatty acid esters, which are readily hydrolysed by acid and alkali, they are stable and effective over a wide range of pH values. A particular characteristic of non-ionic surfactants is their inverse solubility – that is, as the temperature rises the solubility decreases, until a point is reached at which the surfactant reaches its limiting solubility and therefore begins to precipitate out, causing cloudiness of the solution. The temperature at which this occurs, known as the cloud point, depends upon the number of oxyethylene units in the non-ionic molecule in relation to length of the hydrophobe. Thus, for any given hydrophobe, the cloud point increases with increasing degree of ethoxylation; for example, dodecanol heptaoxyethylene $C_{12}H_{25}(OCH_2CH_2)_7OH$ has a cloud point of 59°C, while that of the undecaoxyethylene homologue is 100°C. Conversely, for a fixed number of oxyethylene units, the cloud point decreases with increasing size of the hydrophobe. The cloud points of non-ionic agents are also generally lowered by the presence of electrolytes, the effect varying with the electrolyte and its concentration. It is important to bear this in mind when choosing non-ionic agents for use in electrolyte-containing processes. This inverse solubility arises from the solubilisation of the non-ionic molecules by hydrogen bonding of water with the ether oxygen atoms (9.56). As the temperature rises, the energy within these bonds becomes insufficient to maintain their cohesion, and dehydration takes place with a consequent decrease in solubility. A knowledge of the cloud point of a surfactant is useful, not only because of solubility effects but also because the surface activity tends to be optimal just below the cloud point.

$$\text{HOH} \qquad\qquad \text{HOH}$$
$$(-OCH_2CH_2OCH_2CH_2O-)_n$$

9.56 HOH

The tendency of non-ionics to produce foam varies. Some, such as the block copolymers, are even used as defoamers. Their wetting, detergency and emulsifying properties also vary widely, depending to a large extent on the balance between the hydrophobic and hydrophilic (oxyethylene) portions.

The amphoteric agents exhibit excellent compatibility with inorganic electrolytes and with acids and alkalis. Such is their stability in strongly acidic solution that they are even used in cleaning compositions based on hydrofluoric acid [16].

9.8.3 The theory of surface activity

The physico-chemical theory of surface activity is a vast field and no more than broad principles can be touched upon here; classic works exist [8,25–27] for those who require more detail of the relationship between chemical structure and the major surfactant properties of wetting, detergency and emulsification–solubilisation.

Surface activity is generally related to the balance between the hydrophobic and hydrophilic portions of the molecule. For example, among the anionic surfactants C_8–C_{12} alkyl hydrophobes tend to be predominantly wetting agents, whilst the C_{12}–C_{18} analogues exhibit better detergency and emulsifying properties. The alkylsuccinates and sulphosuccinates are particularly powerful wetting agents. Clearly, as the hydrophobic character of the surfactant is increased, aqueous solubility decreases and oil solubility increases. Thus the balance between the hydrophobic and hydrophilic moieties of a surfactant is a critical factor in determining its major characteristics. This is referred to as the hydrophile–lipophile balance, or HLB (the word 'lipophile', of course, being analogous to 'hydrophobe'). Whilst the HLB value is of general use in expressing the characteristics of a surfactant, it is of particular value in describing the formation of emulsions. For some general purposes the HLB can be used qualitatively (referring, for instance, to low, medium or high HLB), but for more precise work it is preferable to use a quantifying scale. Such a scale, put forward in the 1940s [2,28], covers a range of values from zero (the lipophilic or hydrophobic extreme) to a hydrophilic extreme of 20 or higher, with a value of 10 approximately representing the point at which the hydrophilic and hydrophobic portions are in balance. This scale is especially useful in describing the properties of the non-ionic ethoxylates. For example, a low HLB value (4–6) signifies a predominance of hydrophobic groups, indicating that the surfactant is lipophilic and should be suited for preparing water-in-oil emulsions. A value in the 7–9 range indicates good wetting properties. As the value shifts towards increased hydrophilicity other properties predominate, values of 8–18 being typical for surfactants that will give oil-in-water emulsions, and values of 13–15 for surfactants that show useful detergency. The HLB values required for solubilising properties are generally in the range 10–18.

The HLB of a relatively pure poly(oxyethylene) adduct can be calculated from theoretical data [2,28]. For these agents the HLB is an indication of percentage by mass of the hydrophilic portion, divided by five to give a conveniently small number. For example, if the hydrophilic portion of a purely hypothetical non-ionic agent accounted for 100% of the molecule (such a product cannot, of course, exist), its HLB is 20. Similarly a more plausible product in which 85% of the molecule is accounted for by the hydrophilic portion has an HLB of 85/5 = 17. The ICI Americas Inc. method of calculating the theoretical HLB of a sorbitan monolaurate non-ionic having 20 oxyethylene units per molecule is given in Eqn 9.1 (total relative molecular mass = 1226, of which 1044 is contributed by the hydrophilic portion) [28].

$$\text{HLB} = \frac{1044}{1226} \times 100 \times \frac{1}{5} = 17.0 \tag{9.1}$$

As explained earlier, however, the actual constitution of a surfactant rarely conforms to its nominal structure. Consequently the theoretical method of calculation is of limited utility, practical methods being more reliable. The HLB value may be determined directly by analysis or by comparison with a range of surfactants of known HLB values. An analytical method for the sorbitan monolaurate described above uses Eqn 9.2 [28]:

$$\text{HLB} = 20\left(1 - \frac{S}{A}\right) = 20\left(1 - \frac{45.5}{276}\right) = 16.7 \tag{9.2}$$

where S is the saponification number of the ester and A is the acid number of the recovered acid. The saponification value of a product is the mass in milligrams of potassium hydroxide required to saponify one gram of the product; it can be found by saponification of the product with an excess of potassium hydroxide followed by back-titration of the remaining alkali with hydrochloric acid. The acid value of an acid is the number of milligrams of potassium hydroxide required to neutralise a standard quantity, and can again be found by titration. The comparative methods should always be used for the non-ionic surfactants that are not based on ethylene oxide, and also for ionic surfactants since the hydrophilic influence of the ionic group exceeds that indicated by the mass percentage basis (this can lead to apparent HLB values higher than 20).

Once the HLB values of a range of surfactants are known it is an easy matter to calculate the HLB value of a mixture as follows:

Individual HLB		Fractional HLB
45% of surfactant A	16.7	$0.45 \times 16.7 = 7.52$
35% of surfactant B	4.0	$0.35 \times 4.0 = 1.40$
20% of surfactant C	9.6	$0.20 \times 9.6 = 1.92$
		Total HLB = 10.84

When preparing an emulsion, emulsification tends to be most efficient when the HLB of the agent matches that of the oil phase. Often a mixture of surfactants makes a more efficient emulsifying agent than a single product having the same HLB value as the mixture; similarly, if the oil phase to be emulsified is itself a mixture, its components will each contribute to the effective HLB value. It is this effective HLB value that is the main criterion in designing a suitable emulsifying system. The effective HLB value can be found by carrying out preliminary emulsification tests with agents of known HLB values. A useful procedure [28] uses two such emulsifying agents of widely differing HLB values mixed in various proportions so as to give a range of intermediate HLB values. The HLB value of the mixture that gives the best emulsion of the oil phase under test then corresponds to the effective HLB value of the oil phase. Further tests can then be carried out with different chemical types of agents around this effective HLB value in order to find the optimum emulsifying system.

9.8.4 Micelle formation

All surfactants in solution tend to form more or less ordered agglomerates of molecules, known as micelles. Pure water has a surface tension of about 72×10^{-3} N/m. As surfactant is added gradually to it, the surface tension falls quite rapidly (Figure 9.1) until, at a certain concentration of surfactant, it begins to level off more or less sharply. At the point at which this levelling out takes place, the critical micelle concentration (CMC in Figure 9.1), the surfactant molecules begin to orient themselves in clusters within the body of the solution, these clusters being more or less lamellar or spherical (Figure 9.2).

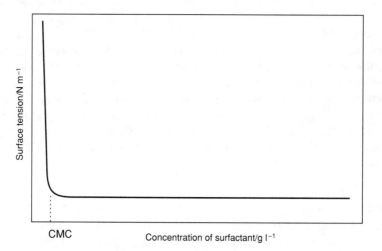

Figure 9.1 – Surface tension of water against surfactant concentration

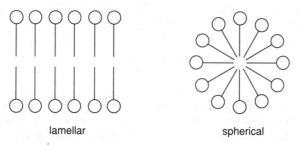

lamellar   spherical

Figure 9.2 – Micelle formation

In water the surfactant molecules orient themselves with their hydro-phobes at the centre of the cluster. The CMC is typically quite low, perhaps 0.5–0.2 g/l. At concentrations lower than this the molecules orient them-selves only at the interfaces of the solution, and it is this effect which brings about the lowering of surface tension. Once the CMC is reached the interfaces become saturated and as the concentration increases micellar clusters of molecules begin to form in the bulk of the solution; there is little further reduction in surface tension beyond the CMC, nor are there changes in the other surfactant properties such as wetting and foaming. In general, the CMC decreases with increasing size of the hydrophobe, and the CMCs of non-ionic agents tend to be lower than those of ionic types, since with the non-ionics micelles can form more easily in the absence of polar charges. This ability to form micelles is vital to the efficacy of surfactants as emulsifying, dispersing and solubilising agents.

REFERENCES

1. G C Johnson, *Amer. Dyestuff Rep.*, **73** (May 1984) 22.
2. C A Ferguson, *Canadian Textile J.*, **95** (July 1978) 41.
3. G M Gantz, *Amer. Dyestuff Rep.*, **57** (Nov 1968) 885.
4. G P Sheridan, *Dyer*, **163** (Feb 1981) 31.
5. H T Pratt, *Amer. Dyestuff Rep.*, **70** (Feb 1981) 31.
6. A J Sabia, *Text. Chem. Colorist*, **12** (Aug 1980) 178.
7. H Rath, *Lehrbuch der Textilchemie*, 3rd Edn (Berlin: Springer–Verlag, 1972).
8. A M Schwartz and J W Perry, *Surface-active agents* (New York: Robert E Krieger, 1949, reprinted 1978).
9. B R Bluestein and C L Hilton, *Amphoteric surfactants* (New York: Marcel Dekker, 1982).
10. E Jungermann, *Cationic surfactants* (New York: Marcel Dekker, 1970).
11. W M Linfield, *Anionic surfactants* (New York: Marcel Dekker, 1976).
12. J W McCutcheon, *Synthetic detergents* (New York: MacNair–Dorland, 1950).
13. N J Schick, *Non-ionic surfactants* (New York: Marcel Dekker, 1967).
14. N Schonfeldt, *Surface-active ethylene oxide adducts* (London: Pergamon Press, 1969).
15. J P Sisley and P J Wood, *Encyclopaedia of surface-active agents* (New York: Chemical Publishing Co., 1972).
16. A S Davidsohn and B Milwidsky, *Synthetic detergents*, 7th Edn (Harlow, Essex: Longman, 1987).
17. *Sulphated castor oil and castor oil soap* (Stockport: Ellis Jones & Co.).
18. A Riva and J Cegarra, *J.S.D.C.*, **103** (1987) 32.
19. H Egli, *Textilveredlung*, **8** (1973) 495.
20. W Mosimann, *Text. Chem. Colorist*, **1** (1969) 182.
21. J Cegarra, Proc. IFATCC, Barcelona (1975).
22. J Cegarra, A Riva and L Aizpurua, *J.S.D.C.*, **94** (1978) 394.
23. J Cegarra and A Riva, *Melliand Textilber.*, **64** (1983) 221.
24. S B Moore, R A Diehl, J M Barnhardt and G B Avery, *Text. Chem. Colorist*, **19** (May 1987) 29.
25. J L Moillet, B Collie and W Black, *Surface activity* (London: Spon, 1961).
26. W W Niven, *Fundamentals of detergency* (New York: Reinhold, 1950).
27. L I Osipov, *Surface chemistry* (New York: Reinhold, 1962).
28. *The HLB system – a time-saving guide to emulsifier selection* (Publication 103–3 10M) (Wilmington, Delaware: ICI Americas, 1976, revised 1984).

CHAPTER 10

Classification of dyeing and printing auxiliaries by function

Terence M Baldwinson

10.1 ELECTROLYTES AND pH CONTROL

The simplest auxiliaries of all are the neutral electrolytes such as sodium chloride and sodium sulphate. These are used in large quantities for dyeing cellulosic materials with direct or reactive dyes and wool with anionic dyes. The major effect of electrolytes on dyes of this type is to increase the degree of aggregation of the dye molecules in solution by the common-ion effect, the degree of aggregation varying markedly with dye structure (see section 3.1.2). The electrolyte suppresses the ionisation of the dye in solution, thereby effectively reducing its solubility in the dyebath and modifying the equilibrium in favour of movement of the dye molecules from the solution to the fibre. The object, of course, is to use the optimum amount of salt to give the required rate and extent of exhaustion of the dyebath; too little electrolyte is ineffective whilst too much may aggregate the dye to an extent that may inhibit its diffusion into the fibre, thus giving a tendency to surface coloration only, or even bringing about precipitation. The aggregating effect of electrolytes varies, sodium chloride having a stronger effect than sodium sulphate, but it is generally decreased by raising the temperature.

This effect, which we may term the 'salting-on' effect, is the result of interactions between electrolyte and dye. However, there may also be interactions between electrolyte and fibre, giving rise to a positive levelling action as the electrolyte anions compete with the dye anions for the cationic sites in the fibre. Surfactants (see Chapter 9) can of course be regarded as electrolytes, although by hydrophobic interactions they tend to form micelles in concentrated solution and hence may be referred to as colloidal electrolytes. In some respects their levelling action is analogous to that of simple inorganic electrolytes – that is, ionic hydrophobes compete with dye ions of similar charge for sites of opposite charge in the fibre.

The great majority of coloration processes demand some control over the treatment pH, which varies from strongly alkaline in the case of vat, sulphur and reactive dyes, to strongly acidic for levelling acid dyes. The concept of pH is a familiar one; its theoretical derivation can be found in all standard physical chemistry textbooks and has been particularly well explained in relation to coloration processes [1,2] both in theory and in practice. We are concerned here essentially with the chemistry of the products used to control pH and their mode of action. It has been said [2] that 'Unfortunately, pH control appears simple and easy to carry out. Add acid and the pH decreases; add base (alkali) and the pH increases. However, pH is the most difficult control feature in any industry' [3].

The control of pH in textile coloration processes is ensured by three fundamentally different techniques:
(a) the maintenance of a relatively high degree of acidity or alkalinity
(b) the control of pH within fairly narrow tolerances mainly in the near-neutral region
(c) the gradual shifting of the pH as a coloration process proceeds.

Approach (a) is normally the easiest to control, and is used in the application of levelling acid and 1:1 metal-complex dyes to wool and nylon, and of the reactive, sulphur and vat dyes to cellulosic fibres. The agents traditionally used are the stronger acids and alkalis such as sulphuric, hydrochloric and formic acids, sodium carbonate and sodium hydroxide. In certain operations, particularly fixation in steam (as in printing), steam-volatile acids are replaced with non-volatile products such as citric acid. Use of approach (a) can lead to the misconception already mentioned, that pH is easy to control, particularly as the dye–substrate systems involved are not normally sensitive to minor pH shifts. Nevertheless, strong acids and alkalis can react to produce quite drastic changes in pH; this can occur, for example, when alkali is carried over from wool scouring into initially acidic dyebaths. Wool and nylon absorb acid from dyebaths, thereby inducing a change in the dyebath pH, but wool will absorb significantly more acid than nylon [4] – a factor to be borne in mind when comparing results on these two fibres, especially in those systems using 'half-milling' acid dyes for which the controlling agent is generally the weaker acetic acid; such systems represent a compromise between approaches (a) and (b) and are moderately sensitive to change in pH.

Approach (b) needs greater awareness of the factors that not only determine pH but also help to stabilise it against interferences. Most of the dye–fibre systems requiring approach (b) are operated in the near-neutral region (pH 4–9) and are much more sensitive to minor changes in pH. In addition, the pH of the water supply may vary, or drift during heating. Even the pH of pure water changes on heating, from 7.47 at 0°C to 7.00 at 24°C and 6.13 at 100°C, but that of the process water used in dyehouses and printworks can change much more drastically, most commonly showing an increase. Changes in pH on heating may counteract the intended response of process liquors, especially in the central pH range associated with approach (b); even more critical can be the effect of any acids or alkalis carried over from previous processes.

The dye–fibre systems of obvious interest for approach (b) are milling acid and 1:2 metal-complex dyes on wool and nylon, basic dyes on acrylic fibres and disperse dyes on various fibres. With wool and nylon there is often some overlap with approach (c) (see page 403).

Where control is not too critical, simple electrolytes of weak bases with strong acids (such as ammonium sulphate) or strong bases with weak acids (such as sodium acetate) are often used to produce slightly acidic or slightly alkaline media respectively. Ammonium acetate is also commonly used, producing a less acidic effect than ammonium sulphate. Occasionally acetic acid and sodium carbonate are used, necessitating careful control and monitoring. These simple expedients are not suitable for systems requiring more sensitive control, however, and use of single electrolytes such as ammonium sulphate and sodium acetate more properly belong to control systems based on approach (c). More precise control is achieved by use of buffering systems. By the use of electrolyte pairs, these systems set the initial pH and exert a protective action that tends to resist changes arising from contaminants entering by way of the substrate or the water supply.

Buffering systems are generally based on combinations of
- a weak acid together with the salt of this acid formed from a strong base, or
- a weak base together with the salt of this base formed from a strong acid.

The most commonly used example of the first type is acetic acid/sodium acetate, which functions well over the pH range 3.8–5.8. Acetic acid with ammonium acetate is also used although it is less effective, especially in boiling open dyebaths from which the ammonia can escape into the atmosphere, thus allowing the pH to fall. Such acetate buffers have the advantage of low cost. Somewhat more expensive are the phosphate buffers, of which the most common is a mixture of sodium dihydrogen orthophosphate (NaH_2PO_4) and disodium hydrogen orthophosphate (Na_2HPO_4). Here, as with most polybasic acid systems, the distinction between the acid and its salt seems blurred at first sight. In fact, sodium dihydrogen phosphate is the 'acting acid' and disodium hydrogen phosphate is its salt. The tribasic orthophosphoric acid and its three salts can be used to produce a series of buffers, each active within a particular pH range:
- orthophosphoric acid and the monosodium salt, main buffering region pH 2.5–3.5
- the mono- and di-sodium salts, main buffering region pH 6–8
- the di- and tri-sodium salts, main buffering region pH 10.5–11.

This can be seen from the titration curve for phosphoric acid [1] shown in Figure 10.1. In practice the mono- and di-sodium salt system is used most extensively, since this covers the pH range over which precise control is most often needed. These phosphate buffers are more resistant than the acetate type to temperature-induced changes.

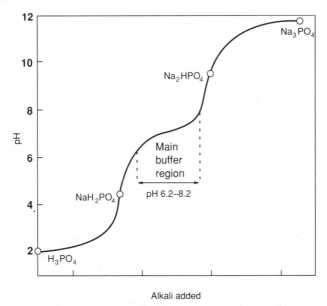

Figure 10.1 – Orthophosphate buffer system

The most common buffering system containing a weak base together with its salt formed with a strong acid is ammonia with ammonium sulphate. Some useful buffers are obtained from combinations of unrelated acids/bases and salts. The following combinations find occasional use in textile coloration processes, but the acetates and orthophosphates are most frequently used:
– pyrophosphoric acid ($H_4P_2O_7$) and its salts (pH 3–9)
– boric acid, sodium tetraborate (borax) and sodium hydroxide (pH 8.1–10.1)
– citric acid and sodium hydroxide (pH 2.1–6.4)
– sodium carbonate and sodium bicarbonate (pH 9.3–11.3).

The pyrophosphate buffer is of particular technical interest as it can be used over the relatively wide pH 3–9 range. Unlike the orthophosphate titration curve, that for the tetrabasic pyrophosphate system is almost straight (Figure 10.2) [1]. This linearity means that effective buffering action is available across the whole pH range simply by using various 'acidic' and salt components and varying their proportions; even so, however, it does not seem to be widely used.

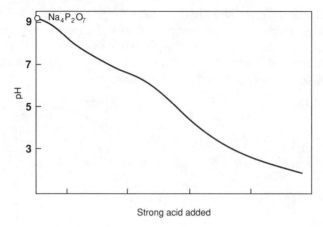

Figure 10.2 – Pyrophosphate buffer system

The mechanism of buffering can be described by reference to the acetic acid/sodium acetate system. In aqueous solution sodium acetate can be considered to be practically completely ionised (Scheme 10.1), the equilibrium being wholly to the right-hand side. Since acetic acid is a weak acid it is only slightly ionised, and the equilibrium represented by Scheme 10.2 lies mainly to the left-hand side. This low degree of ionisation is even further suppressed in the presence of sodium acetate as a result of the common (in this case acetate) ion effect operating through the law of mass action. The undissociated acetic acid is, in effect, a 'bank' of hydrogen and acetate ions that can be brought into play as a neutralising mechanism when either acidic or alkaline products enter the system (either by deliberate addition or adventitiously). If a small amount of an acidic substance is added to the mixture, the added hydrogen ions combine with acetate ions to form undissociated acetic acid, which has only a minimal effect on the pH of the system. If an alkaline substance is added to the buffer, the added hydroxide ïons react with the bank of hydrogen ions to form undissociated water and so again the ionic balance and hence the pH remain essentially the same. The mechanisms of other buffering systems are similar: buffering action is increased by adding more of the components, keeping their proportions constant.

$$CH_3COONa \rightleftharpoons Na^+ + CH_3COO^-$$

Scheme 10.1

$$CH_3COOH \rightleftharpoons H^+ + CH_3COO^-$$

Scheme 10.2

Approach (c) for pH control involves a deliberate shift of pH during the processing cycle, in a consistent direction rather than randomly. Systems of this type are particularly useful for non-migrating acid dyes on wool and nylon, and have long been known in this connection. More recently, similar systems have been proposed for reactive dyes on cellulosic fibres. The simplest and most widely used of these systems consist of the salts of strong acids with weak bases or of strong bases with weak acids, examples being ammonium sulphate and sodium acetate respectively. Ammonium sulphate, for instance, dissociates in aqueous media to yield the dominant strong-acid species of sulphuric acid, so lowering the pH (Scheme 10.3) at a rate that increases with temperature, especially when the ammonia formed can be released from open dyebaths. Ammonium acetate functions in the same way but does not yield as great a pH shift. Similarly, a solution of sodium acetate tends to produce the dominant strong-alkali species of sodium hydroxide (Scheme 10.4), thus increasing the pH.

$$(NH_4)_2SO_4 + 2H_2O \rightleftharpoons H_2SO_4 + 2\,NH_4OH \qquad NH_4OH \longrightarrow NH_3 + H_2O$$

$$\Updownarrow$$

$$2H^+ + SO_4{}^{2-}$$

Scheme 10.3

$$CH_3COONa + HOH \rightleftharpoons NaOH + CH_3COOH$$

$$\Updownarrow$$

$$Na^+ + OH^-$$

Scheme 10.4

Acetic acid (b.p. 118°C) is not as readily boiled off as ammonia from open dyebaths but is rapidly flashed off in steam and dry heat fixation processes, thus developing the maximum degree of alkalinity under these conditions. The sodium salts of less volatile acids, such as sodium citrate, can be used to develop a lesser degree of alkalinity.

If the process demands a gradual shift from about pH 9 to a slightly acidic pH, ammonium sulphate together with ammonia can be used. This gives a safer, more uniform development of acidity than can be achieved by making additions of acid to an alkaline bath, although the degree of acidity developed will clearly depend on the ease with which ammonia can escape from the system. In enclosed or partially enclosed machines this system does not function so efficiently [5–7].

Another method of obtaining a pH shift in the direction of acidity is to use organic esters that hydrolyse to alcohol and acid under the conditions of processing. Ethyl lactate (Scheme 10.5) and diethyl tartrate (10.1) are recommended for applying milling and chrome dyes to wool [8]. γ-Butyro-lactone (10.2), which hydrolyses during processing to 4-hydroxybutyric acid, and 2-hydroxyethyl chloroacetate (10.3) have been recommended. Such hydrolysable esters can be used alone, beginning at a near-neutral pH, but are more commonly used in conjunction with an alkali to give a higher starting pH. Thus γ-butyrolactone and sodium tetraborate (borax) to give pH shift from about 8 to 5.6 have been recommended for the dyeing of wool [9], as has 2-hydroxyethyl chloroacetate with sodium hydroxide for the dyeing of nylon [10]. Such hydrolysable esters are sometimes sold under proprietary trade names, such as Sandacid V (S). The disadvantages of hydrolysable esters appear to be their higher cost, a limited pH range and, where the dyebath is to be reused, the need for increasing quantities of ester to overcome the buffering effect caused by the accumulation of salts [2,11].

$$CH_3CHOHCOOC_2H_5 \; \underset{}{\overset{H_2O}{\rightleftharpoons}} \; CH_3CHOHCOOH + C_2H_5OH$$

Scheme 10.5

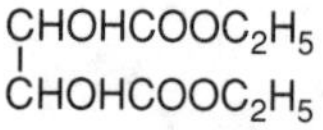

CHOHCOOC$_2$H$_5$
|
CHOHCOOC$_2$H$_5$

$$ClCH_2-\overset{\overset{\textstyle O}{\|}}{C}-O-CH_2CH_2OH$$

10.1 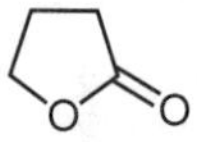   *10.2* 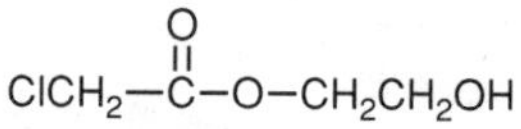   *10.3*

The use of strong acids and bases for control of pH-shift systems is obviously fraught with difficulties, particularly where the operation is carried out manually. If a sophisticated automatic monitoring and dosing system is used, however, the use of such compounds has certain very worthwhile advantages:

(a) The adjusting chemicals are the cheapest available
(b) The whole range of pH values can be controlled by using just two chemicals
(c) Since a buffering system is not built up in the bath, the pH can be shifted in any direction to any degree, easily and with the minimum addition of chemicals
(d) As a result of (c), any variation in the intrinsic pH of the substrate or water supply can be easily neutralised
(e) Exhausted dyebaths can often be reused as there is no build-up of buffering agent
(f) There are no environmental problems.

The Dosacid W control and dispensing unit, developed by Ciba–Geigy and Polymetron, uses such a system. Its development and use have been described by Mosimann [12]. Such a system is universally applicable; it is not restricted to pH-shift systems.

10.2 SEQUESTERING AGENTS

The tendency of soaps and other carboxylates to form insoluble complexes with the calcium and magnesium ions in hard water is mentioned in sections 9.4 and 9.8.2. Apart from decreasing the efficiency of the anionic surfactant, the deposition of the insoluble complex on the textile substrate can cause problems in subsequent processing and particularly in coloration. Even trace amounts of certain transition-metal or alkaline-earth elements may cause processing difficulties. The formation of 'iron spots', particularly in bleaching, is well known: multivalent transition-metal cations catalyse the decomposition of hydrogen peroxide (although divalent calcium and magnesium ions have a stabilising effect) and localised staining or tendering of the fibre may occur. In coloration trace-metal ions can react with certain dyes, giving rise to precipitation, discoloration, unlevel dyeing and/or reduced fastness properties. The processing water is the most obvious source of such extraneous metal ions, but other potential sources should not be overlooked. For example, trace metals may be dissolved from the surfaces of machinery and fittings. The substrate may already contain such metals, as may also any chemicals or dyes used. Hence these problems cannot always be avoided simply by ensuring the supply of suitable water – indeed, the over-zealous treatment of water can actually lead to the presence of troublesome aluminium ions that were not originally present! Such problems can be solved using chemicals that react preferentially with the metal ion, effectively preventing it from interfering with the mainstream reaction or process. Such chemicals are aptly known as sequestering agents.

Sequestering agents work by a mechanism of complex formation, often in the form of chelation. A chelating agent contains substituents suitably located to form one or more chelate rings by electron donation to the metal ion (see section 5.2), the resulting complex remaining soluble and innocuous under the conditions of processing. The most useful donating atoms are nitrogen, as found in amines or substituted amines, and oxygen in the form of carboxyl, phosphate or ionised hydroxy groups. As in the formation of dye–metal chelates (such as chrome mordant and metal-complex dyes), at least two electron-donating atoms in the sequestering agent structure must be arranged so that a stable ring can be formed with the metal ion, the highest stability resulting from five- and six-membered rings.

A great many products exhibit sequestering abilities but relatively few are of commercial value in textile processing, the three main types being, in order of importance [13,14]:

– aminopolycarboxylates
– phosphates, mainly inorganic
– hydroxycarboxylates.

The aminopolycarboxylates are powerful chelating agents; the most common is undoubtedly ethylenediaminetetra-acetic acid, generally known as EDTA. Such products are sold either as the free acids or as sodium salts; EDTA is more usually sold as the di- or tetra-sodium salt (10.4). Another useful member of this class is diethylenetriaminepenta-acetic acid (DTPA), again generally used as its sodium salt (10.5); a third is nitrilotriacetic acid (NTA), also as its sodium salt (10.6).

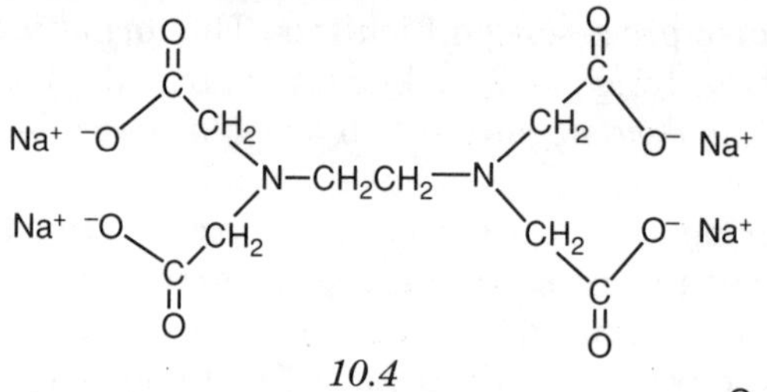

10.4

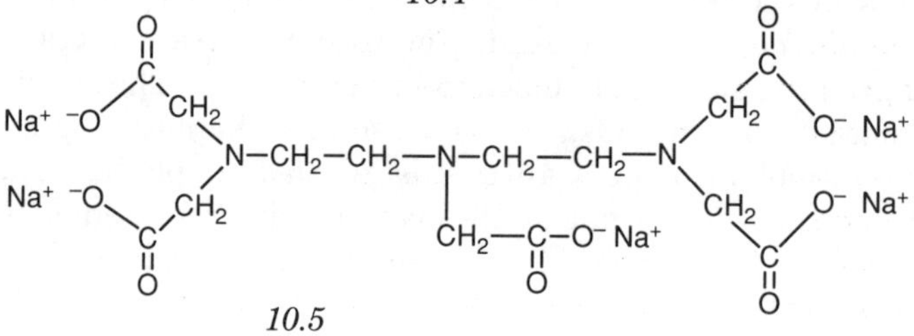

10.5

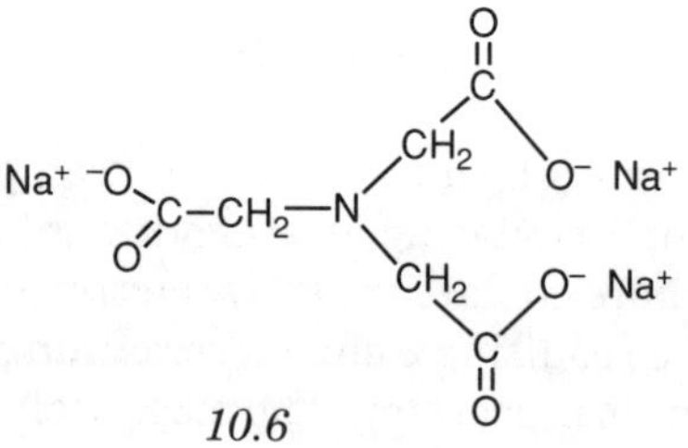

10.6

Also useful in certain circumstances are derivatives of these aminopoly-carboxylic acids in which one or more of the carboxymethyl groups has been replaced by a hydroxyethyl group to give a hydroxyaminocarboxylic acid. The most important examples of this type are N-(hydroxyethyl)ethylene-diaminetriacetic acid (10.7; HEDTA), in which one of the carboxymethyl groups of EDTA has been replaced by a hydroxyethyl group, and NN-bis(hydroxyethyl)glycine (10.8; DEG), in which two of the carboxymethyl groups of NTA have been so substituted.

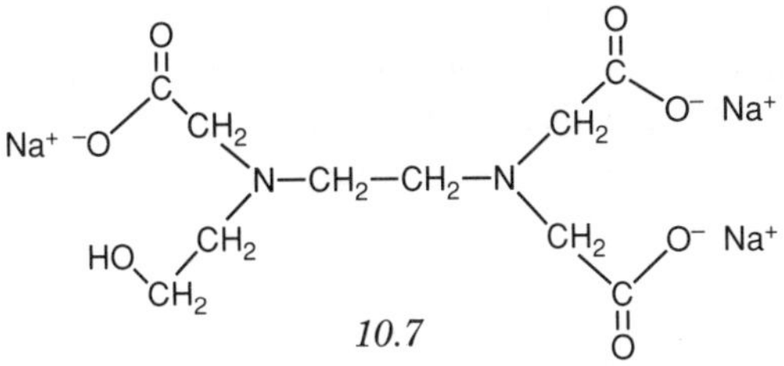

$$Na^+ \ ^-O \overset{\displaystyle O}{\overset{\|}{C}} \diagdown CH_2 \diagdown N-CH_2-CH_2-N \diagup CH_2 \overset{\displaystyle O}{\overset{\|}{C}} \diagup O^- \ Na^+$$

10.7

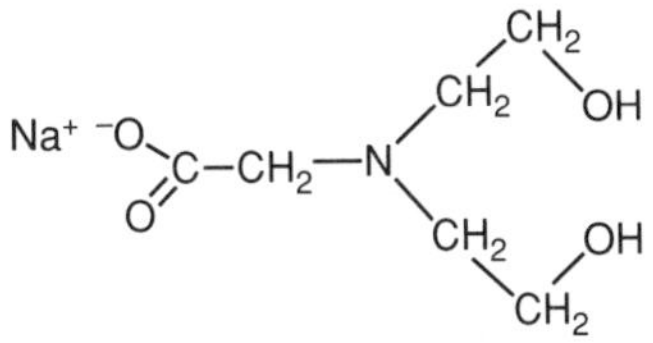

10.8

These aminopolycarboxylates act as sequestering agents by forming structures in which each metal ion is chelated into one or more five-membered rings. It is often assumed that one molecule of sequestering agent reacts with one ion of the metal, and for many practical purposes this is a valid assumption. The nature of the complexes actually formed, however, may depend on other factors such as the pH of the medium. It is difficult to represent such structures in detail, particularly as water of solvation is usually involved. It is convenient to adopt a simplified representation, omitting the water of solvation, as for the EDTA–calcium complex shown in structure 10.9, in which the arrows represent coordination bonds and the calcium ion is held by three five-membered rings. At pH values below 11 the structure tends to be more like that shown in 10.10, which also resembles the complex formed with NTA (10.11).

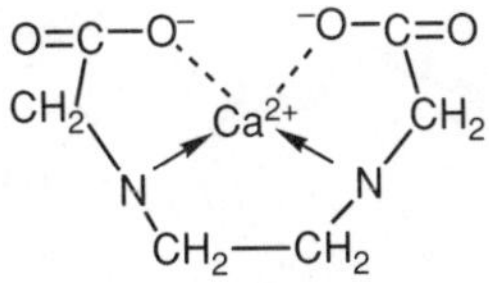

10.9

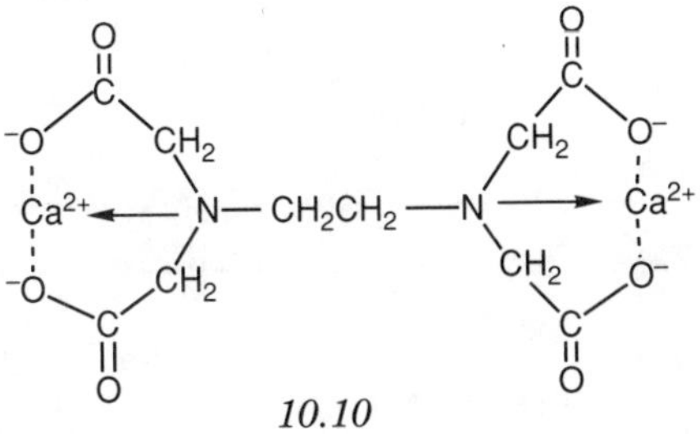

10.10

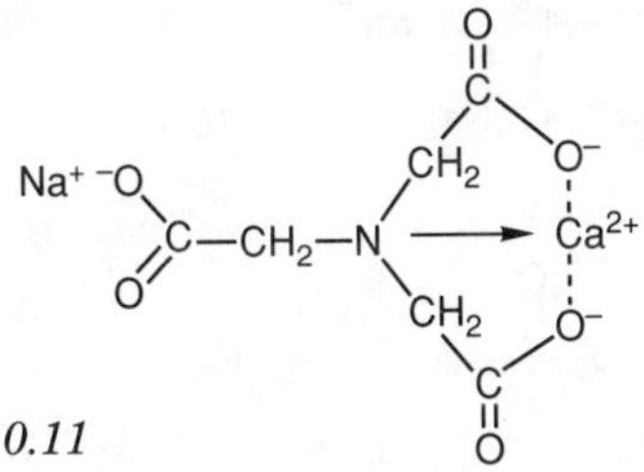

10.11

A more elaborate representation of an EDTA–metal complex, which gives some indication of the three-dimensional aspects of the structure, shows a complex of five five-membered rings (10.12) [13];. A similar representation of a DTPA–metal complex shows a system of eight five-membered rings.

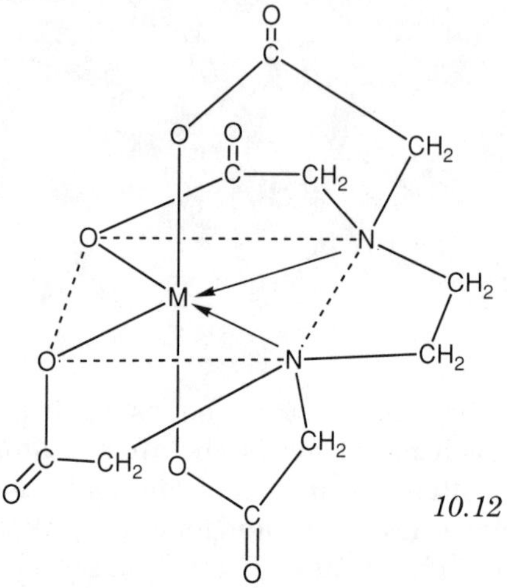

10.12

Various polyphosphates are effective sequestering agents under appropriate conditions. The best known of these is sodium hexametaphosphate [$Na_2(Na_4P_6O_{18})$]. Others are sodium polyphosphate (10.13), sodium tripolyphosphate (sodium triphosphate) (10.14), sodium trimetaphosphate (10.15) and sodium pyrophosphate (10.16). These function by withdrawing the troublesome metal cation into an innocuous and water-soluble complex anion by a process of ion exchange as shown in Scheme 10.6 for sodium hexametaphosphate.

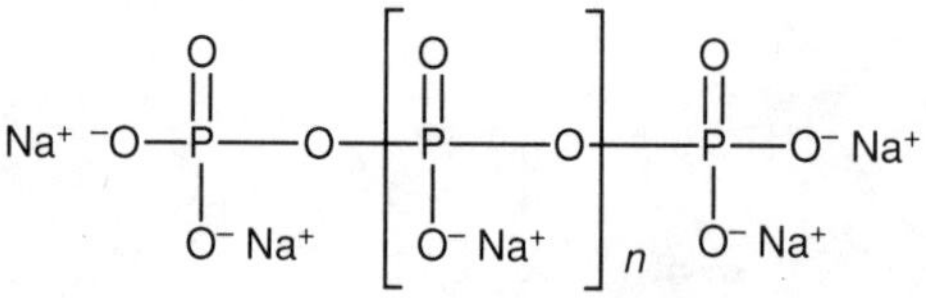

10.13

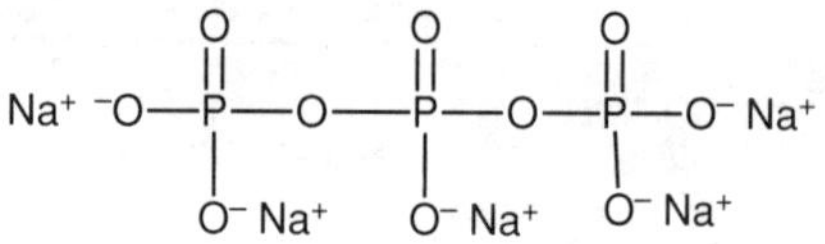

10.14

10.15

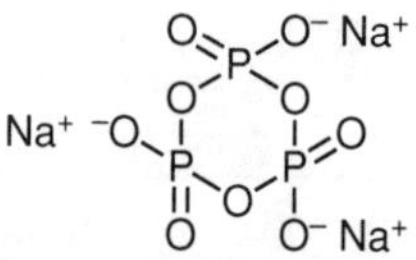

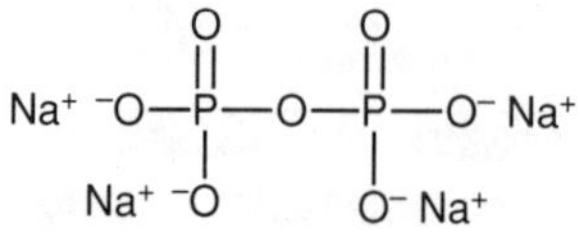

10.16

$$Na_2(Na_4P_6O_{18}) + 2\,Ca^{2+} \rightleftharpoons Na_2(Ca_2P_6O_{18}) + 4Na^+$$

Scheme 10.6

The disadvantage of the polyphosphates is that at the temperatures used in many textile processes – 100°C or higher – they can be hydrolysed into simpler phosphates that cannot retain the metal atom in the sequestered form. For example, disodium dicalcium hexametaphosphate hydrolyses on prolonged boiling to yield the insoluble calcium orthophosphate. This is one of the main reasons why polyphosphate sequestrants are used much less extensively than the more versatile and stable aminopolycarboxylates. A structural compromise between these two types of compound can also give products with sequestering properties, although they are phosphonates rather than phosphates since they contain –C–P–, rather than –C–O–P–, linkages. Examples of these phosphonated aminopolycarboxylates are ethylenediaminetetramethylphosphonic acid (10.17; EDTMP), diethylenetriaminepentamethylphosphonic acid (10.18; DETMP) and nitrilotrimethylphosphonic acid (10.19; 'aminotrimethylene phosphonate', or ATMP). The consumption of these compounds in textile processing is small in relation to that of the aminopolycarboxylates; they are mainly used in detergent formulations [15,16] as sodium, potassium, ammonium or alkanolamine salts.

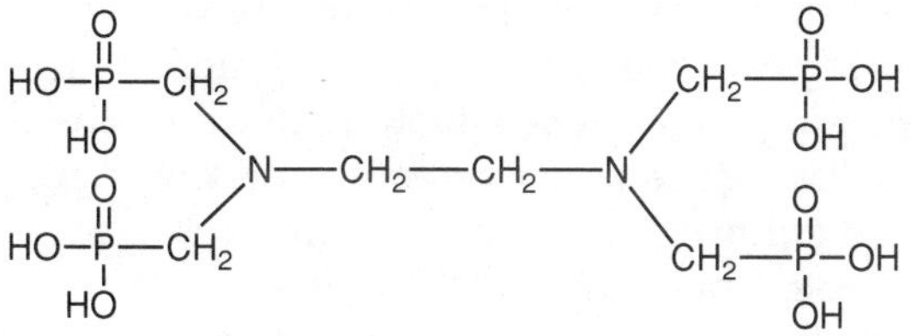

10.17

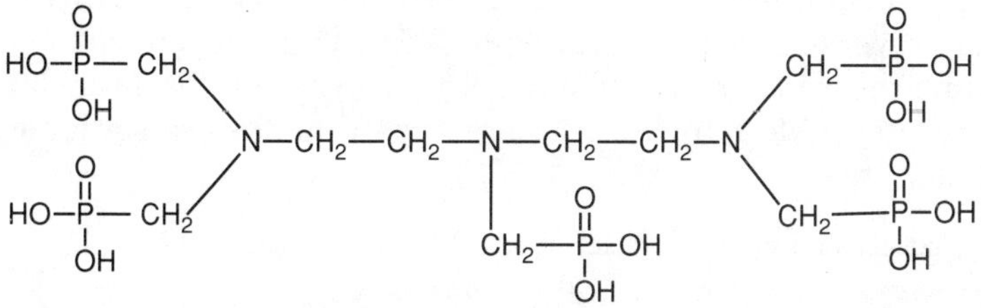

10.18

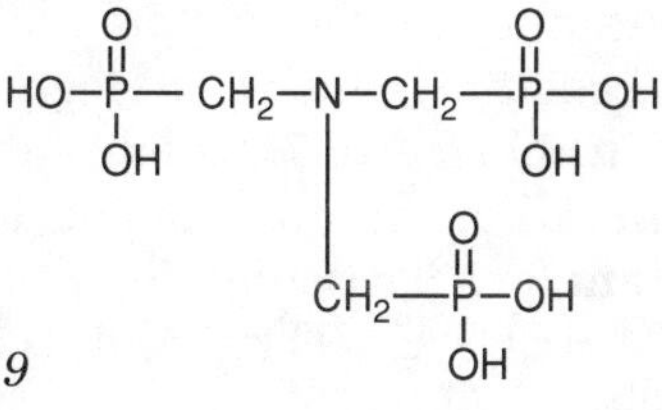

10.19

The hydroxycarboxylic acids provide a range of sequestering agents of which the best known are citric acid (10.20), tartaric acid (10.21) and gluconic acid (10.22); the poisonous oxalic acid (10.23) is now rarely used. These acids are are much less important as sequestering agents than either the aminopolycarboxylates or the polyphosphates, however.

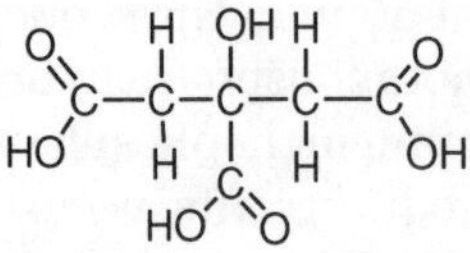

10.20 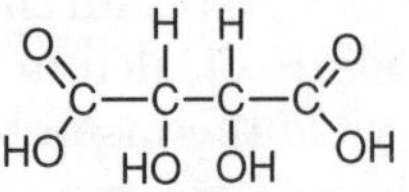   10.21 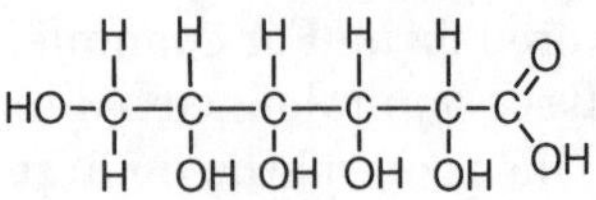   10.22

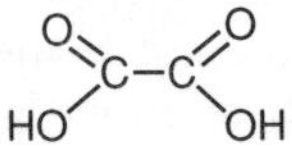

10.23

Sequestering agents are probably used rather indiscriminately by most textile processors, in amounts far in excess of the stoichiometric quantities required by the particular set of conditions. Instructions often simply state 'add 0.5–1.0 g/l of a suitable sequestering agent such as EDTA'. Whilst this is convenient for most purposes, it is worth bearing in mind that the action of sequestering agents is governed by physico-chemical factors that, among other things, determine a hierarchy of efficacy. When the type and concentration of trace-metal ions to be sequestered is known, a more discriminating approach can be adopted regarding the choice of agent. In some cases, including the treatment of water, this more precise specification of type and quantity can be important.

Little need be said here about the simple ion-exchange reactions such as that between sodium hexametaphosphate and calcium. It is useful, however, to consider in more detail those reactions involving chelation (Scheme 10.7). This is a reversible reaction, the equilibrium being dependent on the process pH and the concentrations of the reacting species. While chelated complexes are less stable at higher temperatures, this effect can be ignored in practice.

sequestering agent + metal ion ⇌ chelated complex

Scheme 10.7

The stability of the complex is generally expressed in terms of its stability constant, which is the logarithm of the equilibrium constant of the reaction in Scheme 10.7. A high stability constant indicates a high sequestering effect. For example, amongst the aminopolycarboxylates the stability constant for a particular metal ion generally increases in the order NTA < HEDTA < EDTA < DTPA. Metals can also be listed in order of increasing stability constant: $Mg^{2+} < Ca^{2+} < Mn^{2+} < Al^{3+} < Zn^{2+}, Co^{3+} < Pb^{2+} < Cu^{2+}, Ni^{3+} < Fe^{3+}$. Thus for the series of sequestering agents and metals mentioned, the magnesium–NTA complex has the lowest stability and iron(III)–DTPA the highest. This scale of values effectively constitutes a displacement series. This means, in general, that in any system containing more than one metal it is the metal forming the most stable complex (that is, the complex having the highest stability constant) that chelates preferentially. When these ions have been completely chelated, any remaining sequestering agent then begins to sequester the metal that forms the complex having the next highest stability constant. Similarly if iron(III) enters a system in which, for example, calcium is already chelated, the iron will displace the calcium since the iron complex has the higher stability constant, and the calcium will only remain chelated if sufficient sequestering agent is present to sequester both iron and calcium.

Adding protons or hydroxide ions to the system will influence the position of the chelation equilibrium. The stability constant of a complex is thus influenced by the pH of the system, and pH is an important consideration in the choice of sequestering agents. The inorganic polyphosphates tend to be most efficient under slightly acid conditions whilst the aminopolycarboxylates generally work best under neutral or alkaline conditions, although they still show some usefulness, and are used, at pH values of around 4.5. Generalisations like these can be misleading, however, since efficiency varies from one metal ion to another at different pH values for each sequestering agent. The phosphates are good sequestrants for magnesium and calcium but are considerably less effective for trivalent cations, which can be successfully sequestered with NTA, EDTA and DTPA up to about pH 9. At higher pH values iron(III) tends to be precipitated from these complexes. It was mainly for this reason that the hydroxyaminocarboxylates were developed, this basically being their main use. For example, HEDTA will sequester iron(III) ions at pH 9 and DEG works well at pH 12. Although effective with most metal ions, DEG will not sequester calcium or magnesium, and HEDTA is also not as efficacious with these hard water ions as are the aminopolycarboxylates. At pH values above 12 iron(III) can be sequestered with triethanolamine (10.24), either alone or together with EDTA.

$$HOCH_2CH_2 \diagdown N \diagup CH_2CH_2OH$$
$$| $$
$$CH_2CH_2OH \qquad 10.24$$

Most divalent and trivalent ions, with the exception of the alkaline-earth metals, are effectively chelated by the hydroxycarboxylates citric and tartaric acid, and citric acid will also sequester iron in the presence of ammonia. Another hydroxycarboxylate, gluconic acid, is especially useful in caustic soda solution and as a general-purpose sequestering agent.

Clearly, the efficiency of sequestering must be optimised *for a particular set of conditions*. Thought needs to be given especially to the pH of the system and to whether broad-spectrum or specific sequestering is required. The extent of knowledge of the trace-metal ions present will determine whether a precise addition or an arbitrary excess of agent is needed. Finally, in some circumstances problems can arise in the use of certain sequestering agents that can remove the metal from a dye, with subsequent changes in shade and/or fastness properties. Metal-complex acid dyes and mordanted dyes are obviously vulnerable, but many direct and reactive dyes also contain such metals.

Further uses of sequestering agents are mentioned in Chapter 12.

10.3 PREPARATION OF SUBSTRATES

Although this chapter is concerned with auxiliaries used in coloration processes, the success of any such process relies on the state of the substrate presented for coloration; moreover, thorough preparation can often do much to reduce the need for auxiliaries in subsequent processes. The subject of substrate preparation has been discussed in detail elsewhere [17]; in the brief treatment given here, the emphasis is on the chemistry of the products used rather than on the technology of processing.

10.3.1 Scouring

The purpose of scouring is to reduce the level of fats, waxes, oils, dirt and so forth on the substrate. Apart from the aesthetic benefits of clean fabric, the major technical reason for scouring is to improve the extent and uniformity of absorbency for subsequent processes, especially coloration. Usually the object is the complete removal of all extraneous matter but on occasion only partial removal is the aim, since a certain residue of oils, for example, will aid such processes as spinning, weaving or knitting. Scouring is particularly important with natural fibres, which obviously contain much more extraneous matter than do synthetic fibres.

In scouring, surface-active products function as primary, rather than auxiliary, agents as the basic requirements are for good wetting power and detergency, the latter property generally including the ability to remove, emulsify and suspend the extraneous matter in the liquor. Not all good detergents possess good wetting properties; hence a combination of surface-active agents to provide both wetting and detergency may be preferable. Detergency can be significantly improved by the use of additional (i.e. auxiliary) compounds usually referred to as 'builders', the chief of which is undoubtedly alkali in the form of sodium carbonate or hydroxide, although alkaline phosphates such as trisodium orthophosphate, sodium pyrophosphate and sodium tripolyphosphate are also used; phosphates, indeed, have been used for many years as an integral part of household washing powders [15]. Alkalis function mainly through the saponification of the waxes, fats and oils on the substrate, thus rendering them water-soluble and more amenable to removal and suspension by detergent. If the processing water or the substrate contains cations such as those of calcium, magnesium or iron, a sequestering agent should be added to the scouring liquor; as well as their ability to sequester metals, many of these agents also possess useful detergent-enhancing powers. The aminopolycarboxy-lates are generally preferred, both for their sequestering ability and for their stability in warm to hot alkaline liquors. Polyphosphates are occasionally used at lower temperatures but are less efficient in alkaline media. For special purposes, organic solvents may be incorporated in the scouring media as these greatly aid the removal of greasy matter, particularly mineral oil, which may be a component of any lubricating oils applied to the substrate; examples include pine oil (especially), trichloroethylene, perchloroethylene, triethanolamine and glycols.

Soaps are occasionally still used for scouring, although anionic and non-ionic synthetic detergents are almost always preferred. Fatty alkyl sulphates, sulphonates and phosphates are commonly used among the anionics, while ethoxylated fatty alcohols and, especially, ethoxylated octyl- and nonyl-phenol are the most common non-ionic products used. Proprietary scouring agents range from single-component surfactants to complex, specially formulated mixtures that contain some or all of the above-mentioned types of component matched to give a balanced or compatible product. As mentioned in section 9.8.3, better emulsifying properties are generally obtained with a carefully selected blend of surfactants rather than with a single product. In selecting a suitable product, thought should be given to the ease with which it can be rinsed out of the substrate and to any effects that residual quantities may have on subsequent processes. Fabrics destined for printing, in particular, need the highest degree of uniform absorbency and cleanliness [18], free from residual surfactants that may cause bleeding or haloing of the printed design into the surrounding area.

Scouring is of critical importance in wool processing: important because the raw fibre contains 20–60% of extraneous matter [6] in the form of grease, suint, dirt, sand and vegetable matter, and critical because the fibre is so easily damaged by hot alkaline treatments. Soaps (such as sodium oleate, which has good detergency and is easily washed out) together with sodium carbonate have been widely used at 40–50°C; very greasy wools have been scoured using alkali alone to saponify the grease, forming a soap [6]. In recent years, however, even the traditionally conservative wool processors have mostly adopted synthetic detergents, applied under neutral conditions to help preserve the quality of the wool [16]. Raw wool is now usually scoured with non-ionic surfactants, the octa/nona-ethoxylated nonylphenols being preferred for their detergency, although ethoxylated straight-chain alcohols are used where better biodegradability is required. The advantages of non-ionic detergents over soaps include greater efficiency under neutral conditions, stability in hard water, lower cost and more efficient removal of grease (although this is one area where over-degreasing can be a disadvantage). Syndets are desorbed more easily in difficult rinsing situations (in yarn cheeses, for example), although they are not as efficient as soap for the suspension of dirt. In place of the alkaline sodium carbonate, the tendency is to use neutral sodium sulphate as a detergent builder. Aside from the raw wools, the trend nowadays for lubricating the fibre is to use [19]

(a) water-miscible polyglycol lubricants; these are mainly used on carpet yarns and can readily be scoured with neutral non-ionic surfactant

(b) mineral wool oil (mineral oil with a non-ionic lubricant), normally extracted using a non-ionic surfactant although in some cases a little alkali may also be useful

(c) a combination of mineral oil, olein fatty acids and triglycerides; non-ionic surfactant with sodium carbonate can be used for partial removal, but where more complete removal is required (as it is where subsequent shrink-resist processes are carried out) soap and sodium carbonate must be used

(d) natural vegetable and/or animal oils; these are mostly used on woven worsteds and are scoured traditionally with soap and sodium carbonate, although even here there is a gradual trend towards more neutral systems.

Solvent scouring has also been carried out on wool with, for example, perchloroethylene in which 8–18% water on the weight of wool has been emulsified with a surfactant.

The other major natural fibre, cotton, also contains a significant proportion of extraneous matter such as seeds, fats, waxes, colouring matter and dirt as well as substances such as sizes and lubricants applied during processing. Unlike wool, however, it has outstanding stability to alkali and withstands strongly alkaline treatments ranging from severe caustic kier boiling to milder treatments with soap and soda [17,20–22]. It is difficult to detach the effect of scouring from the complete sequence of desizing, scouring, mercerising and bleaching, since they all contribute to improved absorbency and cleanliness; desizing and bleaching will be considered later, however. Caustic treatment in kiers is carried out at the boil or in some cases at up to 120°C, using 1–2% o.w.f. alkali. This treatment bursts the seed motes and saponifies fats and waxes, converting the fatty esters into sodium salts and glycerol. This *in situ* formation of soaps naturally aids cleaning. Nevertheless, synthetic detergents are often added to aid penetration through wetting and to increase detergency. The surfactants must be highly stable in the strongly alkaline conditions, as well as in hard water. Anionic surfactants of the fatty alkyl sulphate, sulphonate and phosphate types are preferred. A synergistic mixture is beneficial, one component $(C_{10}-C_{13})$ to aid wetting, the other $(C_{14}-C_{16})$ as a detergent. The sulphosuccinates, often a first choice for wetting ability, cannot be used here as they are hydrolysed under such strongly alkaline conditions. A sequestering agent is usually added in order to remove metals that would create problems in subsequent bleaching. Addition of a mild reducing agent guards against alkaline oxidative tendering of the fibre through oxycellulose formation and also promotes a degree of bleaching. A commercial kier scouring agent may contain some or all of these components. Suppression of foam may also be a requirement (see section 10.8.2). Semi-continuous and continuous scouring systems are more common nowadays [22]. The auxiliary needs in these pad–steam processes are generally the same as those for batch scouring, except that the selection and balancing of the components is much more critical in order to secure optimum treatment under the short dwell times.

Compared with wool and cotton, the scouring procedures for synthetic fibres are relatively simple since these fibres contain fewer impurities, most of which have at least some degree of water solubility; the most important are sizes and lubricants. The major sizes used are poly(vinyl alcohol), carboxymethylcellulose and poly(acrylic acid), all of which are completely or partially water-soluble. Sometimes aliphatic polyesters are used.

Secondary acetate and triacetate fibres generally respond to a light scour with soap or synthetic detergent, usually at 60–75°C, although temperatures can range from 30 to 90°C [23], this being sufficient to remove soil, oil, sighting colour and any antistatic agent. Anionic synthetic detergents, such as the poly(oxyethylene) sulphates, are preferred for all fibres that are subsequently to be dyed with disperse dyes since low cloud-point non-ionic scouring agents, if carried over into the dyeing process, can interfere with the stability of the dye dispersion at higher temperatures. Addition of a sequestering agent is helpful in hard water. Care should be taken if alkali is added, especially on secondary acetate, since these ester fibres can be hydrolysed to cellulose under hot alkaline conditions. Nevertheless the S-finishing process uses this alkali sensitivity to effect a carefully controlled surface saponification of the fibre to improve drape and antistatic properties [24]. The process uses sodium hydroxide together with an anionic surfactant to aid wetting and uniformity of treatment. It is more usually carried out on the triacetate fibres, and reduces the total acetyl content from about 62 to 59%.

Polyamide and polyester fibres are generally adequately scoured using an alkyl poly(oxyethylene) sulphate and sodium carbonate [25]. Recently some polyester materials have been subjected to 'causticisation' treatments with sodium hydroxide in the presence of a cationic surfactant [22,23] to give a lighter fabric with a silkier handle; this process involves etching (localised saponification) of the polyester surface and is broadly analogous to the S-finish used on acetate fibres. As mentioned earlier, non-ionic scouring agents are best avoided when disperse dyes are to be used for subsequent coloration.

Conversely, when scouring acrylic fibres, anionic surfactants should be avoided [23] because they are liable to restrain the uptake of basic dyes. These fibres are usually scoured with an ethoxylated alcohol, either alone or with a mild alkali such as sodium carbonate or a phosphate.

10.3.2 Desizing

Desizing is essentially a part of the scouring process, and rapid removal of size is very important in the present trend towards continuous preparation processes. Starch-based products and especially solubilised starches are still the sizes most commonly used on cellulosic goods [22]. They are most frequently removed by enzyme treatment, which since it affects only the starch product ensures that the cellulosic fibre is undamaged; bacterial amylase is increasingly replacing malt and pancreatic enzymes [22]. On substrates other than 100% cellulose the tendency is to use completely or partially soluble sizes such as poly(vinyl alcohol), carboxymethylcellulose and poly(acrylic acid). Stiffening and lubricating agents, such as paraffin wax, may also be present. These are relatively easily removed, sometimes by warm water alone, or with detergent and alkali as described in section 10.3.1; detergents are always needed where lubricating agents are present. Where detergents are used in conjunction with an enzyme desizing system, it is worth remembering that non-ionic surfactants are less likely to deactivate enzymes than are anionic types. Heat treatments, such as fabric setting, can impair the solubility of poly(vinyl alcohol), carboxymethylcellulose and poly(acrylic acid) sizes; an oxidative desizing treatment using a detergent in the presence of alkaline hydrogen peroxide in its unstabilised form is then useful.

10.3.3 Bleaching

Bleaching with sodium hypochlorite has long been the mainstay of the bleaching industry, and although there have been no significant developments in process techniques in recent years, it is still widely used on a batchwise basis on account of its low chemical costs and in spite of its labour- and time-intensive characteristics [17,22]. Although bleaching can be accelerated by lowering the pH and/or raising the temperature, this so dramatically increases the risk of damage to the cellulose that such processes have not been adopted on a commercial basis. The traditional process uses sodium hypochlorite carefully controlled by addition of sodium carbonate at pH 10–11, the bleaching action then being governed by Scheme 10.8 [17]. Lower pH values lead to liberation of potentially damaging hypochlorous acid and ultimately to free chlorine (Scheme 10.9).

$$NaOCl \rightleftharpoons Na^+ + OCl^-$$

Scheme 10.8

pH 5.0-5.5
$$HOCl \rightleftharpoons H^+ + OCl^-$$

pH < 5
$$4 H^+ + 2 OCl^- \rightleftharpoons Cl_2 + 2H_2O$$

Scheme 10.9

If bleaching powder is used in place of sodium hypochlorite, the pH is controlled by adding lime [17]. Hypochlorite bleaching is followed by an antichlor treatment, usually with bisulphite, to remove residual chlorine. An intermediate dilute acid scour may also be given, this being essential if bleaching powder and lime have been used in order to remove the calcium.

Chlorite bleaching, using sodium chlorite ($NaClO_2$) under acidic conditions (pH≈4) is sometimes used on cellulosic and synthetic fibres. The reaction in the presence of cellulose can be conveniently represented as in Scheme 10.10 [20], although this is to some extent a simplification [17].

$$Cell—CHO + 3 HClO_2 \rightleftharpoons Cell—COOH + 2 ClO_2 + HCl + H_2O$$

Scheme 10.10

Chlorine dioxide, the active bleaching agent, is less liable than hypochlorite to damage cellulose. It is unpleasant and toxic, and can seriously damage stainless steel; its evolution during bleaching must be carefully controlled, and special corrosion-resistant equipment must be used. As Scheme 10.10 shows, acid (HCl) is also liberated and obviously tends to lower the pH. Hence it is common practice to begin the process at a higher pH (4.5–5.0), allowing the reaction to proceed towards the optimum pH of 4.0 ± 0.2. This shift can be controlled using an acid acceptor such as triethanolamine, a polyamine or ammonium persulphate, together with a buffer such as sodium acetate or phosphate [17]. The presence of metals in the liquor or on the fabric is not generally troublesome in chlorite bleaching. As well as controlling chlorine dioxide emission by careful control of pH, surfactants or other chemicals can be used that can trap the chlorine dioxide in stable foam and/or form a complex with it.

In contrast to the chlorine-containing chemicals, hydrogen peroxide has become widely adopted for continuous bleaching, offering considerable savings in labour, water and energy costs that more than offset the increased chemical costs. The basic mechanism of bleaching may be summarised by Scheme 10.11, the active bleaching component being the perhydroxyl ion.

$$H_2O_2 \longrightarrow HO_2^- + H^+$$

Scheme 10.11

But, as shown by Dickinson [17], many factors are involved and the actual mechanism is more complex. Most of the hydrogen peroxide sold for textile bleaching is acidic (pH 4.5–5.0) and contains additives that effectively stabilise it at this pH. Bleaching, however, is generally best carried out at pH 10.5–11.0. Under such alkaline conditions different additives are required for the stabilisation of the peroxide, which is necessary to avoid undesirably rapid decomposition with loss of bleaching efficiency and/or damage to the fibre.

The most common stabilising agents have been the colloidal sodium silicates. The formulae of silicates are best represented in terms of the ratio of sodium oxide to silica, as in sodium metasilicate ($Na_2O:SiO_2$) and orthosilicate ($2Na_2O:SiO_2$). These silicates, however, are crystalline forms in which this ratio is 1 or greater. In the colloidal forms originally preferred for peroxide bleaching the ratio is less than 1; for example, in the so-called 'alkaline glass' form the ratio is 1:2, whilst in the so-called 'water glass' form it varies from 1:1.6 to 1:1.38. The colloidal silicates are efficient and economical stabilisers but care is needed to ensure efficient washing-off in order to avoid silicaceous deposits on the fabric and equipment. Although such colloidal forms have been preferred, the crystalline meta- and ortho-silicates can also be used, and may provide easier washing-off. The required degree of alkalinity is generally obtained by the addition of sodium hydroxide, sodium carbonate or a phosphate, the amount of alkali varying with the type and quantity of silicate used. Since the bleaching action as represented by Scheme 10.11 yields acid, sufficient alkali is required for neutralisation as well as absorption by the cellulose. The mechanism by which these stabilisers work is complex, although the elements of buffering action and sequestering of transition-metal ions, such as those of iron(III) and copper(II), undoubtedly contribute. Magnesium ion also plays an essential part in the mechanism and must be added (as the sulphate, for example) if sufficient is not already present in the system. It is important to recognise that whilst transition-metal ions catalyse the destruction of peroxide, the alkaline-earth elements stabilise it. In the absence of calcium and magnesium even silicates can act as bleach activators [14].

The problems associated with silicaceous deposits have led to the adoption of more costly organic stabilising agents that also aid in plant cleaning and reduce the incidence of reprocessing. These organic stabilisers are often commercially blended products which may or may not contain magnesium salts [17], the three main types being aminopolycarboxylate sequestering agents, protein degradation products and selected surfactants. The preferred sequestering agents, in terms of both sequestering ability and stability to oxidation, are DTPA (10.5), either as its sodium or its magnesium salt, and its hydroxy derivatives [13]. Relatively simple methods of evaluating the efficiency of stabilisers have been used, but more reliable results are obtained with statistical experimental methods involving a realistic simulation of the bleaching process [26,27].

Wool is usually bleached with peroxide [6] at alkaline pH although acidic conditions (pH 3–3.5 with formic acid) can also be used. Sulphur stoving, a bleaching process used only on wool, employs sulphur dioxide generated by burning sulphur. Aqueous reduction bleaching systems include (a) a cold dilute solution of sodium bisulphite and sulphuric acid, (b) a solution of sulphur dioxide in water (sulphurous acid) and (c) a dilute solution of sodium dithionite. Occasionally potassium permanganate followed by treatment with oxalic acid has been used.

Cotton is bleached mainly with peroxide, although hypochlorite or chlorite may be used in batchwise processes. Certain alkaline peroxy compounds are of minor interest for wool or cotton bleaching, including sodium peroxide (Na_2O_2), hydrated sodium perborate ($NaBO_2.H_2O_2.3H_2O$) and sodium percarbonate or sodium carbonate peroxyhydrate ($2Na_2CO_3. 3H_2O_2$).

Most synthetic fibres need no bleaching, but where it is necessary either peroxide or chlorite bleaches are recommended. Fluorescent brightening agents suitable for use in the bleaching of natural and synthetic fibres are discussed in Chapter 11.

10.3.4 Mercerising

The objective of mercerising is to swell the cotton fibre, increasing its lustre, strength and dyeability. Traditionally a cold solution of 25–26% by mass of sodium hydroxide is used, although better penetration and more even treatment is obtained with the more recent hot mercerising technique [17,22,28]. The addition of a wetting agent to the mercerising liquor gives better penetration and more even treatment, the main requirements being for a combination of stability and powerful wetting action under such strongly alkaline conditions. Low propensity to foaming is generally another important requirement, although detergency, as opposed to wetting, is not usually necessary. The wetting power, however, becomes more important if the goods have not already been well scoured. Until recently products based on cresylic acid (a mixture of o-, m- and p-cresols) were popular [29] as they were more effective than conventional surfactants. Cresylic acid alone was ineffective, however, and required co-solvent additives such as alcohols, ethers, ketones, lower fatty acid amides or cellosolve. Such products have largely been replaced by cresol-free alternatives. According to Davidsohn and Milwidsky [15], a commonly used basis is sulphated 2-ethylhexanol (10.25). Like cresylic acid, this is ineffective alone and must be blended with about 10% each of butanol and unsulph-

$$CH_3CH_2CH_2CH_2 \diagdown$$
$$CHCH_2OSO_3H$$
$$CH_3CH_2 \diagup$$

                                    10.25

ated 2-ethylhexanol to give an effective product in terms of solubility, stability and wetting power.

Most of the commercial products listed today [30] are described either as mixtures of non-ionic and anionic wetting agents, or as sulphonated and sulphated alcohols. The lower fatty phosphate esters are also used.

10.3.5 Wool processing

Milling is a process peculiar to wool and is carried out to develop its felting propensity [6]. Some goods such as felt hats and blankets are milled under slightly acidic conditions, sulphuric acid being the main agent. Acid milling is particularly useful for dyed goods, which may not have adequate resistance to neutral or alkaline treatments. Alkaline milling conditions are still, however, largely used for woven piece goods traditionally known as milling cloths, maximum milling taking place at around pH 10, using soap. The higher-melting soaps, such as those based on tallow and palm oils, are preferred to give the required gelatinous solution and lubricating properties [20]. Greasy woollens are often milled in sodium carbonate alone, which saponifies the grease to a soap. Even with such woven pieces, however, there is a gradual trend [19] towards milling in almost neutral conditions, for which milling aids based on non-ionic and anionic surfactants are useful. Some wool yarns are milled nowadays simply by tumble drying the wet yarns, whilst knitted garments are milled in rotary-type machines using non-ionic surfactants with sodium bicarbonate or polyphosphates. Solvent-based systems in which a small amount of water is emulsified in the solvent by an appropriate surfactant are also used [19], this often forming part of a sequence in which scouring, milling and shrink-resist treatments are all carried out in the same machine.

Another process peculiar to wool is carbonising, in which heat and a mineral acid (such as sulphuric acid or aluminium chloride) are used to oxidatively decompose the cellulosic impurities. Surfactants, which must be stable to the conditions of hot acidic treatment, help the wetting and penetration of the wool, ensuring more uniform treatment with less damage to the wool. Alkylnaphthalenesulphonates such as structure 10.26, as well as non-ionic surfactants such as structure 10.27, are widely used [6,29].

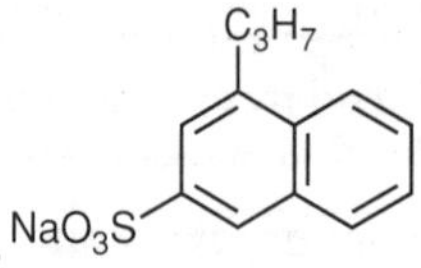

10.26

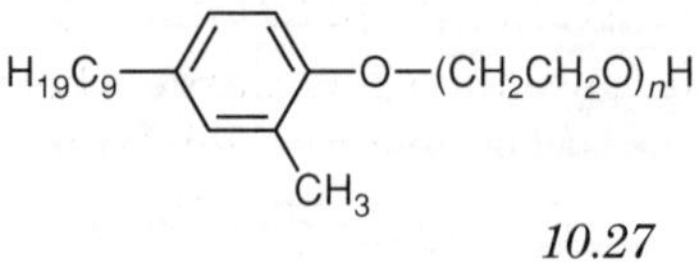

10.27

Shrink-resist processes for wool have come into prominence in recent years, especially those producing machine-washable wool. These processes can have a decisive bearing on the selection of dyes as regards fastness properties. Numerous approaches have been suggested, involving oxida-

tive modification of the epithelial scales, the deposition of a polymer on the fibre, or a combination of both, but relatively few are in significant commercial use today. The following have been estimated [19] as being of major current commercial significance:
- the chlorination–Hercosett process
- oxidative processes, particularly those based on sodium dichloroisocyanurate and permonosulphuric acid.

Other processes used to a much smaller extent include
- polymer-only processes using Synthappret BAP (BAY) or Lankrolan SHR3 (Diamond Shamrock)
- solvent treatments using silicones or Synthappret LKF (BAY).

Undoubtedly the most important of these processes today, accounting in 1982 for almost three-quarters of the world production of fully machine-washable wool [19], are those using a combination of mild acid chlorination and a polymer, of which the most widely used is the basic polyamide–epichlorohydrin resin known as Hercosett 57 (Hercules). The Dylan GRC process (Precision Processes) is also a chlorination–resin treatment, using Polymer G; details of this process, however, are only available to licensees.

The earlier oxidative processes used acidified sodium hypochlorite, but met with difficulties in achieving consistent, uniform treatment without excessive fibre damage. These have now largely been overcome by processes based on the use of sodium dichloroisocyanurate (10.28) under acidic conditions, such as the well-known Fichlor (Fisons) and Basolan DC (BASF) processes.

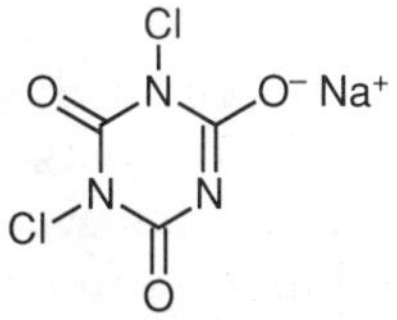

$$\text{10.28}$$

The use of this 'chlorine generator' provides a more gradual and controlled release of chlorine than can be obtained with hypochlorite. Additives used include dioctylsulphosuccinates as wetting agents, and an acidifying medium such as acetic acid with a buffer such as sodium formate/formic acid or permonosulphuric acid (H_2SO_5) (Dylan X2 process of Precision Processes).

Less significant are polymer–solvent processes, perhaps the most important being that based on Synthappret LKF [31]. This is an 80% solution in ethyl acetate of a partly polymerised isocyanate of the type represented by structure 10.29, which is applied from perchloroethylene; exposure to atmospheric moisture over 4–5 days induces further polymerisation to give

$$
\begin{array}{l}
\text{—OCONHRNCO} \\
\text{—OCONHRNCO} \quad \text{R = alkyl} \\
\text{—OCONHRNCO}
\end{array} \qquad 10.29
$$

a polyurethane finish that is insoluble in both water and perchloro-ethylene.

Polymers which can be applied from aqueous solution include Synthap-pret BAP, the bisulphite adduct of Synthappret LKF and Lankrolan SHR3, which is a thiosulphate (Bunte salt) derivative of a polyether; the former is applied in conjunction with a polyacrylate or polyurethane dispersion (Sirolan BAP process) [19]. Some silicone-based polymers are also used.

10.3.6 Combined processes

The economics, at least on paper, of combining two or more processes to gain major savings in time and energy have long been sufficiently attrac-tive to motivate research in this direction. For example, one-stage desize–scour, scour–bleach, desize–scour–bleach, scour–dye and even (paradoxically enough) bleach–dye operations have been, and are, oper-ated. The major disadvantage of such combined processes stems from the difficulty of operating a single process, especially compounded where there is a high probability of incompatibility, as in enzyme desizing–bleaching or in bleaching–dyeing. In addition, any process that is combined with scouring and/or desizing may be subject to interference from the products removed by those processes. Under these circumstances the choice of chem-ical additions becomes critical. For example, in combined desizing–bleaching the enzyme must be stable to oxidation and both processes must be efficacious under the same conditions of time, temperature and pH. Similarly any other products used, such as surfactants for wetting and detergency or metal-sequestering agents, must fulfil their primary task and not interfere with other functions, while themselves being unaffected by the other ingredients and process conditions.

Scour–dye operations in particular need very careful planning backed by detailed knowledge and experience, especially in regard to the ways in which the detergents and the products that they remove affect the stability and exhaustion of the dyes. In the combined scouring and dyeing of wool or nylon with acid dyes the detergent should ideally also function as a levelling agent – or, rather, the levelling agent must also function effi-ciently as a scouring agent. The crucial factor in scour–dye processes involving disperse dyes is the stability of the dye dispersion in the presence of the detergent and of the impurities extracted from the fibre; this becomes increasingly critical with higher temperatures (say 130°C) and with difficult substrate forms and machines (such as tightly woven fabrics on beams). Hence such operations are more frequently used in, for example, jet dyeing. Incompatible surfactants and greasy soil can have disastrous effects on dye dispersions, leading to agglomeration of dye particles and deposition of coloured oily stains on the substrate, with extensive breakdown of the dispersion in severe cases. Surfactants can also have a highly selective effect on the rate and extent of exhaustion of disperse dyes and must therefore be selected with due regard for this property.

In spite of these difficulties successful combined processes are indeed operated, although they require vigilant monitoring. The economies gained must not be offset by any counter-claims of lost processing time and costs of damage and reprocessing. It would be surprising if the manufacturers of dyes and chemicals were more enthusiastic than textile processors about such combinations, since the former are understandably more cautious about guaranteeing the efficacy, compatibility and stability of individual products in circumstances for which they were not really designed. Yet in an area where environmental and economic factors limit research into new products, the fusing of normally sequential processes into a single one will remain a worthwhile economical and technological goal.

10.4 DISPERSING AND SOLUBILISING AGENTS

10.4.1 Dispersing agents

Dispersing agents are substances that promote the more or less uniform and stable suspension of relatively small particles in a given matrix. We are concerned here with the most common type of dispersion encountered in textile coloration, the solid-in-water systems typified especially by disperse dye technology, as well as the insoluble forms of vat and sulphur dyes. Pigments are also extremely important examples of solid-in-liquid dispersions but form a specialised case fully dealt with in Chapter 2. Also excluded from this section are other systems that depend mainly on a large increase in viscosity for their suspending action; these are more appropriately dealt with in section 10.6.

Any preparation of solid particles in a liquid medium is more or less unstable as a result of (a) gravitational settling effects and (b) attractive forces between particles tending to lead to particles adhering, thus increasing the susceptibility of the system to gravitational effects. Two aspects need to be considered: the initial preparation of the dispersion, and its subsequent stabilisation during storage and use; only rarely will one agent satisfy the needs of both. Individual dyes vary widely in their requirements and any given dye may require different treatments depending, for example, on its micro-crystalline form and the application processes in which it is to be used. Therefore specific types of dispersing agents, or mixtures of them, are frequently needed to obtain the optimum dispersing action. There are three main groups of such agents:

- surfactants, mainly of the anionic and non-ionic types
- water-soluble polyelectrolytes, most usually of the anionic type
- polymers.

The chemistry of surfactants has already been described. They usually play a subsidiary role in dispersions involved in textile coloration. The polymer group includes water-soluble products such as acrylic acid copolymers, sulphonated polyvinyl compounds, alginates and carboxymethylcellulose. These are less important as dispersing agents for disperse, vat and sulphur dyes, although much more so in areas such as pigment technology and as thickening or anti-migration agents in printing and continuous dyeing (see section 10.6). The polyelectrolytes thus form the major group of dispersing agents of concern to us here, particularly in the manufacture and use of disperse dyes. Two types are important [32]: the condensation products of formaldehyde with arylsulphonic acids, and the ligninsulphonates.

As with surface-active agents, the detailed chemistry of these products is a good deal more complicated than is indicated by the nominal structures frequently quoted. Most commercial products are mixtures of which the nominal structure represents a basic type only. Indeed, the detailed chemistry of the more complex products is still only partially understood. These provisos should be borne in mind when considering the structures given below.

The sulphonated aromatic condensation products form a large and varied group, since formaldehyde will condense with many aromatic compounds [32], including sulphonated arylamines, phenols and aliphatic ketones; the range of commercially important products is relatively limited, however. One of the oldest is the condensation product of naphthalene-2-sulphonic acid and formaldehyde (10.30) in which the degree of condensation is thought to correspond to between two and ten naphthalene units, although the quantitative distribution of the condensates varies widely. Also of importance are the similarly structured condensation products of (a) phenols with formaldehyde and sodium sulphite (structures 10.31 and 10.32, depending on molar ratios) and (b) p-cresol and 2-naphthol-6-sulphonic acid with formaldehyde and sodium bisulphite (10.33 and 10.34). The types represented by structures 10.31–10.34 are also widely used as syntans (see section 10.7.1).

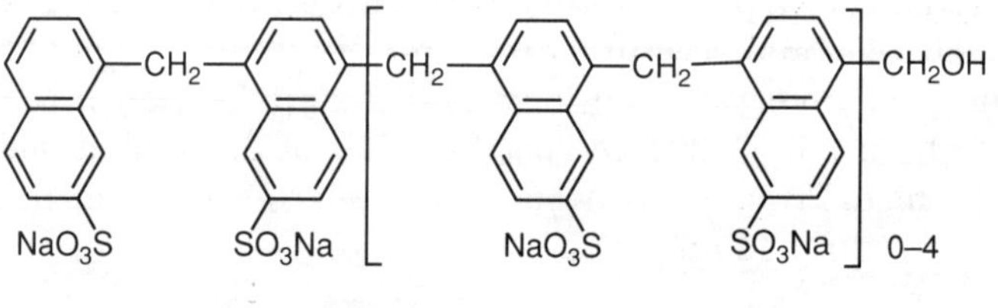

10.30

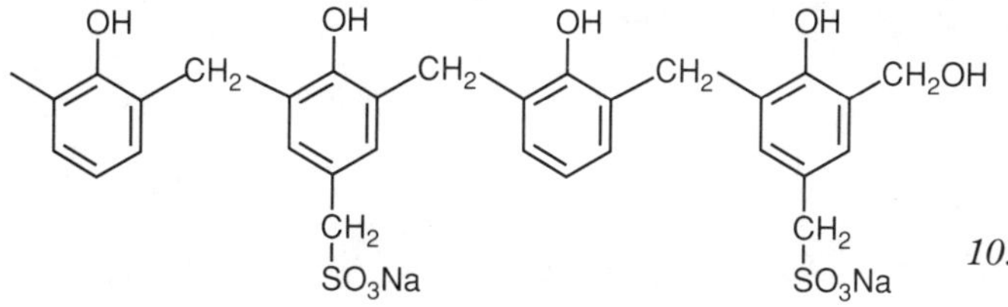

10.31

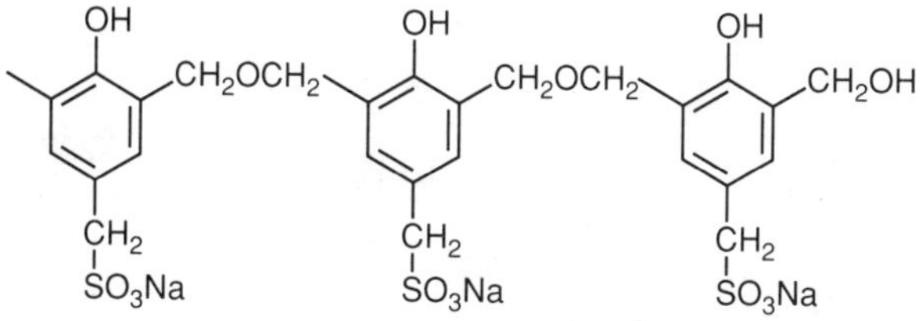

10.32

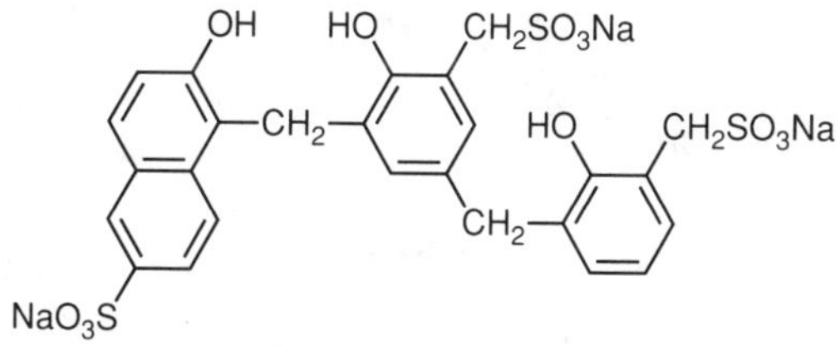

10.33

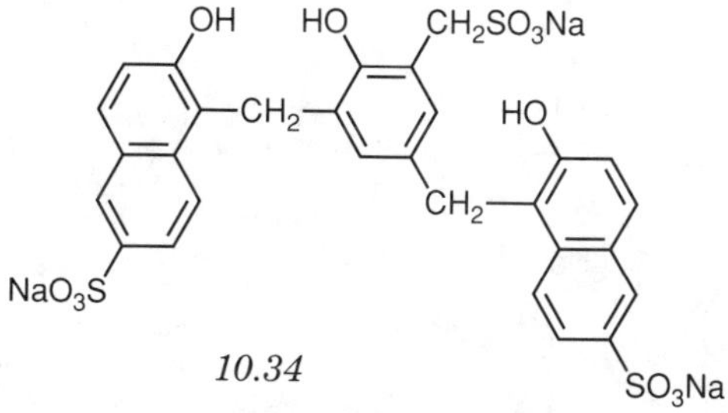

10.34

The ligninsulphonates comprise a variable group of products derived from wood pulping. Their highly complex structures are only partially understood, although enough is known to enable representative structures to be proposed, showing the major functional groups. There are two distinct processes whereby lignins are obtained. The first is an acidic digestion process in which the wood is pulped by sulphite or bisulphite. The second is an alkaline process, the so-called kraft process, in which the wood is treated [33] with sodium sulphide in autoclaves at pH 13 and 160–175°C. The product is precipitated by careful addition of acid, filtered off and washed free from inorganic species, and then sulphonated to increase its aqueous solubility. Structure 10.35 has been proposed as being representative of kraft lignin prior to sulphonation [33]. An alternative partial representation of a lignin structure [32] is that of structure 10.36, which shows

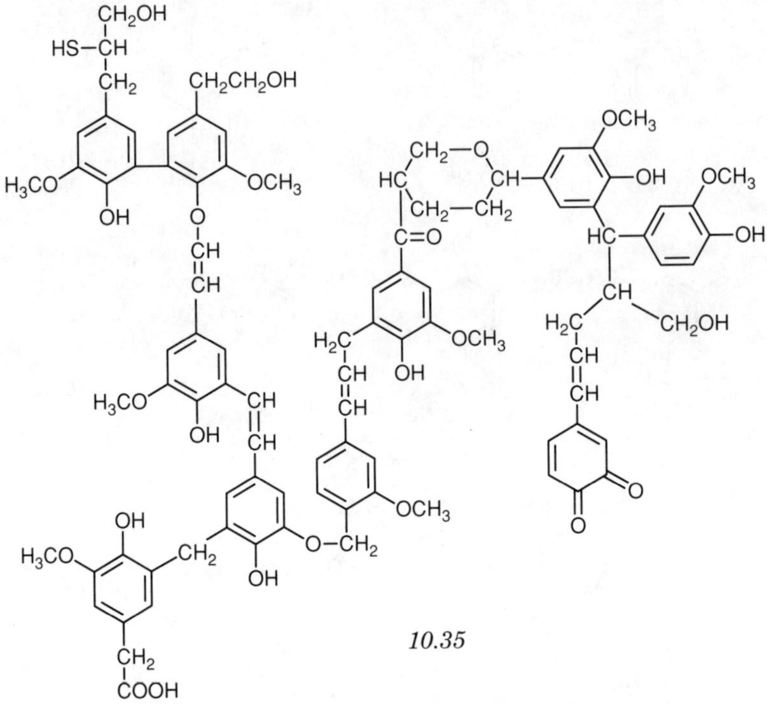

10.35

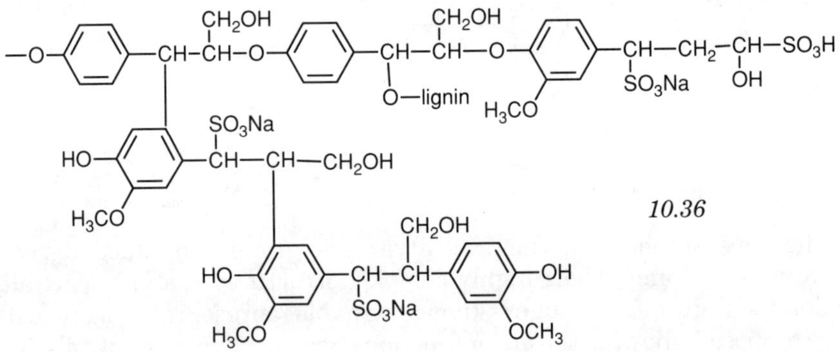

10.36

sulphonation as having taken place mainly at the –CH=CH– link. The molecular configuration is such as to give spherical particles. The final nature of the product varies enormously depending, amongst other things, on

(a) its purity, especially the content of electrolytes such as sodium sulphate

(b) the number of hydroxy groups present

(c) the degree of sulphonation

(d) the relative molecular mass (2000–1 000 000) and its distribution.

This wide variability need not be a disadvantage provided it can be controlled to give reasonable consistency from batch to batch, since this enables products to be engineered to give the optimum efficiency for the particular application concerned. The kraft lignins provide greater scope for modification, particularly of the degree of sulphonation and molecular size, and are also much more amenable to production in low-electrolyte forms [33].

The basic similarity between these major types of dispersing agents and the surface-active agents discussed earlier lies in their amphiphilic nature (the possession of a combination of hydrophobic and hydrophilic moieties). The polyelectrolytes, however, are of much larger molecular size than are the other types.

In converting a conglomerate mass of relatively coarse particles into an aqueous dispersion (as in the manufacture of disperse dyes) there are two broad phases to be considered. In the first phase the dual aim is that of mechanically grinding the particles down to the required size and of obtaining as narrow a range of particle size as possible during the actual preparation of the dispersion. Maintaining these particles in a stabilised suspension constitutes the second phase.

Particle size alone is not the main criterion; its distribution is equally important. This is because all dispersions are metastable. As well as tending to settle as a result of gravitational forces, there is also a thermo-dynamic tendency towards a reduction in the free energy of the system, which is manifest in a continuing increase in particle size leading ulti-mately to a severe deterioration in the dispersion (as already mentioned). Smaller particles tend to be attracted towards larger particles, with which they then form even larger particles; the opportunity for particle growth is therefore much less when all the particles are the same size than when the range of sizes is large.

The actual comminution of the coarse particles is usually carried out mechanically – for example, by grinding an aqueous slurry of the colorant in a revolving mill containing relatively large, hard and inert grinding media such as pebbles. The process is facilitated by efficient wetting of the particles and lowering of interfacial tension. It is therefore helpful to add dispersing agents that have some surface activity and good wetting properties. Micro-fissures are created as the particles are broken down. The surface-active properties of the dispersing agent enable it to penetrate these micro-fissures, hindering agglomeration and facilitating further comminution; its ionic nature enables it to be adsorbed and oriented on the surfaces of the particles, providing a protective sheath of like repellent charges, the forces of which eventually exceed the forces of attraction between the particles and thus stabilise the dispersion. The stability of this protective sheath becomes of critical importance during the second phase (that of stabilising the suspension of particles, both in storage and in subsequent use). Hence different dispersing agents may well be required to provide optimum dispersing and stabilising power in the two phases.

The dual amphiphilic nature of the polyelectrolyte condensates and ligninsulphonates described above, with their hydrophobic groups juxtaposed with many polarisable ionic groups, renders them very efficient dispersing agents. It is necessary, however, to make a careful choice from the various grades of dispersing agents available with respect to their molecular size and charge distribution. Optimum dispersing ability depends on matching the steric, hydrophobic and ionic properties of the dispersing agents relative to the characteristics of the particles to be dispersed. The forces that may be operative in adsorption of surfactants on to disperse dye particles have been listed [32] as ion exchange, ion pairing, hydrogen bonding, London/van der Waals dispersion forces, polarisation of π-electrons on aromatic systems and hydrophobic interaction. It may be gathered from this that anionic and non-ionic surfactants, judiciously selected, may be used in conjunction with the polyelectrolytes to aid the dispersing mechanism [32].

10.4.2 Solubilisation

It is necessary to differentiate between simple solutions and the process of 'solubilisation' in colloidal solutions. A non-colloidal solution is a homogeneous single-phase mixture of a solute dissolved in a solvent, examples being an aqueous solution of sodium chloride or a solution of methylnaphthalene in acetone. The term 'solubilisation' refers to the homogeneous mixing of an otherwise insoluble agent, the 'solubilisate', into a liquid medium by addition of a solubilising agent, invariably a surfactant. This agent acts as an amphiphilic bridge between solubilisate and medium. For example, methylnaphthalene will not dissolve to any great extent in water, but its colloidal solubilisation in water, to give an apparently clear 'solution', can be brought about by the use of a surface-active agent such as nonylphenol poly(oxyethylene) sulphate. Hence the distinction between 'solution' and 'solubilisation' in non-colloidal and colloidal situations generally.

Solubilisation can be viewed as one end of a reversible colloidal continuum that begins with wetting and proceeds through dispersion or emulsification to solubilisation, each of these stages being characterised by the size and nature of the particles. In this sense solubilisation is an extension of emulsification (or dispersion) in which the proportion of surfactant has been increased to the level where the discrete droplets (or particles) that characterised the emulsion (or dispersion) have become completely absorbed into the surfactant-medium phase. In some cases the surfactants used to produce an emulsion (or dispersion) may need modification (a change of hydrophile–lipophile balance) before complete solubilisation can be brought about. Similarly, if a solubilised system is diluted by addition of the liquid medium, a point will usually be reached at which the solubilised system changes to an emulsion (or dispersion). It is indeed possible to have all the stages of wetting, emulsification (or dispersion) and solubilisation present at the same time to different degrees.

It is beyond the scope of this section to discuss the complex physico-chemical parameters of solubilisation [34] in detail. It follows, however, that since solubilisation is essentially an extension of emulsification (or dispersion), the factors discussed in section 9.8.3 in regard to emulsification are also pertinent to solubilisation. Theory in this area is a useful guide but much still depends on empiricism for, as in emulsification, each system to be solubilised will present its own specific requirements in regard to the type and amount of surfactant(s) required. In some cases solubilisation is aided by the addition of a small amount of a water-miscible solvent such as an alcohol or glycol, whereas the presence of electrolytes can have a deleterious effect. Temperature too can be important; a system that is an emulsion (or dispersion) at one temperature may become solubilised at a different (usually higher) temperature, and vice versa.

Solubilisation is usually met in textile wet processing under two circumstances: in the deliberate preparation of a solubilised product for use as an auxiliary agent, as in the proprietary carriers formulated for dyeing polyester with disperse dyes, or as a concomitant of the process itself, as in the solubilisation of fats and oils during scouring processes and in the disperse dyeing process – both situations where more than one stage of the colloidal continuum of wetting–dispersion/emulsification–solubilisation may be present at any one time.

10.5 LEVELLING AND RETARDING AGENTS.

Level dyeing problems can be broadly divided into two categories [35]:
(a) gross unlevelness throughout the material: this type of unlevelness is primarily related to the dyeing equipment or process; the substrate is often uniform in properties, both chemically and physically
(b) localised unlevelness: this is primarily related to physical and/or chemical non-uniformity of the substrate; typical examples are barriness in nylon or polyester dyeing and skitteriness in wool dyeing.

There are also two fundamental mechanisms that can contribute to a level dyeing:
(a) control of the exhaustion of dye so that it is taken up evenly
(b) migration of dye after initially unlevel sorption on the fibre.

Either or both of these mechanisms may operate to a greater or lesser extent in a given dye–fibre system, although the general trend in recent years towards better fastness properties often dictates the use of dyes that show low, if any, propensity to migration, thus placing the emphasis for level dyeing on the control of exhaustion. Physical factors such as temperature and liquor/substrate contact (such as the rate of liquor circulation in a jet, beam or package machine) can be used to exert some degree of control over these mechanisms. Lower rates of heating usually favour more even uptake of dye, and high temperatures tend to increase migration or diffusion. In some cases level dyeing can be influenced by dyebath pH and/or the presence of electrolytes. This section is, however, more concerned with the control of levelness by means of chemical auxiliaries, generally known as levelling or retarding agents.

Since levelling agents are invariably surfactants, they may be anionic, cationic, non-ionic or amphoteric in nature. Sometimes combinations of these are used. The chemical structure of commercial products is seldom revealed, however; hence only general principles can be covered here. The main mechanisms by which levelling agents operate [35–40] are as follows:

(a) non-ionic agents usually form water-soluble complexes with the dye, some degree of solubilisation being involved

(b) ionic agents are primarily dye- or fibre-substantive; in the former case they tend to form complexes with the dye and there is competition between the levelling agent and the fibre for the dye, while in the latter case the competition is between levelling agent and the dye for the fibre.

In complex formation the principle, as far as levelling action is concerned, is usually the same irrespective of whether non-ionic or ionic agents are used, although the mode of complexing is different. The attractive forces between agent and dye create a counterbalancing mechanism against dye–fibre attractive forces, restraining the uptake of dye by the fibre. As the temperature of the dyebath increases the complex gradually breaks down, progressively releasing the dye for more gradual sorption by the fibre. Clearly, for an effective levelling agent that functions by this mechanism the stability of the agent–dye complex, which is governed by forces of attraction between agent and dye, is crucial. If these forces are such that a relatively unstable complex is formed, restraining or levelling action may be inadequate. On the other hand, strong forces of attraction may result in a complex that is too stable to break down as the temperature rises, so that the dye is effectively entrapped by the agent in the solution phase and is not available for sorption by the fibre. The object therefore is to formulate the levelling agent such that it forms a dye complex of optimum, rather than maximum, stability relative to the conditions of application. This is done by adjusting the hydrophilic–lipophilic balance of the surfactant. The difficulty lies in the fact that the dye–agent interaction is so specific that different members of a range of dyes may each require a different balance. Hence commercial levelling agents may contain more than one surfactant.

A difficulty that arises with ionic levelling agents is that they may form an insoluble precipitate with ionic dyes of the opposite charge; this can be obviated in various ways. In the first instance attention should be paid to the concentration of the surfactant: where initial addition of surfactant to the dyebath causes precipitation of the agent–dye complex, further additions of surfactant often lead to its solubilisation. Alternatively, a further surfactant may be added to solubilise the complex; a non-ionic agent will not in itself react with either the dye or the original ionic surfactant to form a further insoluble complex, but its addition may further complicate the relationship between the hydrophobic–hydrophilic balance of the ionic agent and the dyes to be complexed. Due regard also needs to be paid to the cloud point of the non-ionic agent under the conditions of use. This does not preclude the use of a relatively hydrophobic non-ionic agent, since its cloud point may be effectively raised in the presence of the ionic agent (subject to further interferences from any electrolytes or solvents present in the dyeing system). Similarly, if there is any danger from the cloud point of a non-ionic surfactant used as the primary levelling agent (as with disperse dyes, for example), a suitable anionic surfactant may be added to effectively raise the cloud point – again, paying due attention to any effect the anionic may have on the complexing–liberating performance of the non-ionic agent.

The third method of obviating precipitation of an ionic agent–ionic dye complex is to choose what effectively amounts to a 'modified' ionic agent. Ethoxylated anionic and ethoxylated cationic agents are particularly useful in this respect. The ethoxylation tends to reduce the ionic character of the agent thus giving rise to weaker, more controllable, forces of attraction for dye ions, and the oxyethylene chain can further function as a dispersing–solubilising agent for the agent–dye complex. In a sense this is basically similar to using a mixture of ionic and non-ionic agents as described above, except that a single agent is used, thus facilitating the aim of obtaining the optimum complexing–liberating balance.

Dye–agent complexes of lower net charge are formed when the ionic agent is added to the ionic dye solution. As the concentration of agent is increased a point is reached at which all the dye is complexed and its ionic charge has been neutralised. Beyond this point, as more agent is added, the agent–dye complex takes on the charge of the complexing agent (i.e. the opposite to that of the dye itself). This brings about a change in the partition coefficient of the complex between water and organic solvents [35], modifying the electrical and solution properties of the dye, and so altering its affinity for the fibre.

Fibre-substantive levelling agents are usually of the same ionic type as the dye, that is, anionic agents are used with anionic dyes and cationic agents with cationic dyes, the aim being to create a system in which levelling agent and dye both compete for the sorption sites in the fibre. Just as the complexing type of levelling agent has to be carefully chosen so as to obtain the optimum complexing–liberating properties, so must the competing type of levelling agent be chosen such that its ionic power gives the optimum level of competition relative to the dye–fibre system concerned. If the ionic power is too weak, it will not function as an effective levelling agent; if it is too strong, it may exert blocking effects, preventing sorption of the dye. Ideally the balance should be such that the ionic agent is adsorbed by the fibre more quickly than is the dye, but the agent–fibre bond needs to be weak enough to permit subsequent displacement of the ionic agent by the dye ions.

TABLE 10.1

Levelling agent types and their uses

Type of levelling agent	Recommended for use with	
	Substrate	Dye class
Non-ionic	Cotton	Azoic, vat, direct
	Wool, nylon	Milling acid, metal-complex
	Polyester	Disperse
Non-ionic/anionic	Polyester	Disperse
	Wool, nylon	Milling acid, metal-complex
Non-ionic/cationic	Wool	Acid, mordant, reactive, metal-complex
Anionic	Wool, nylon	Acid
	Cotton	Direct
	Polyester	Disperse
Weakly anionic	Polyester	Disperse
Anionic/cationic	Wool, nylon	Acid, metal-complex
Cationic	Acrylic	Basic
	Wool, nylon	Acid, metal-complex, reactive
Weakly cationic	Wool, nylon	Acid, mordant, metal-complex
Cationic/polymeric	Cotton	Vat, sulphur
Amphoteric	Wool	Acid, mordant, metal-complex, reactive

As the forces of dye–fibre interaction vary from one dye to another, the ionic power of the levelling agent must be suitably adjusted through its hydrophilic–hydrophobic balance to give the optimum properties. This can be done either by careful choice of a single surfactant or by the use of mixtures, which has gained prominence in recent times. For example, the strongly anionic character of a long-chain alkyl sulphonate or sulphate can be modified (toned down) by mixing it with a more weakly anionic poly(oxyethylene) sulphate or with a non-ionic agent.

Some levelling agents operate both by complexing and by competition. For example, in the application of acid dyes a weakly cationic agent may be used to complex with the dye and an anionic agent may also be used as a competing agent. This combination is useful because unlevelness may arise from different mechanisms. Unlevelness arising from process or equipment variables can often be controlled by dye–agent competition, whereas localised dye-uptake variations generally respond better to dye–agent complex formation. Evidently, in this combined system the balance of properties is highly critical. In particular the oppositely charged surfactants must not mutually precipitate; hence the more weakly ionic ethoxylates are of particular interest, since the oxyethylene moiety assists solubilisation of any complex so formed. A purely non-ionic agent may also be used to prevent coprecipitation of the ionic types. Amphoteric agents, in a sense, fall within this combined system.

Theoretical considerations are clearly useful in formulating suitable levelling agents; nevertheless, a good deal of empiricism is always involved in formulating well-balanced agents for specific dye–fibre systems. Table 10.1 shows the general types of levelling agents now being offered [30] and their uses; more detail is given in Chapter 12 relative to each class of dye.

Many, but not all, levelling agents promote migration of dye in addition to retarding dyeing, and such agents will obviously be a further aid to level dyeing. In some cases, however, higher concentrations of levelling agent are needed to obtain significant migration and this may interfere unduly with dye sorption. Levelling agents are also widely used as stripping agents, either alone for non-destructive stripping or together with, for example, reducing agents such as sodium dithionite for destructive stripping. When used for this purpose, their hydrophilic–hydrophobic balance is not as critical as when they are used simply as levelling agents, and higher concentrations are often used in order to maximise rather than optimise desorption of the dye.

10.6 THICKENING AGENTS, MIGRATION INHIBITORS AND HYDROTROPIC AGENTS USED IN PRINTING AND CONTINUOUS DYEING

Most, if not all, textile printing and continuous dyeing processes are characterised by the use of auxiliaries that considerably increase the viscosity of the application medium compared with conventional batchwise dyeing processes, the aim being to facilitate and stabilise the local application of colour prior to its actual fixation to the fibre. Such auxiliaries are generally known as thickening agents in printing and as migration inhibitors in padding operations.

They are characterised by undergoing marked macromolecular swelling in solution due to solvation (hydration in aqueous systems). While the principal role of thickening agents is to increase the viscosity of print pastes or pad liquors, certain other properties are also of importance, such as stability and rheology of the print paste, adhesion and brittleness of the dried thickener film, the effect on colour yield and penetration, ease of preparation and removal, and cost; these are usefully covered elsewhere, however [41–52].

Miles [49] lists four means of thickening print pastes, by use of
(a) a relatively low concentration of a long-chain thickening agent
(b) a relatively high concentration of a shorter-chain thickener or one having a highly branched chain structure
(c) an emulsion
(d) a finely dispersed solid such as bentonite (derived from clay).

The first two types, and particularly the first, are the most frequently used today; combinations of the above are also possible.

Thickening agents can be of natural or synthetic origin. Various natural gums and starches have been used traditionally in different printing styles. Unfortunately the materials from which they are derived are also valuable sources of foodstuffs, and the urgent need to feed an ever-growing world population has acted to stifle supply of the products for industrial use. In 1978, for example, though guar gum and starch were still widely available, the supply of alginate and locust bean gum had dwindled alarmingly, resulting in escalating prices as well as shortages [46]. Consequently there is an increasing requirement for synthetic replacements.

10.6.1 Natural thickeners
Natural thickeners are derived from plants, either by extraction from part of the plant itself or from a plant secretion; their biosynthesis is also now a possibility. The products are generally polysaccharides and are thus closely related to cellulose. They consist of homo- or hetero-polymers of simple hexoses, most commonly glucose, mannose and galactose [46]. Linear and branched segments are normally present, the degree of branching being important in relation to the technical properties of the product. They bear some structural similarities to the anionic polyelectrolyte dispersing agents described in section 10.4.1. In particular, the nature of the side groups (mainly, though not always hydroxy or carboxyl groups) has a decisive effect on viscosity and other technical properties. Some, such

as native starch, are used as derived directly from their sources; others, such as starch ethers, are treated to introduce substituents or bring about controlled hydrolysis and lower their viscosity. As with other complex auxiliaries already discussed, their detailed structure is still not completely understood, and the formulae given are only indicative of their structures.

Although native starch is less important nowadays as a thickening agent for textile printing, some starch derivatives still make a significant contribution. Starch has two components, both of which are made up of linked α-glucoside units (10.37). In amylose, which accounts for some 20–30% of the polymer and has a relative molecular mass in the range 2–6 × 10^5, the α-glucoside units are linked in a linear 1,4 arrangement (10.38). Cellulose (10.39), by contrast, consists of β-glucoside chains. In amylopectin (r.m.m. 4.5×10^4 to 4×10^8) the linear α-1,4-linked main chain is randomly branched at the 6-position every 15–30 glucose units to give an α-1,6-anchored side chain (10.40).

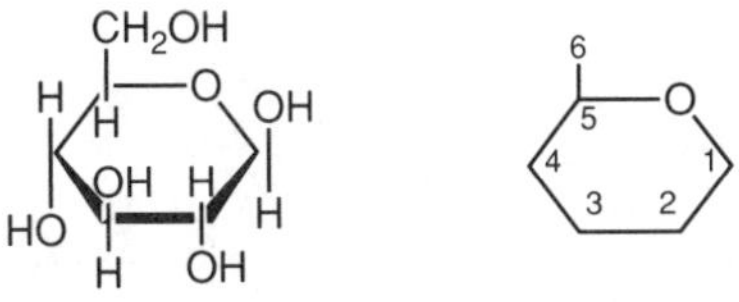

10.37

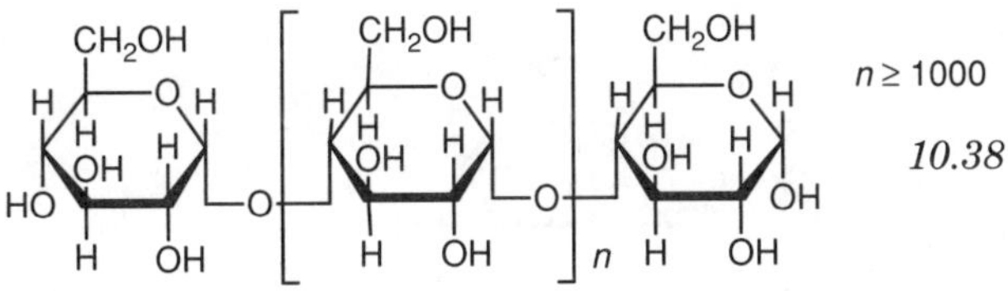

$n \geq 1000$

10.38

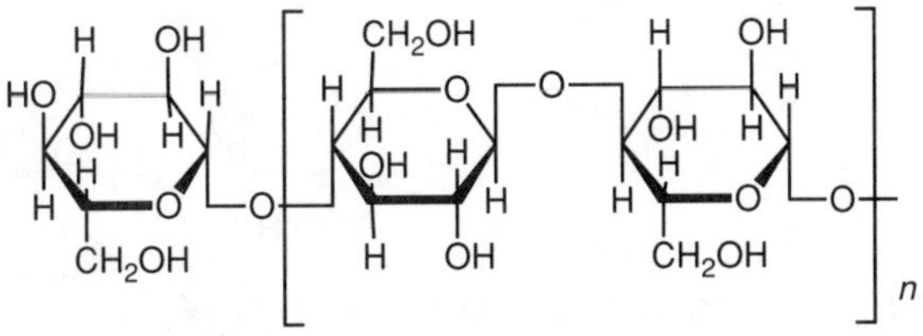

10.39

The amylose component is substantially crystalline, forming helical structures that uncoil in an aqueous solution. It can also aggregate to give a gel or precipitate, an undesirable phenomenon known as retrogradation. Amylose is completely hydrolysed by the β-amylase enzyme. Amylopectin is substantially amorphous, having a globular structure that can expand considerably in aqueous solution. Its branched chains give rise to a much

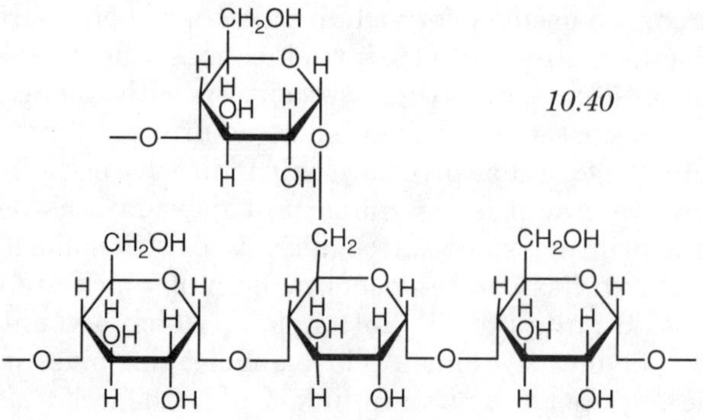

10.40

more stable solution, substantially free from retrogradation, and it is much more resistant to the action of β-amylase. Starches containing little or no amylose are known as 'waxy starches'.

The properties of starch, from a printing point of view, can be improved by conversion to British gum (10.41). This is done by a dry roasting treatment at 135–190°C, which can be accelerated by trace quantities of acid, to give random hydrolysis of the 1,4-links to decrease the chain length and the formation of 1,6-links (branching); the effect is to increase the solubility and stability although reducing characteristics, which can affect certain susceptible dyes, are enhanced by formation of more aldehyde end-groups. Control of the hydrolysis and branching reactions yields a varied range of products.

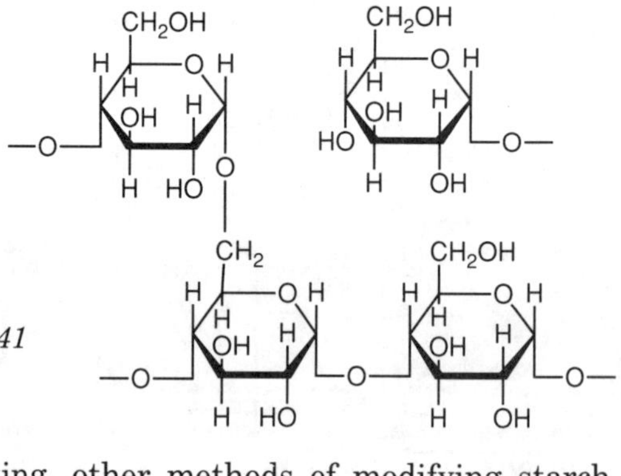

10.41

Besides roasting, other methods of modifying starch are available. Etherification and esterification, to give starch ethers and starch esters, are both practised although the ethers, being resistant to hydrolysis in acidic or alkaline media, are much the more important as thickening agents for textile printing. The starch may first be partially decomposed before etherification, and the degree of etherification itself may be varied. The most important products are the carboxymethyl (10.42), hydroxyethyl (10.43) and methyl (10.44) starches (the structures illustrated use the

glucose unit as an example, showing the primary hydroxy group substituted). The degree of alkylation is said to be low or high depending on
whether it is less or greater than 0.3 substituents per glucose (or other)
unit; the products are termed modified starches if the degree of substitution is low and starch derivatives if it is high. Crossbonded starches can be
obtained by treating, for example, a starch ether of low degree of substitution with bifunctional agents such as ethylene oxide, propylene oxide,
epichlorohydrin or phosphates. The corresponding derivatives of cellulose
can also be made and used as thickening agents if the chain length is
appropriate. The steric hindrance effect of the substituents gives thickening agents of improved all-round properties and many derivatives have
ousted their parent products in terms of commercial importance.

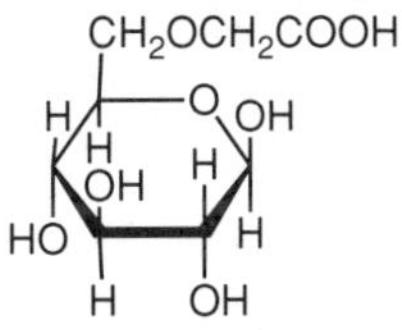

10.42	10.43	10.44

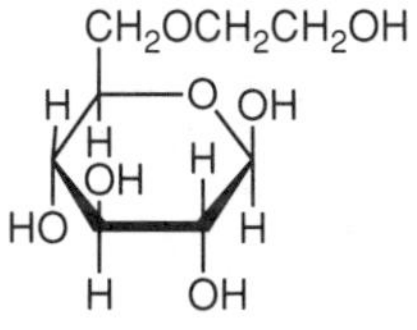

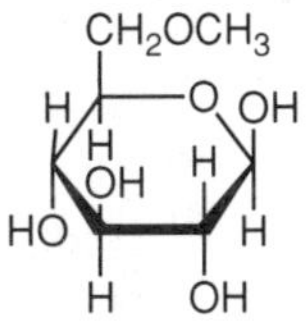

Locust bean gum and guar gum are chemically very similar, both being
based on D-galactomannoglycan (10.45; for locust bean gum $m = 3$, and for
guar gum $m = 1$); this is structurally related to starches. Typical chain
lengths are $n = 375$ for locust bean gum and $n = 440$ for guar gum. Warm
water is required to effect complete dispersion of the former, but the latter
disperses readily in cold water, because of reduced molecular association
resulting from the greater number of side units. As with the starches,
modified gums can be obtained. In particular, etherification improves the
cold water dispersibility of locust bean gum.

10.45

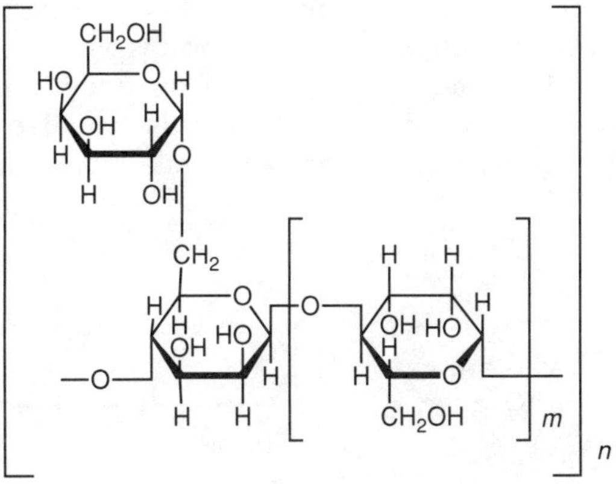

Locust bean gum forms an interesting and unusual crosslinked complex by the association of *cis*-dihydroxy groups in mannose chains with borate ions, diagrammatically represented in structure 10.46. This complex forms a gel, which has been made use of in printing with vat dyes in a two-stage fixation process; the crosslinks are relatively weak, being in a state of dynamic equilibrium, and are ruptured in the presence of hydrotropes such as glycerol.

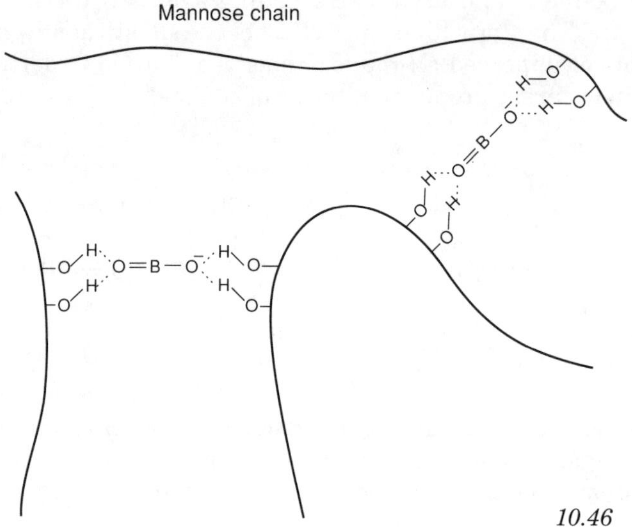

10.46

Of great importance as thickening agents are the alginates derived from seaweeds. These are based on alginic acid (10.47; $n = 60$–600) of which the major commercial salt is sodium alginate, although calcium (particularly in mixture with sodium), magnesium and ammonium alginates, as well as amine salts, are also available. Their relatively very low reactivity with reactive dyes is a particular advantage. This is a result of the replacement of primary hydroxy groups by carboxyl groups which, as well as being non-reactive towards reactive dyes, create an anionic polyelectrolyte, the ionised carboxylate anions of which repulse the dye anions in alkaline media. Carboxylated polymers will form gels with multivalent metal ions.

10.47

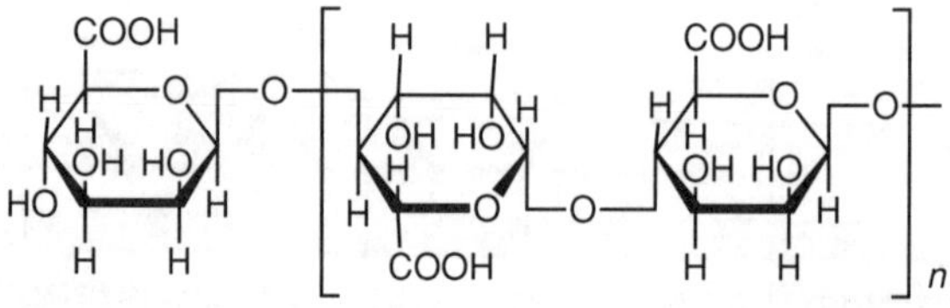

This behaviour, like the locust bean gum–borate complex mentioned earlier, has been exploited in the two-stage flash-ageing process for vat dyes in printing. Alginate esters (such as the hydroxypropyl ester) have also been used.

Other natural polysaccharides used as thickening agents are gum arabic, gum tragacanth and xanthate gum, but these are of less importance nowadays.

10.6.2 Synthetic thickeners

Polymers based on acrylic acid have been known for many years [50] yet it is only since the late 1970s that the use of thickening agents based on them has come into prominence in textile printing [44,46,50]. Clarke and Miles [50] have culled representative schematic formulae (10.48 and 10.49) and other data from the technical publications of two major manufacturers [53–55]. The basic similarity of these two formulae for linear grades is readily apparent. The commercial products represented by structure 10.48 are available as linear grades ($n = 50$–750) and there are crosslinked grades where the value of n is said to be 'unmeasurable'. The products represented by structure 10.49 cover a range of n values from 3200 to 30 000, of which only the longer-chain grades are of significant interest for textile printing in the form of their sodium or ammonium salts. Related synthetic thickeners have included poly(vinyl alcohol), copolymers of acrylic acid (1 mol) with divinylbenzene (0.01 mol) and maleic anhydride–alkene copolymers crosslinked by a diamine.

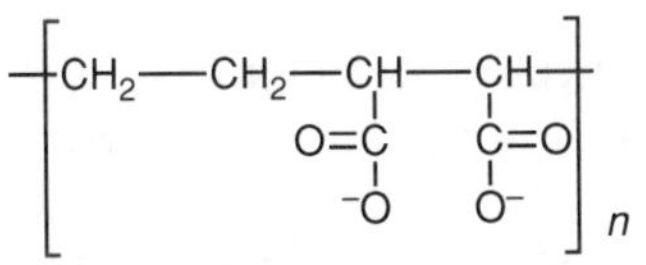

10.48 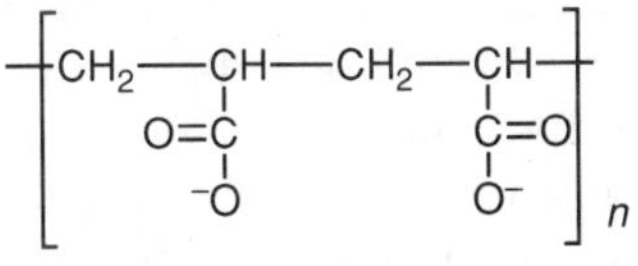   10.49

These products are usually supplied to the printer as 'partially neutralised polyacids', and further neutralisation is carried out by the printer when making up the print pastes. This neutralisation is often a critical process. For certain applications, such as resin-bonded pigments, neutralisation is carried out with ammonia; this has the advantage that during subsequent baking the ammonia is driven off to liberate the free polyacid, which then catalyses the activation of the bonding resin. Otherwise neutralisation is carried out with non-volatile alkalis such as sodium hydroxide.

Like the emulsion thickeners described in section 10.6.3, the synthetic thickeners can be described as emulsified dispersions. The dry polyacid powders on which they are based are difficult to handle and before marketing require formulation as an emulsified paste or dispersion that can be more easily manipulated. The aim is first to disperse the powder in a non-swelling medium such as a hydrocarbon [56] or more specifically white spirit distillate [50,54,55], with the addition of at least one surfactant [56] to assist wetting and dispersion. In one case [50,54,55] a surfactant of low HLB is added at this stage and another of higher HLB is used in the subsequent aqueous dilution phase, when the polyacid/hydrocarbon dispersion is converted into an oil-in-water emulsified dispersion with a concomitant increase in viscosity as the polyacid becomes swollen by the water. Considerably more swelling takes place during subsequent partial neutralisation by alkali. It is usually at this stage that the products are supplied to the printer, who then develops the viscosity to its required potential during preparation of the print paste by dilution and perhaps further addition of alkali. The mechanism of neutralisation is rather complex and has been explained by Clarke and Miles [50].

A major drawback of the synthetic thickeners so far marketed is their sensitivity to electrolytes, including the anionic dispersing agents that are often present in dyes, particularly disperse dyes; this can result in a pronounced loss of viscosity, which can be overcome to some extent by increasing the concentration of thickening agent. The preferred method is to eliminate as far as possible the presence of electrolytes and anionic dispersing agents, however; this is why some disperse dyes have been produced in low-electrolyte form containing non-ionic, in place of the usual anionic, dispersing agents.

10.6.3 Emulsion thickeners

When immiscible liquids are emulsified the viscosity increases, and this fact can be made use of to prepare thickenings for textile printing. The emulsions used contain a hydrocarbon solvent (usually white spirit), surfactant(s) and water; the oil phase must account for at least 70% of the whole [43,49,52]. The earlier preference was for water-in-oil emulsions (that is, at least 70% of the product was water) in which typical surfactants were ethoxylated alcohols, acids or amides with a low degree of ethoxylation, perhaps 5–8 oxyethylene units per molecule, morpholine/oleic acid or lauric/palmitic and stearic acid esters with sorbitol [43]. But over the last thirty years or so manufacturers have developed oil-in-water (≤70%) emulsions for which appropriate surfactants are higher ethoxylated alcohols, acids or amides, or a wide variety of alkylaryl types. For any type of emulsion, the HLB of the emulsifying agent(s) is clearly of great importance [52].

The size of the droplets in the emulsion is inversely related to its viscosity, typical diameters ranging from 100 to 7000 nm [49]. Theoretically up to 75% of oil can be incorporated in an aqueous emulsion, assuming uniformly spherical droplets, but distortion due to packing allows significantly higher proportions of oil phase to be added; presumably the oil droplets are stabilised by a surrounding layer of like charges, the type and strength of the charge depending on the surfactant(s) used. Consequently the stability of the emulsion tends to be impaired by any additions that reduce the charge on the droplets.

Emulsion thickener systems differ markedly from those based on synthetic thickeners by virtue of their much greater content of hydrocarbon and surfactant phases. For example, Barrett [56] has quoted typical recipes for an emulsion system and for a synthetic one based on Alcoprint PTF (Allied Colloids) for use in a pigment-binder system (Table 10.2). The synthetic system does, of course, contain small amounts of emulsifier and hydrocarbon since, as described above, these are incorporated into the thickener before it is sold to the printer; nevertheless the amount in the total system is clearly very small. It is essentially the large amount of hydrocarbon solvent used in emulsion thickenings that constitutes their biggest disadvantage today in terms of costs and environmental problems, and they are now used only in the less environmentally sensitive countries.

Emulsion thickeners are usually mixed with low concentrations of either natural or synthetic thickeners, especially when applying fibre-substantive dyes as opposed to pigments; these additions act as film formers, taking the place of the binder used with pigments to increase the retention of the dye by the substrate prior to fixation.

TABLE 10.2

Composition of emulsion and synthetic thickeners (parts per thousand)

	Emulsion system	Synthetic system
Water	110	848
Emulsifier	10	
Binder	120	120
Fixing agent	10	10
White spirit	700	
Alcoprint PTF		17
Catalyst	20	
Ammonia (sp.gr. 0.880)		5
Humectant	30	
Total	1000	1000

10.6.4 Continuous dyeing

The foregoing discussion has concentrated on the use of thickening agents for textile printing. Similar types of product are used to thicken pad liquors in continuous dyeing processes, although they are often referred to then as migration inhibitors rather than thickening agents. All the polysaccharides previously mentioned, especially the alginates, locust bean, guar and xanthate gums, modified starches and celluloses, can be used in continuous dyeing [45], but by far the most widely used of these are the alginates. Concentrations tend to be significantly lower than those used in printing since the dyeing process requires a lower viscosity, permitting easy penetration into the fabric during padding. In addition to the alginates, polyacrylates (see section 10.6.2), polyacrylamides and polyethoxylates are also used [51]; the last-named are mixed polyglycol ethers of fatty alcohols with ethylene oxide (or propylene oxide) – that is, the non-ionic block copolymers described in section 9.6, which function by virtue of a low cloud point (about 25°C). The functions of these products in pad applications are twofold: (a) they should favour the uniform application of dye by padding, and (b) they should effectively inhibit any tendency of the dye to migrate during the subsequent intermediate drying process (hence the term 'migration inhibitors'); in the absence of an inhibitor, dye liquor tends to migrate towards hotter regions of the fabric during drying, causing either patchiness or an undesirable two-sided effect. Whilst viscosity plays an important part in facilitating the uniform absorption of dye liquor, it is less effective than coagulation for inhibiting migration. The polyacrylates are particularly effective [51].

In continuous dyeing products to assist rapid wetting and even penetration of the fabric are invariably added to pad liquors along with the migration inhibitor. Many types of surfactant can be used, including phosphate esters (which are particularly effective [51]), sulphonates, sulphates, sulphosuccinates and ethoxysulphates. Care should be taken to ensure that the type of product chosen, and its concentration, do not depress the degree of fixation of the dye. (Wetting agents are rarely used in printing since they would tend to promote bleeding or haloing of printed areas.)

Polyacrylamides of chain length (n) 7000 to 14 000 (higher than used for migration inhibitors) are also useful pad liquor additives [51] in that they increase liquor pick-up and sometimes colour yield, notably with pigments, and when used with azoic dyes can eliminate the need for the intermediate drying process.

10.6.5 Hydrotropic agents

In many printing and some continuous dyeing processes the colour yield of dyes can often be improved, sometimes markedly, by the use of an auxiliary that tends to increase the aqueous solubility of the dye, particularly when using highly concentrated pastes or liquors under conditions that tend to eliminate moisture. There is clearly an analogy here with the mechanism of solubilisation discussed in section 10.4.2, since the hydrotrope acts as an amphiphilic bridge between the dye solubilisate and the aqueous medium. Surfactants can therefore function as hydrotropes and are sometimes used as such in continuous dyeing processes. 'Non-surfactant' hydrotropes are more widely used in printing, where surfactants tend to be avoided because their concomitant powerful wetting properties promote bleeding and haloing of the print.

By far the most widely used compounds are urea (10.50) and thiourea (10.51). However, dye–fibre systems are so varied that many hydrotropes are of interest under specific conditions. Schlösser [43] has mentioned numerous compounds along with their particular uses, including urea, thiourea, triethanolamine (10.24), NN-diethylethanolamine (10.52), sodium N-benzylsulphanilate (10.53), sodium NN-dibenzylsulphanilate (10.54), ethanol, phenol, benzyl alcohol, resorcinol, cyclohexanol (10.55), ethylene glycol, glycolic acid (10.56), 2-ethoxyethanol (10.57), diethylene glycol (10.58), 2-ethoxyethoxyethanol (10.59), 2-butoxyethoxyethanol (10.60), thiodiethylene glycol (10.61) and glycerol (10.62), the last-named in particular being useful with practically all classes of dyes.

10.50 $\begin{array}{c} H_2N \\ H_2N \end{array}\!\!>\!\!C=O$ $\begin{array}{c} H_2N \\ H_2N \end{array}\!\!>\!\!C=S$ 10.51

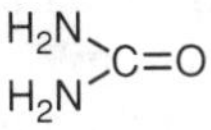

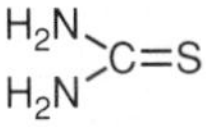

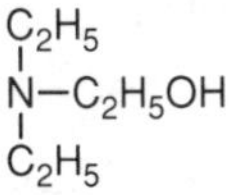

10.52 $\begin{array}{c} C_2H_5 \\ | \\ N-C_2H_5OH \\ | \\ C_2H_5 \end{array}$ $NaO_3S-\!\!\langle\!\!\bigcirc\!\!\rangle\!\!-NHCH_2-\!\!\langle\!\!\bigcirc\!\!\rangle$ 10.53

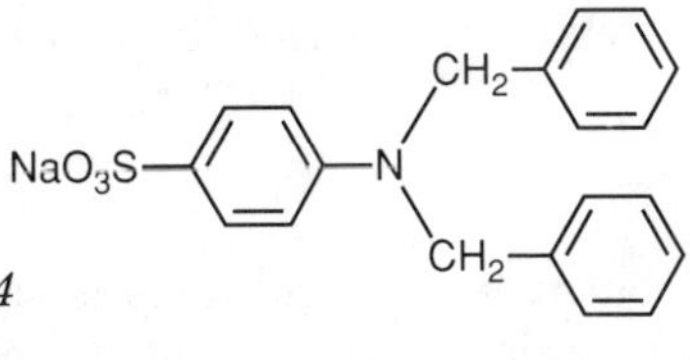

10.54 $NaO_3S-\!\!\langle\!\!\bigcirc\!\!\rangle\!\!-N\!\!\begin{array}{c} CH_2-\langle\bigcirc\rangle \\ \\ CH_2-\langle\bigcirc\rangle \end{array}$ $\langle\bigcirc\rangle\!\!-OH$ 10.55

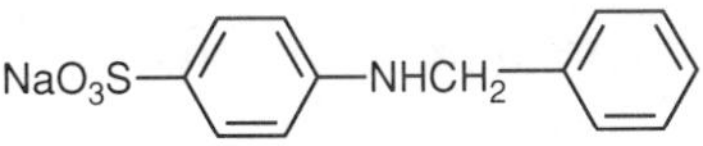

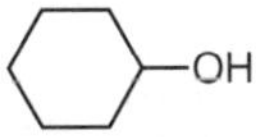

$HOCH_2COOH$ $CH_3CH_2OCH_2CH_2OH$

10.56   10.57

$HOCH_2CH_2OCH_2CH_2OH$ $CH_3CH_2OCH_2CH_2OCH_2CH_2OH$

10.58   10.59

$$CH_2OH$$
$$|$$
$$CHOH$$
$$|$$

CH₃(CH₂)₃OCH₂CH₂OCH₂CH₂OH   HOCH₂CH₂SCH₂CH₂OH CH_2OH

10.60   *10.61*   *10.62*

Most hydrotropic agents, though not surfactants in the usual sense of the word, do act to lower the surface tension of water, this being an important prerequisite for their solubilising action. Hydrogen bonds, together with weaker dipolar and van der Waals forces, contribute to this interaction, the active centres in the hydrotropic molecules being proton-donating groups (such as hydroxy, amino and amido groups) and proton-accepting atoms (such as the nitrogen atom of tertiary amines) [43]. For this reason hydrotropes are also added to the diluent system in the manufacture of certain dyes to improve their apparent solubility.

10.7 AFTERTREATING AND OTHER AGENTS TO IMPROVE FASTNESS PROPERTIES

The use of aftertreatments to improve the intrinsic fastness of dyeings has a long and prolific history, the word 'aftertreatment' in this context referring to a treatment that is not an integral part of the normal dyeing process. This narrows the present discussion to the following:
(a) acid dyes, including metal-complex dyes, on nylon and wool
(b) direct and reactive dyes on cellulosic fibres
(c) disperse dyes on acetate and polyester fibres
(d) sulphur dyes on cellulosic fibres.

Relatively few such processes are in use and the emphasis in this chapter has to be on those that still have some commercial importance today. An excellent comprehensive review covering the period 1880–1980 is available [57].

10.7.1 Acid dyes

By far the most important aftertreatment for acid dyes is the so-called syntan process widely used on nylon, which has superseded the classic full back-tan process. This involved treatment of the dyed nylon first with 'tannic acid' (a highly complex gallotannin or polygalloylated glucose, such as structure 10.63, which hydrolyses to give digallic acid (10.64) or gallic acid (10.65) [57,58]), followed by further treatment with potassium antimonyl tartrate (tartar emetic) (10.66).

It has been replaced on grounds of its high cost, instability to hot alkali, undesirable effects on fabric handle and light fastness, changes in colour (usually dulling) during treatment, and diffusion and degradation of the

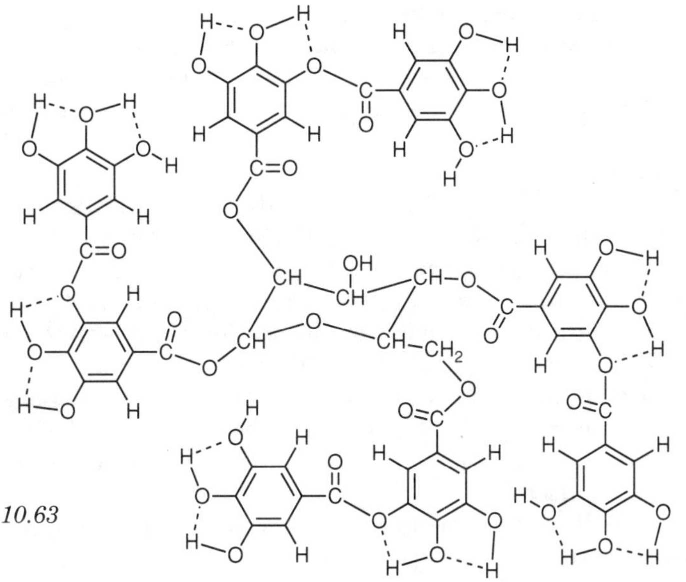

10.63

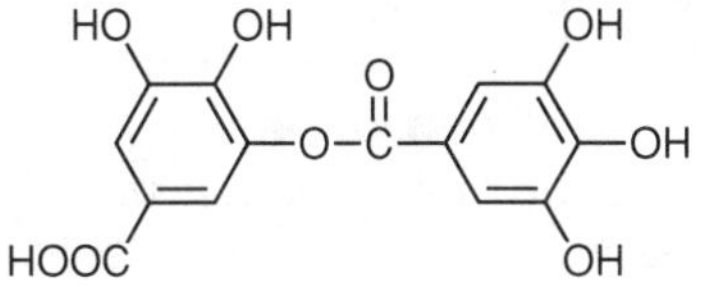

10.64 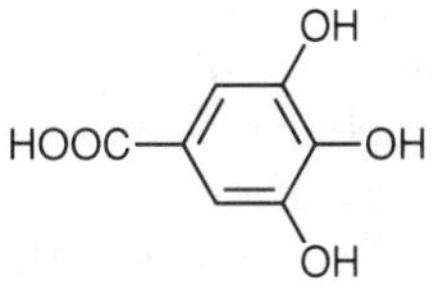   10.65

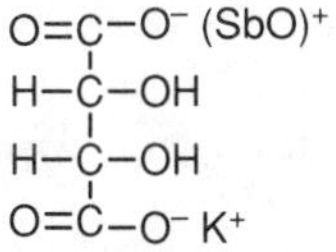

10.66

antimonyl tannate complex during subsequent steam- or heat-setting, [57], as well as for health and environmental reasons. Its presumed mechanism is complex [57,58].

The synthetic tanning agents (syntans) that have superseded the back-tan have the advantage of being applied in a single process but, like the naturally derived gallotannins, tend to be polyphenolic compounds. In fact, compounds of this class have been described in section 10.4.1 as condensation products of formaldehyde with sulphonated phenols, naphthols or naphthylamines. Structures 10.31–10.34 are typical of these compounds although, as mentioned earlier, they form a large and varied group. Cook [57] has pointed out that the precise structural details of many current commercial syntans for nylon are hidden within a plethora of patent literature, much of which pertains to their uses as leather syntans or even as mordants for cotton dyeing. In addition to the type of product mentioned in section 10.4.1 analogous sulphur-containing products, such as those derived from thiophenols, have been used as well as heavy-metal phenolates.

Empiricism has guided the screening of syntans for nylon. Both the affinity of the syntan for the fibre and its diffusion rate are important, and the required values are obtained by balancing the degree of sulphonation and range of molecular sizes present. Moreover, many of these products are used not only as aftertreating agents for the improvement of wet fastness, but also as blocking agents to inhibit absorption of dye either partially or completely – for example, in the dyeing of wool/nylon blends to restrain the usually preferential uptake of dye by the nylon, or to produce resist effects, particularly in printing. The balance of properties required in the syntan may therefore vary somewhat, and is influenced by the class of dye with which it is to be used.

A brief simplified mechanism whereby syntans are thought to work can be described, at the risk of incompleteness. Their rapid sorption by the fibre under the (usually acidic) conditions of application is largely the result of electrostatic attraction between the negatively charged sulphonic acid groups and the protonated amino groups in the fibre. Hydrogen bonding between uncharged polar groups, and hydrophobic bonding between the hydrophobic moieties in the syntan and the fibre, create conditions for the formation of complexes. Maximum improvement in wet fastness results when the complexes are formed at the fibre surface, since any treatment leading to diffusion of the syntan complex into the fibre tends to yield lower fastness. Hence a 'barrier effect' seems to be involved. Some syntans will also give an improvement to the wet fastness of disperse dyes on nylon, although their use in this respect is not significant. Even with acid dyes, the response to the syntan treatment in terms of improved wet fastness varies markedly from dye to dye.

10.7.2 Direct and reactive dyes on cellulosic fibres
The fact that the aftertreatment of direct dyes has a long history is not surprising since, as a class, their general wet fastness is not particularly good. Their prime advantages are ease of application and economy compared with dyes of higher fastness (reactive, sulphur or vat) – hence the continued search for highly effective aftertreatments that improve wet fastness without excessive additional cost. More recently some of the aftertreatments used for this purpose have also been applied to reactive dyes, as will be described later.

One of the earliest aftertreatment processes employed diazotisation of free amino groups in the adsorbed dye, followed by coupling (development) with a suitable component such as a phenol, naphthol or amine; 2-naphthol, *m*-phenylenediamine, resorcinol and 1-phenyl-3-methyl-5-pyrazolone (10.67) were particularly popular. Obviously, this was only possible with dyes containing a diazotisable amino group, an example being C.I. Direct Yellow 59, the classic primuline (a mixture of structures 10.68a and b), which was converted on the fibre from a greenish-yellow to a bluish-red by diazotisation and development with 2-naphthol. The reverse process – application of a dye containing a phenolic group and aftertreatment with a solution of a diazotised amine, such as *p*-nitroaniline – was also used.

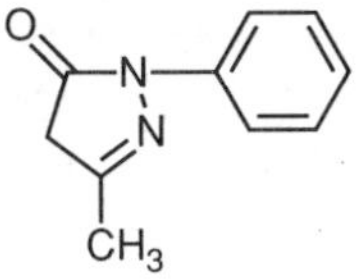

10.67

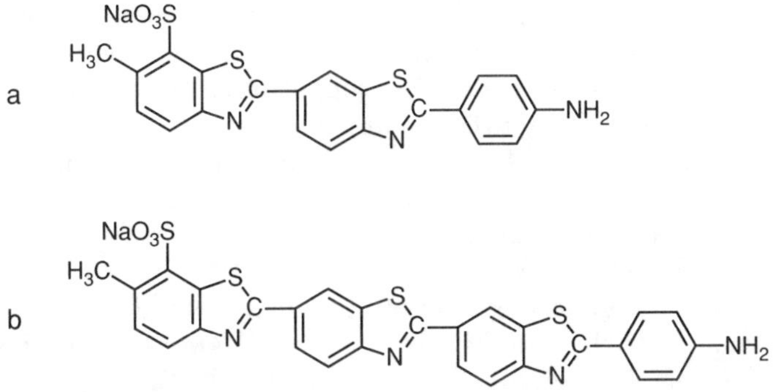

a

b

10.68

Formaldehyde aftertreatment was employed to link together pairs of amino-substituted dye molecules by a methylene bridge (10.69). The required reactivity of the sites in the dye towards formaldehyde was ensured by pairs of *o*- and *p*-directing electron-donating groups using resorcinol, *m*-phenylenediamine and *m*-aminophenol.

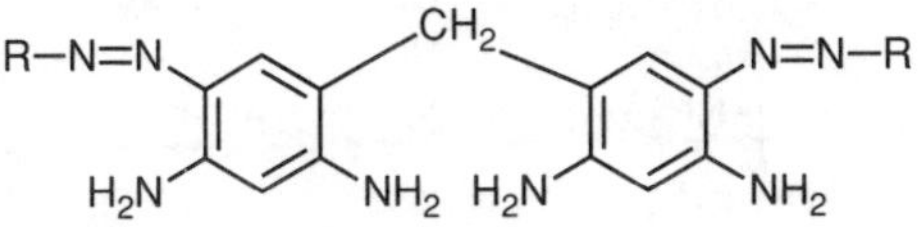

10.69

A third approach used copper salts, especially copper(II) sulphate, in conjunction with dyes containing chelatable groupings such as salicylic acid or *o,o'*-dihydroxyazo moieties. Indeed, special ranges of 'copperable' direct dyes, for which the treatment with copper(II) sulphate is really part of the dyeing process rather than an optional aftertreatment, have been introduced. In the past the main use of this chelation treatment was to bring about an improvement in light fastness, but it is little used for this purpose nowadays.

Since direct dyes are anionic in nature, many cationic surfactants such as quaternary ammonium compounds can be used as aftertreatments to form surfactant–dye complexes of reduced aqueous solubility and therefore higher wet fastness. The improved fastness related only to non-detergent agencies such as perspiration and water, however; in soap-based washing processes the stronger interaction between the anionic soap and the cationic agent tended to cleave the dye–cation complex, thus effectively negating the aftertreatment even after a single mild wash. The aftertreatment also brought about a change in shade and a reduction in light fastness, although the latter could sometimes be countered by a combined or subsequent treatment with a metal salt such as copper(II) sulphate, as described in the preceding paragraph.

All the aftertreatment processes so far described have declined considerably in commercial importance in recent years and are now rarely carried out (with the exception of the after-coppering of 'copperable' direct dye ranges). Nevertheless, their common principle of creating on the fibre a larger molecular complex of reduced solubility and a correspondingly lower rate of desorption has survived in today's use of 'resin-type' fixing agents. The principle of cationic aftertreatment, in particular, has seen noteworthy development.

The earliest cationic treatments stemmed from the development of crease-resist finishes for cellulosic fabrics [59]. One such, promoted specifically for its colour fastness improvements when applied as an aftertreatment to direct dyeings, was a condensation product of formaldehyde and dicyandiamide (10.70; X = Cl or Br) of which the classic example was Fibrofox of Courtaulds, launched during the economic difficulties of the Second World War [60]. Many similar compounds [61] have succeeded it, such as condensation products of formaldehyde with melamine (10.71), polyamines with cyanuric chloride (10.72), and chloroalkanes with poly(ethylene imine) (10.73; R = alkyl).

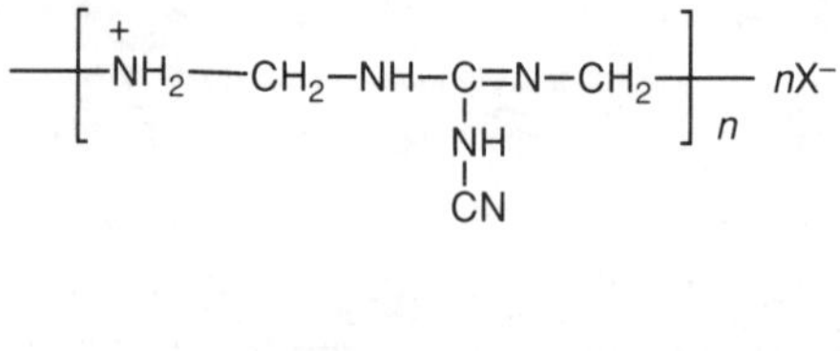

10.70

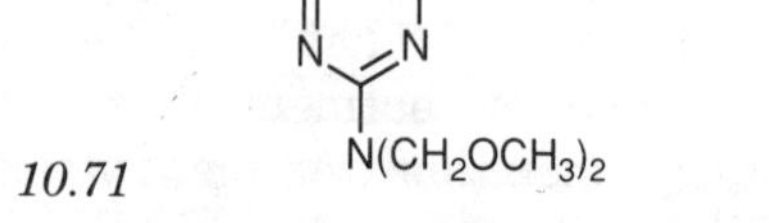

10.71

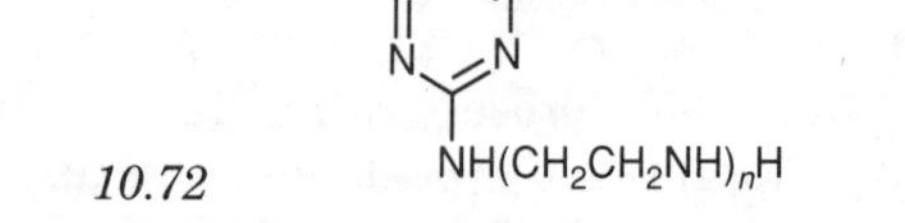

10.72

$$[RNH(C_2H_4NH)_xC_2H_4\overset{+}{N}H_3]\ \ Cl^-$$ *10.73*

These condensates were an improvement on the simpler cationic surfactants mentioned earlier, and products of this type are still widely available [30]. Their interaction still relies on electrostatic bonding between agent cation and dye anion; hence the major weakness remains fastness to washing with anionic detergents such as soap. More recently this limitation of the monofunctional cationic agents has been overcome by the development of bi-, tri- and tetra-functional agents which carry reactant groups capable of forming more permanent (i.e. covalent) bonds by reaction with other suitable groups in the dye and/or the hydroxy groups in the fibre. Studies on the functionality and reactivity of various multifunctional crosslinking agents [62] led to the selection of 1,3,5-triacylhexahydro-*s*-triazines (10.74; R = CH_2CH_2Cl, $CHClCH_2Cl$, $CCl=CH_2$ or $CH=CH_2$) as being particularly effective, their efficiency arising from the lability of the three substituents and the strong polarising effect of the carbonyl groups.

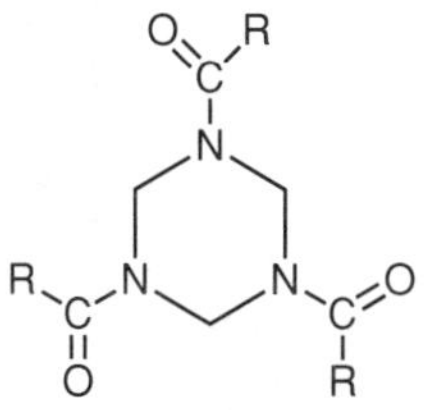

10.74

The trisacryloyl derivative (R is $CH=CH_2$) was subsequently developed as a fixing agent for use with the Basazol (BASF) dyes in the printing of cellulosic fibres, in conjunction with urea as hydrotrope [62]. It has also been shown [63] that aftertreatment with 1,3,5-trisacryloyl-*s*-triazine or the tris-β-chloropropionyl derivative improves the wet (including wash) fastness of direct dyes, provided the dyes contain suitable nucleophilic groups. The same compounds have useful properties with reactive dyes (other than the Basazols) in giving increased colour yield through fixation of hydrolysed dye, an aspect discussed in more detail below.

The basic mechanism of multifunctional fixation agents has been well described by Robinson [61] (Figures 10.3 and 10.4); however, the multifunctional products are no better than the monofunctional types when used with 'ordinary' direct dyes that do not contain suitable reactant groups through which to link the fixative. Direct dyes suitable for forming additional bonds have been termed 'reactant-fixable' dyes and are mostly of the copper-complex type. Thus brightness of shade is limited.

A range of bifunctional (Indosol E-50), trifunctional (Indosol EF) and tetrafunctional (Indosol CR) fixatives has recently been developed by

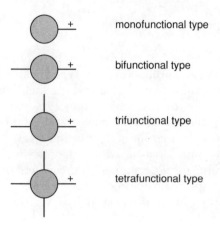

Figure 10.3 – Fixing agents showing various degrees of functionality

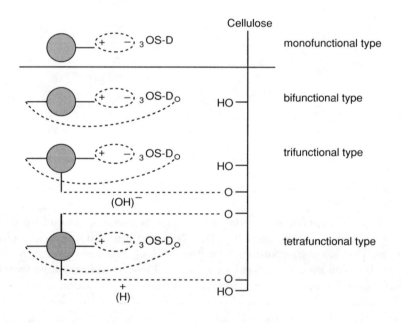

Figure 10.4 – Modes of reaction of the various fixing agents [61]

Sandoz [61,64] for use with a selected range of copper-complex (Indosol) dyes. The bifunctional type, which reacts only with the dye, is applied in a fresh bath at about 60°C and gives fastness to washing up to 50–60°C through the formation of a large dye–agent complex within the fibre. The trifunctional type additionally forms covalent bonds with cellulose and is applied at 40°C for about 15 minutes, followed by addition of alkali to bring about reaction; this confers a higher degree of wash fastness up to 60°C even with deep shades. Tetrafunctional reactant resins confer the highest fastness, even to washing at the boil. Typical polymers are made by the reaction [65] of an amine such as diethylenetriamine with cyanamide, dicyandiamide (especially), guanidine or biguanide. One of these is mixed with an N-methylol reactant (such as dimethyloldihydroxyethyleneurea) and an acid-liberating catalyst (such as magnesium chloride) to give the commercial product sold as a cationic reactant resin (Indosol CR). It is applied to the dyeing by padding, at which stage a dye–agent complex is believed to be formed. It is then cured at 175–180°C, resulting in covalent reaction between the cationic agent and the N-methylol reactant as well as crosslinking of cellulose chains by the N-methylol compound, conferring not only excellent wet fastness but also improved crease resistance and good dimensional stability.

The multifunctional agents offer an alternative aftertreatment for reactive dyes [61], if problems arise from the presence on the fibre of unfixed and hydrolysed dye, normally removed by 'soaping' – a process that is invariably lengthy and expensive, and not always effective. Multifunctional cationic reactant fixatives will react with both unfixed (still reactive) and hydrolysed (hydroxy-containing) dye; tri- and tetra-functional fixatives will further fix them by covalent bonding to the fibre. Improved wet fastness can also ensue including, when tetrafunctional products are used, considerably improved resistance to hydrolysis of the dye–fibre bond and better fastness to treatments involving chlorine or perborates, nowadays of particular importance in some countries. Deleterious effects on hue and light fastness still have to be carefully considered in the selection of dyes for aftertreatment, however.

10.7.3 Disperse dyes on acetate and polyester fibres

Not all disperse dyes on acetate fibres are resistant to oxides of nitrogen present in the atmosphere. Susceptible dyes, usually those containing active amino or substituted amino groups, can undergo quite profound shade changes depending on the reactivity or basicity of the susceptible group(s). The primary general mechanism of fading is believed to be formation of N-nitrosamines [66]. The problem is best avoided by using dyes that do not fade, but this may not always be possible as these tend to be more expensive and less easy to apply. Some protection can be obtained by treatment of susceptible dyeings, either during or after dyeing, with colourless agents that react preferentially with oxides of nitrogen. Such agents are known as gas-fume inhibitors. Since they act as scavengers of the acidic oxides of nitrogen, they need to be more basic in character than the dyes they protect. Many such basic compounds, generally applied from

aqueous solution or dispersion, have been proposed [67]:
- triethanolamine
- dibenzylamine
- *NN'*-dibenzylethylenediamine
- tetrabenzylmethylenediamine
- tetrabenzylethylenediamine
- diethylaminoethyl phthalate
- α-diethylaminoacetanilide
- *NN'*-diphenylacetamidine
- *NN'*-diphenylformamidine
- 2,4,5-triphenylimidazoline
- *NN'*-diphenylethylenediamine
- *NN'*-bis(2,6-dimethylphenyl)ethylenediamine
- *NN'*-diphenylpiperazine
- aniline
- urea
- thiourea
- *N*-allylurea
- *N*-allylthiourea
- *NN*-diphenylthiourea
- *s*-diphenylguanidine
- 2-hexylpyridine
- dibenzylcyanamide
- ethyl anthranilate
- benzoylacetonitrile
- diethyl malonate
- diphenylmethane
- α-benzil monoxime
- 2,6-di-t-butyl-*p*-cresol
- diethylene glycol
- cobalt(II) acetate.

The most popular and efficient are substantive to the fibre; typical examples are *NN'*-diphenylacetamidine (which tends to yellow on exposure to oxides of nitrogen) and particularly the diphenylated diamines, such as *NN'*-diphenylethylenediamine, which does not yellow. Non-substantive inhibitors applied by padding and drying, such as triethanolamine and melamine, have also been used despite the fact that they are removed on washing. The use and commercial availability of gas-fume inhibitors has declined considerably over the past decade or so [30].

Atmospheric ozone has also been reported as causing fading of certain dyes in some countries [68,69]; diallyl phthalate, used as a carrier in the dyeing of triacetate, is said to be an effective ozone inhibitor [70].

In recent years polyester fibres have been widely adopted for use in automobiles where they can be exposed to prolonged sunlight at high temperature and humidity. Consequently many automotive manufacturers have specified a diversity of extremely severe tests for light fastness [71] and resistance of the fibres to photodegradation [71–73]. Although the selection of dyes of suitably high fastness under these extreme conditions is of primary importance, some additional protection can be achieved by the use of so-called ultra-violet absorbers, these being colourless aromatic compounds with a high propensity to absorb the troublesome u.v. radiation. Such products are usually applied during dyeing and give protection to both dyes and fibres. Typical products include benzoates, benzophenones and benzotriazoles [74]; polyamides and other fibres can also be treated.

10.7.4 Sulphur dyes on cellulosic fibres

The fastness of sulphur dyes to the increasingly severe conditions of washing currently demanded, especially in the presence of peroxide-containing detergents, can sometimes be improved by an alkylation treatment. The best-known products for this purpose are adducts of epichlorohydrin with either ethylenediamine (especially) or ammonium salts [17,75]. Typically the procedure involves the application of 2–3% o.w.f. Solidogen IH (HOE) with 1–2% o.w.f. sodium carbonate (pH 10 and 30–40°C), raising the temperature to 90–95°C and allowing the reaction to reach completion at this temperature, which it does after 10 minutes [17]. This treatment usually replaces the traditional oxidation treatment, except for dyes having a marked yellow leuco form.

10.8 FOAMING AND DEFOAMING AGENTS

10.8.1 Foaming agents

The idea of using a matrix of foam to transfer chemicals and colorants to textiles had its origin in the growing need to save heat energy and water in the aftermath of the so-called oil crisis and recession of the early 1970s. In a sense, it was an antidote to the feverish work carried out in the late 1960s on solvent dyeing. Although this did provide some economies in water and heating requirements, it also posed certain problems, not the least of which was that of solvent recovery in bulk-scale processing. Foam dyeing began with the elegant short-liquor (about 1.5:1) dyeing process devised by Lister [76] and developed commercially as the Sancowad (S) process [77], mainly for garment dyeing in rotary machines. Foam application has subsequently been widely investigated, but the degree of commercial acceptance has proved limited. Whilst continuous dyeing and printing, mainly of carpeting, has become established, most processing is in the application of finishes, where concentration tolerances (cf. shade matching) and evenness of application (cf. level dyeing) are not so critical.

Apart from reproducibility and evenness of application, one of the main problems in the application of foam is dissolving or dispersing relatively large quantities of the principal and auxiliary agents in a very small volume of water, followed by the difficulty of maintaining compatibility of the components and the density and stability of the 'loaded' foam under such conditions. For example, Capponi [78] describes a typical resin finishing treatment requiring the dissolution of some 600 g of resin, softener, catalyst and so forth in 400 g of water. Nevertheless, foam processing does offer advantages, notably in the conservation of water and energy and the reduction of effluent problems.

The foam matrix used in textile wet processing is a stabilised air-in-water system. A foam cannot be made with pure water, however; a foaming agent, usually a surfactant, is needed to give a reasonably stable honeycomb matrix of air cells, each enclosed by a thin viscoelastic film of liquid. A single, approximately hemispherical, bubble on the surface of a liquid is the simplest form, but in the denser matrices most readily associated with foam the bubbles are packed close together, their hemispherical character being compressed to a more cuboidal shape by thinning of the lamellar walls between neighbouring bubbles. Clearly, a reduction in surface tension is one important factor in the creation of foam; others include the elasticity and viscosity of the film walls between the bubbles, and the size and uniformity of the bubbles themselves. Drainage, by gravity, of the liquid from the film walls leads to instability of the foam and tends to a maximum with larger spherical bubbles. In a system consisting of variously sized bubbles, the smaller ones tend to coalesce into the larger, which are thus further increased in size and become less stable because of the increased propensity for liquid drainage. Thus, for maximum stability, the bubbles should be as small and uniform as possible, leading to minimum diffusion of air from bubble to bubble, and maximum entropic and electrical double-layer repulsion. The ideal state is not attainable in practice, however, and all foams are unstable to some degree. Nor is perfect foam stability particularly required in textile application, since at some stage during the process collapse of the foam is generally desirable to ensure maximum deposition of chemicals and/or colorants.

The foaming propensity of surfactants generally reaches a maximum at the critical micelle concentration, beyond which there appears to be little further contribution to foam density. Foam stabilisers are also added in some cases.

Of equal importance in any consideration of foaming mechanism is the purely mechanistic question of actually generating the foam by admixture of air and liquid and the transference of the foam to the substrate, but this is outside the scope of the present book. Several authors [78–93] have described the methods used, the principal ones being summarised by Roberts [80]:

(a) generation is generally by high-speed rotors, with metered air and liquid flows and monitoring to control the density of the foam
(b) application of controlled amounts of foam to the substrate is by knife-on-roller, knife-on-blanket, floating knife, horizontal pad or furnishing roller with doctor blade.

Application may also be by squeegee across a printing screen [84].

Subsequent collapsing of the foam [80] is generally by collapse on the fabric (controlled to some extent by the chemicals used), by vacuum suction of the foam into the fabric, or by means of a pad nip.

The most important auxiliary used is, of course, the foaming agent. In theory any surfactant that foams can be used. In practice the choice is usually between anionic and non-ionic types [79,85,93] (the former being generally the cheaper) and a mixture of both. Consideration must be given to overall compatibility as well as to foaming characteristics: for example, anionic types should generally be avoided when applying cationic products. Long-chain alcohol sulphonates and ethoxylates [79] as well as sulphates and sulphosuccinates [85,93] have been used; a representative selection is given below [85], the first three being anionic and the remainder non-ionic:
– sodium lauryl sulphate
– ammonium lauryl sulphate
– sodium dioctyl sulphosuccinate
– lauryl alcohol poly(oxyethylene)
– decyl alcohol poly(oxyethylene)
– tridecyl alcohol poly(oxyethylene).

Particular effectiveness is claimed for a mixture of anionic and non-ionic types [80], such as a mildly anionic sulphated alcohol ethoxylate with a non-ionic alcohol ethoxylate [79]. Ideally, foaming agents should generate consistent foam easily and show optimum and uniform wetting, should cover a wide range of wettability so as to be adaptable for different situations, should show little or no effect on colour fastness, should be compatible with the other components and should be biodegradable [83].

The main function of the foam-stabilising agent is to reinforce the intercellular film wall by contributing rheological characteristics of visco-elasticity. The increased viscosity may also assist handling. The aim, as so often with auxiliaries, is to achieve an optimum balance, since if the bubbles are too thin and wet too quickly they will collapse prematurely, whilst too stable a film could hinder uniform application. Examples of products used as foam stabilisers [79,81,91] are thickening agents such as the polysaccharides, hydroxyethylcellulose, methylcellulose, carboxymethylcellulose, poly(vinyl alcohol) and poly(acrylic acids), as well as other compounds such as sodium tripolyphosphate, sodium hexametaphosphate (detergent 'builders') and dodecyl alcohol. Foam stabilisers should ideally increase the stability of the foam to the optimum controllable level whilst also allowing for subsequent controllable collapse. They should be compatible with the other components and effective at various concentrations, give pseudoplastic solutions, and should not affect the drape and handle of the fabric [83].

10.8.2 Defoaming agents

Useful though foam may be, there are still many circumstances where its presence and persistence is enough of a nuisance to create a need for foam-destruction products, known as defoaming agents or antifoams.

Just as foams are stabilised by decreasing the rate of liquid drainage from the film walls, they can be destabilised by increasing this drainage, resulting in thinning and eventual rupturing of the film. Defoaming agents generally effect this by two means, the basic object being to displace foam-stabilising substances from the liquid–air interface [78,94,95]. Spreading alone is sufficient with light foams of high blow ratio (those having a high air–liquid ratio); in this case surfactants of relatively low surface tension (i.e. powerful surfactants) will spread over the large surface area of the intercellular film and displace the surfactants that are tending to stabilise it. Denser foams of low blow ratio additionally require penetration of the thicker aqueous film by the defoaming agent. Such a defoamer consists of an emulsified hydrophobic substance, which when added to the foaming system disperses fine droplets of insoluble hydrophobic material within the liquid lamellar walls, thus entering the liquid–air interface, aided to some extent by the solubilising action of the foaming agent(s). This creates a weak link as a result of high interfacial tension, the foam then tending to rupture at the interface between defoamer and foamer. In practice, the system is a finely balanced one requiring careful formulation of the composite defoaming agent. This is evident from a consideration of the energy of the system (Eqn 10.1):

$$\Delta E = \gamma_F + \gamma_{FD} - \gamma_D \tag{10.1}$$

where ΔE = decrease in free energy (or entry coefficient for the droplets [95])

γ_F = surface tension of the foaming agent(s)

γ_{FD} = interfacial tension between defoamer and foamer

γ_D = surface tension of the defoamer.

In an effective defoaming system, the entry coefficient ΔE must be positive. Since in practice the surface tension of the foaming system is predetermined by circumstances, it follows that in formulating the defoaming agent only the surface tension of the defoamer (and hence the interfacial tension between defoamer and foamer) can be manipulated.

The main requirement for an effective defoamer [94,95] is that the agent should be insoluble in the foaming system and should have a high rate of spreading. Spreading will be aided if the defoamer has a lower surface tension than that of the foaming system. The interfacial tension between defoamer and foaming system must be high, but not so high as to inhibit spreading. A low degree of attraction between defoamer and foaming system (i.e. a high interfacial tension) is aided by non-polar defoamer systems that do not contribute positively to the surface viscosity of the lamellar walls.

For maximum efficiency the defoamer should be added to the system as foaming becomes troublesome, since its active life-span is inevitably limited by the system's thermodynamic instability. Its principal activity is on the liquid–air interface; therefore there is little point in adding it before sufficient liquid–air interfaces are formed. Secondly the insoluble active ingredient of the defoamer must, given the nature of the system in which it is working, eventually become more or less solubilised, or at least emulsified, into the bulk liquid system, thus losing its activity, and in some circumstances actually promoting foaming.

Defoamers are generally of anionic or non-ionic character and fall into two groups. The first group consists of water-soluble surfactants with polar and non-polar moieties. These compounds are effective only over a narrow range of conditions, functioning simply as spreading agents, and are seldom used alone. Such surfactants are readily absorbed into the bulk of the foaming system where, not surprisingly, they contribute to the foaming. This system is more frequently used, however, as the vehicular or 'carrier' basis of the second group of defoamers, which are much more widely used. These more active defoamers are emulsions of water-insoluble silicones or organic-based types of low volatility and high spreading power. The active organic-based defoamers include:

(a) fatty acids, their glycerides and other esters, including fats, waxes and oils such as mineral and vegetable oils (castor oil, for example); also fatty alkyl-amines and -amides
(b) higher alcohols, such as the isomeric octyl alcohols (2-octanol and 2-ethylhexanol), cyclohexanol, lauryl and cetyl alcohols and others
(c) polyglycols, especially poly(propylene-1,2- or -1,3-glycol)
(d) insoluble alkyl esters of phosphoric acid, especially tributyl phosphate.

A current survey [30] indicates that practically all these types are represented.

The active ingredients in silicone-based defoamers have traditionally been polyalkylsiloxanes, especially poly(dimethylsiloxane) (10.75), and silica (SiO_2); the latter may be chemically bonded to the polysiloxane to render its surface hydrophobic [95,96]. Some 'spotting' problems have been

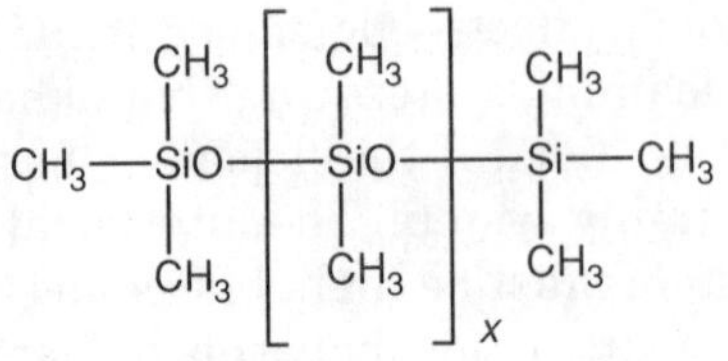

$$
CH_3-\underset{\underset{CH_3}{|}}{\overset{\overset{CH_3}{|}}{Si}}O\left[\underset{\underset{CH_3}{|}}{\overset{\overset{CH_3}{|}}{Si}}O\right]_x\underset{\underset{CH_3}{|}}{\overset{\overset{CH_3}{|}}{Si}}-CH_3 \qquad 10.75
$$

experienced with these defoamers owing to incompatibility of the antifoam emulsion with certain dye dispersions, especially at high rates of shear in the high-temperature dyeing of polyester with disperse dyes. This led, some twenty years ago, to a poor reputation for silicone antifoams in this area of application. Improvements have since been made, both to the emulsion system and to the silicone components themselves. Improved derivatives of poly(dimethylsiloxane) include [94] block copolymers with poly(oxyethylene) and poly(oxypropylene) segments represented schematically by structure 10.76.

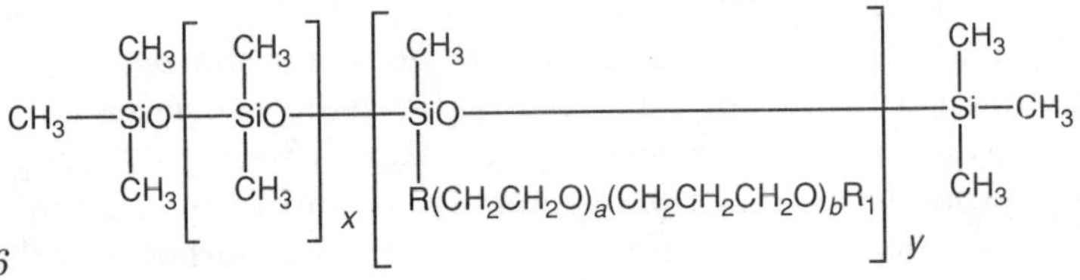

$$
CH_3-\underset{\underset{CH_3}{|}}{\overset{\overset{CH_3}{|}}{Si}}O\left[\underset{\underset{CH_3}{|}}{\overset{\overset{CH_3}{|}}{Si}}O\right]_x\left[\underset{R(CH_2CH_2O)_a(CH_2CH_2CH_2O)_bR_1}{\overset{\overset{CH_3}{|}}{Si}}O\right]_y\underset{\underset{CH_3}{|}}{\overset{\overset{CH_3}{|}}{Si}}-CH_3
$$

10.76

The solubility and other characteristics of these alkoxylated silicones can be adjusted by varying the proportions of dimethylsiloxane and oxyalkylene units. An advantage particularly claimed for these compounds in high-temperature dyeing is their inverse solubility (analogous to the cloud point effect of non-ionic surfactants): that is, as the dyebath temperature reaches its maximum the solubility of the defoamer decreases, thus helping to maintain its effectiveness, whilst the increased solubility on cooling after completion of the dyeing is claimed to overcome the problems of subsequent spotting.

Antifoams are generally supplied for textile use as carefully formulated, relatively dilute, aqueous emulsions; this ensures that the hydrophobic particles are easily dispersed in the foaming system and also helps to safeguard against overdosing, with the attendant danger of spotting. A typical emulsion generally contains, in addition to water and the insoluble hydrophobic defoaming agent, emulsifying agent(s) and thickening agent(s). For emulsification, the most common system [94] is a combination of a low-HLB surfactant with one of high HLB value [such as glyceryl monostearate or sorbitan monostearate with poly(ethylene glycol) monostearate]. Obviously the surfactants used need to be low-foaming types and should provide an optimum level of emulsification, since over-emulsification will tend to negate the activity of the defoamer by inhibiting its interaction with the foaming system. The size of the defoamer droplets, which is largely determined by the emulsification system used and the degree of comminution during manufacture, is critical in relation to the efficacy of the product; too small a size gives inadequate activity whilst if it is too large the stability of the emulsion is affected. The optimum droplet size [94] appears generally to be in the range 2 to 50 μm.

The purpose of the thickening agent is to increase the viscosity and so contribute to the stability of the product, again the aim being to obtain an optimum level of viscosity. Thickening agents that do not gel at the high temperatures used in textile processing are required; hydroxyethylcellulose, alginates and synthetic poly(acrylic acid) products may be used. A small amount of a bactericide such as methyl p-hydroxybenzoate is also often added to safeguard against biological degradation during storage, particularly in regard to the thickening agent.

Some typical detailed formulations for commercial composite antifoams are given by Willig [94]. There are many products on the market but evaluation of their relative efficacy depends on the foaming problems to be overcome. Not only does the chemical type of the active defoamer have to be considered, but its state within the emulsion and the emulsion properties themselves are also of crucial importance.

10.9 AGENTS FOR FIBRE LUBRICATION, SOFTENING, ANTISTATIC EFFECTS, SOIL RELEASE AND SOIL REPELLENCY

Most of the products discussed in this section are finishing agents rather than dyeing or printing auxiliaries. They may be applied before, during or after coloration, however, and thus may influence the choice of dyes and coloration processes, particularly as regards problems experienced during coloration (incompatibility of components) and afterwards (fastness properties).

Many of these products have useful activity in more than one function. Thus a product (and especially a composite commercial product) promoted chiefly as a softener may also have antistatic, yarn lubricating and antisoil properties, and it is useful to bear this diversity of function in mind.

10.9.1 Fibre lubricants

The main consideration here is lubricants used during wet processing rather than in textile manufacture. The basic requirement of a lubricant is that it should form a thin uniform protective coating around the fibre to lower the surface friction and flexural rigidity, thus minimising the formation of durable creases during high-temperature processing. Hence suitable products tend to be relatively hydrophobic surfactants, many of which also contain a proportion of solubilised or emulsified oil or wax (such as mineral oil or paraffin wax) [97,98]. Many problems have been caused through incompatibility of these surfactants, oils or waxes with disperse dyes and auxiliaries in the dyebath. The hydrophobic lubricant phase acts as a solvent for disperse dyes, creating an ideal medium for the formation of tars or scums which, through inadequate emulsification, may be deposited as spots or filtration residues on substrates, particularly in highly concentrated short liquor ratios (as in jig dyeing) and in beam or package dyeing. This problem is exacerbated in polyester dyeing if significant amounts of cyclic trimers are present. Great care and much empiricism is required in the design of a trouble-free fibre lubricant formulation for use in textile wet processing and particular attention needs to be paid to the conditions under which it will be used.

Either non-ionic surfactants or, preferably, the anionic poly(oxyethylene) sulphates and phosphates derived from fatty acids, alcohols or glycols, are suitable. The anionic types perform better than non-ionic agents in high-temperature conditions because they do not give 'cloud point' problems. Even with careful formulation, however, the presence of oils or waxes can give rise to problems in coloration processes, especially as the formulator of the lubricant does not have control over the conditions of use. Consequently there has been a tendency in recent years to promote lubricants based entirely on ethoxylated surfactants (without oils or waxes); these are also hydrotropic and thus impart a temporary antistatic effect on hydrophobic fibres. Quite frequently, however, these ethoxylated lubricants are used as the emulsion basis for carrying other products such as softeners.

10.9.2 Softeners
It is difficult to define in scientific terms the quality of fabric softness and 'hand', since it involves many factors. It is often linked with 'lubricity', especially as similar products can be used for softness and lubrication, and yet is something indefinably more than this; whilst accurate objective methods have been devised for measuring lubricity, the assessment of softness still depends on the subjective judgment of experienced assessors and discerning or fickle customers [98]. The oils and waxes mentioned in section 10.9.1 in connection with lubricants, as well as talc, can also be used as softeners but have now been largely superseded by more effective products. Mooney [98] has given a useful general review of the chemical types and properties of products used and also discussed commercial formulations, application conditions and assessments. The various products are divided into reactive, anionic, non-ionic, amphoteric and cationic types, of which by far the most important today are the cationic and silicone types.

Cationic softeners are undoubtedly the most important, both industrially and domestically. Although many compounds have been used, the most common over many years have been the quaternary alkylammonium compounds, specifically dimethyldistearylammonium methosulphate (10.77) [98], which is favoured for its low cost and wide availability. The preferred anions are methosulphate or ethosulphate since these have a less corrosive effect on steel vessels than the chloride. These compounds generally show maximum cationic activity at around pH 3.5 but are usually applied at higher pH values. Relevant properties of these softeners include aqueous solubility, exhaustion, compatibility with other additives, as well as their temporary antistatic and water-repellency effects. The balance of these properties can be modified by varying the four substituents on the quaternary nitrogen atom or, more precisely, using the related ethoxylated or propoxylated polyamines (10.78), in which the degree of alkoxylation can also be varied. These are more expensive than the simple quaternary ammonium types but are valued as quality industrial softeners. Quaternised imidazolines (10.79) are also useful. In some cases the cationic softening agent is mixed with a non-ionic surfactant, which may serve as a lubricant.

10.77
$$\left[H_{35}C_{17}-\underset{\underset{CH_3}{|}}{\overset{\overset{CH_3}{|}}{N}}-C_{17}H_{35} \right]^{+} \quad SO_4^{-}CH_3$$

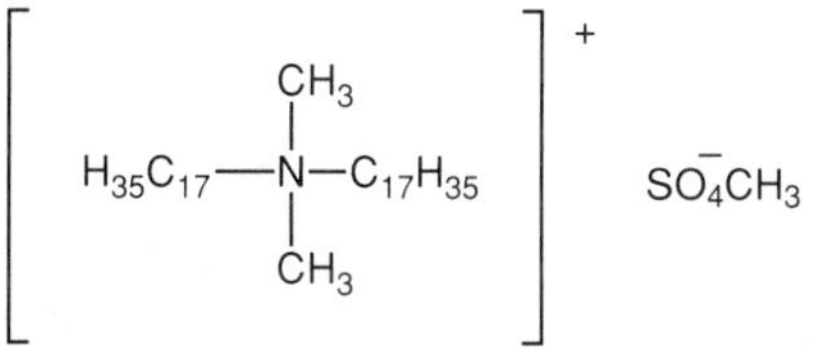

10.78
$$\left[R-\overset{O}{\overset{||}{C}}-NHCH_2CH_2-\underset{\underset{CH_3}{|}}{\overset{\overset{(CH_2CH_2O)_nH}{|}}{N}}-CH_2CH_2NH-\overset{O}{\overset{||}{C}}-R_1 \right]^{+} \quad SO_4^{-}CH_3$$

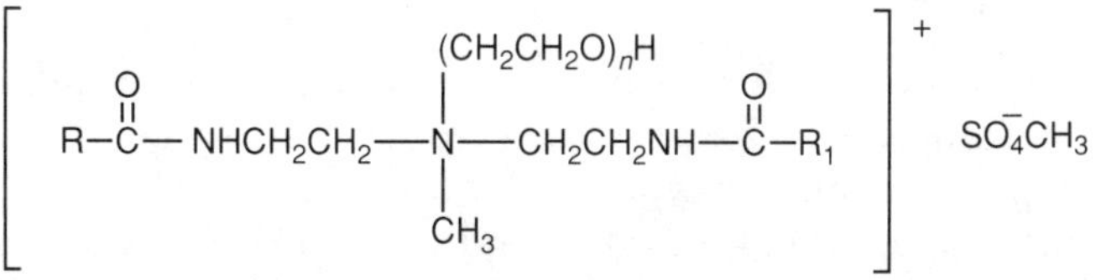

10.79
$$\left[R-\overset{O}{\overset{||}{C}}-NHCH_2CH_2-N \overset{R_1}{\underset{N}{\diagdown}} \right]^{+} \quad SO_4^{-}CH_3$$

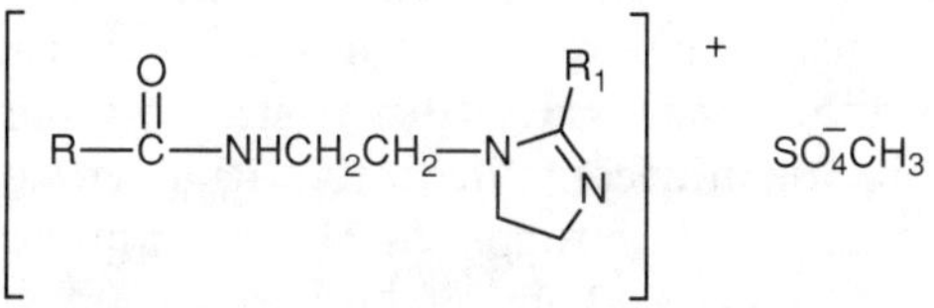

Recent years have seen increasing interest in polysiloxanes as softeners [99–102]. These are similar in structure to the compounds discussed as antifoams in section 10.8.2. Poly(dimethylsiloxane) (10.75) represents the simplest type and is usually applied from an emulsion. It does not react with the substrate and therefore is not durable to washing. More durable softeners are made by modification of the siloxane, typical examples being those containing activated silanic hydrogen (10.80) or silanol (10.81) groups. These can be crosslinked on the fibre by baking in the presence of a suitable crosslinking agent (10.82) and a catalyst (usually organometal-lic). The silanol groups may also be replaced by other functional organic groups such as amines (10.83), epoxides or alcohols. The behaviour of all these polysiloxane products can be varied by controlling the average values of x and y and the range of chain lengths present.

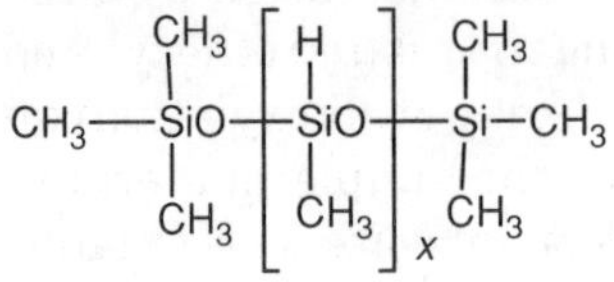

10.80

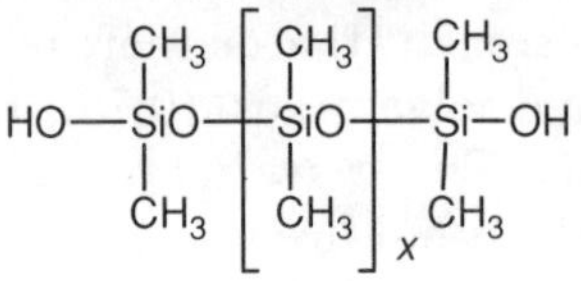

10.81

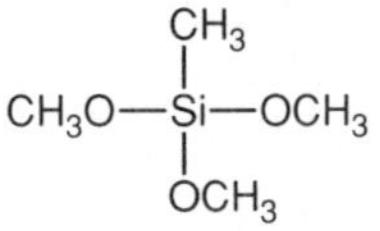

10.82

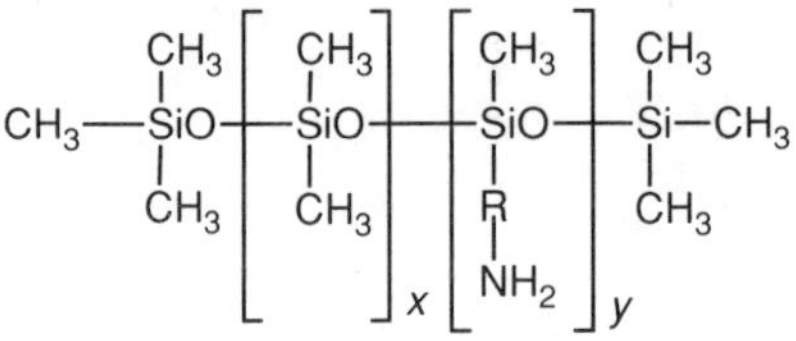

10.83

Many other products can be used as softeners but are commercially of lesser importance because of greater cost and/or inferior properties. Examples are anionic types such as long-chain (C_{16}–C_{22}) alkyl sulphates, sulphonates, sulphosuccinates and soaps. These have rather poor exhaustion properties and are easily washed out. Non-ionic types of limited substantivity and durability, usually applied by padding, include poly-ethoxylated esters of long-chain alcohols, acids, glycerides, oils and waxes. They are useful where other ionic products would pose compatibility problems and they possess useful antistatic properties, but they are more frequently used as lubricants in combination with other softeners, particu-larly the cationics. The properties of some amphoteric softeners such as amino acids (10.84) and sulphobetaines (10.85) are better and more durable than those of the non-ionic types but less durable than those of the cationics; moreover, they tend to be expensive. Other amphoteric types include the zwitterionic forms (10.86) of the quaternised imidazolines already mentioned (10.79); long-chain amine oxides (10.87) also possess softening properties.

10.84 $R-\overset{+}{N}H_2CH_2CH_2COO^-$

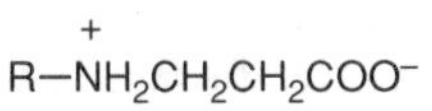

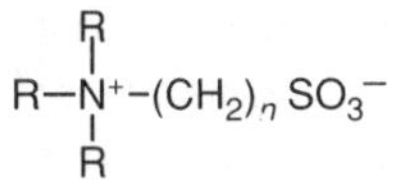

$R-\overset{\overset{\textstyle R}{|}}{\underset{\underset{\textstyle R}{|}}{N^+}}-(CH_2)_n SO_3^-$ 10.85

10.86 $HN\diagup$ ... $N-CH_2CH_2OCH_2CH_2COO^-$ ... R

$R-\overset{\overset{\textstyle R}{|}}{\underset{\underset{\textstyle R}{|}}{N^+}}\longrightarrow O^-$ 10.87

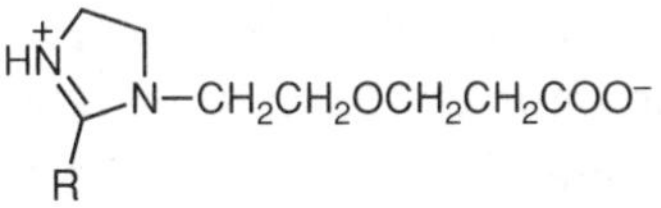

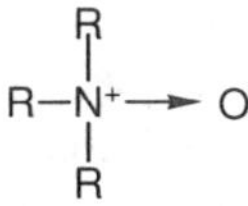

Finally there are reactive types, some of which are N-methylol derivatives of long-chain fatty amides (10.88) while others are triazinyl compounds (10.89). The N-methylol compounds require baking with a latent acid catalyst to effect reaction, whereas chlorotriazines require alkaline fixation conditions. Softeners applicable by exhaustion techniques rather than by padding are usually preferred, but the N-methylol derivatives are particularly useful for combination with crease-resist, durable-press or antisoil finishes. Commercial products are often complex mixtures and may contain, as well as the softener, such products as hydrotropes/ solvents, exhaustion aids (cf. 'builders' used in detergents), antistatic agents, lubricants, bactericides, perfumes and antifoam agents.

10.88 $O=C\diagup\overset{\textstyle NH-\overset{\overset{\textstyle O}{\|}}{C}-R}{\diagdown NH-CH_2OH}$ 10.89

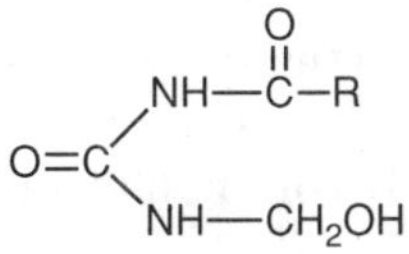

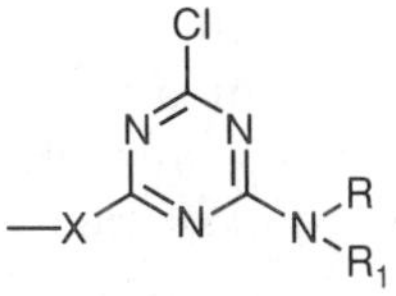

10.9.3 Soil-release and soil-repellent agents

Antisoil products were developed following the increasing use of hydrophobic fibres, particularly nylon and polyester, since experience showed the tenacity of these fibres for oily stains and oil-bound dirt. Durable-press fabrics also tended to soil more easily than untreated fabrics. The subject of soiling and soil removal is more complex than might at first appear [103–107] and involves such aspects as soil resistance, soil adsorption, detergency, soil removal and soil re-deposition. We are concerned here essentially with soils attracted to, and bound mainly at, the fibre surface as opposed to particulate dirt trapped within the interstices between fibres in yarn. The primary objective is to modify the fibre surface (a) to increase the resistance of the fibre to soiling in the first place (i.e. soil repellency) and (b) to ensure that any soil that is deposited is more weakly bound and is hence more easily removed in washing (soil release). Most soils, as might be expected from a predominantly hydrophobic interaction, are held mainly by non-polar bonding (although electrostatic forces may come into play with, for example, coloured anionic stains from food and beverages) so the essence of any antisoil treatment is to render the surface of the fibres more hydrophilic. It also helps if the coating of the fibre is such as to reduce surface irregularity and surface energy. Whilst the two aspects of soil repellency and soil release are interrelated, the actual balance of these properties varies from finish to finish according to requirements. In treatments for carpets, for example, for which frequent washing is hardly desirable, if indeed possible, the emphasis must be on repellency, whereas soil release becomes of greater importance in easily washed articles.

Early soil-release agents, applied particularly to resin-finished cellulosic goods, were water-soluble polymers, many being related to thickeners (see section 10.6) such as starch, hydroxypropyl starch, sodium carboxymethylcellulose, methylcellulose, hydroxyethylcellulose, alginates, poly(vinyl alcohol) and poly(vinylpyrrolidone). These functioned essentially as temporary barriers and 'preferential reservoirs' for soil, which was thus easily removed along with the finish in subsequent washing, when they then helped to minimise re-deposition. Obviously this type of finish lacked durability. More permanent finishes have been developed, and these are generally classified in three groups according to whether they feature (a) carboxyl groups, (b) oxyethylene and/or hydroxy groups and (c) fluorocarbon moieties.

The carboxy polymer type (103,104,108–111] comprise acrylic, methacrylic or maleic acid polymers (all obviously anionic in character) applied mainly from aqueous emulsion and particularly in combination with crease-resist/durable-press resins. This type of chemistry has already been discussed in section 10.6.2. A particularly common example is the copolymer of acrylic acid with ethyl acrylate (10.90).

$$\left[\begin{array}{c} CH_2-CH- \\ | \\ COOH \end{array} \right]_x \left[\begin{array}{c} CH_2-CH- \\ | \\ COOC_2H_5 \end{array} \right]_y$$

10.90

In general the best balance of properties is obtained with 75–85% ethyl acrylate (y) and 25–15% acrylic acid (x), with an average chain length $(x + y)$ of about 1300 units; 65–85% ethyl acrylate with 35–15% methacrylic acid is also suitable. When the content of the acidic monomer component increases beyond these limits the durability to washing tends to decrease, whilst longer chains tend to give a stiffer handle [104].

Soil-release products containing ethoxy or hydroxy groups may be anionic or non-ionic. Many less durable water-soluble polymers have been mentioned already, such as the hydroxy-containing finishes poly(vinyl alcohol), starch, and derivatives of starch and cellulose. When applied together with N-methylol compounds, as in easy-care finishing, they give more permanent antisoil properties. Typical of the ethoxy-containing compounds are poly(ethylene glycol) and poly(ethylene oxide) adducts of functional acids, amines, phenols and alcohols, which may be combined with hydroxy-reactive functional agents as used in easy-care finishes, such as N-methylols or isocyanates.

Essentially non-ionic antisoil agents comprise polyesters, polyamides, polyurethanes, polyepoxides and polyacetals. These are mainly used on polyester and polyester/cellulosic materials, either crosslinked to effect insolubilisation (if necessary) or by surface adsorption at relatively low temperature. Polyester finishes [112,113] have perhaps been most important, particularly for polyester fibre and its blends with cellulose. These finishes, however, have much lower relative molecular mass (1000– 100 000) than polyester fibres, and hence contain a greater proportion of hydroxy (hydrophilic) groups. They have been particularly useful for application in laundering processes and are classically represented by Permalose TM (ICI). These essentially non-ionic types may be given anionic character by copolymerising with, for example, the carboxy types mentioned earlier [114,115]; these hybrid types are generally applied with durable-press finishes.

Polyfluorinated chemicals have been at the forefront of antisoil finishes for some time. Discussion of their chemistry must be restricted here, but it will be sufficient to demonstrate the essential principles. The earlier so-called conventional polyfluorinated products were of the type represented by poly(N-methylperfluoro-octanesulphonamidoethyl acrylate) (10.91) [107]. Such products presented a shield of closely packed fluoroalkyl groups at the fibre–air interface, thus giving low-energy surfaces with excellent oleophobicity, which functioned well as regards resistance to oil-based stains but were less satisfactory as soil-release agents during washing. The soil-release properties were subsequently considerably improved by copolymerising these conventional fluorochemicals with hydrophilic moieties [103,104,107] to give so-called hybrid polymers represented schematically by A–B–A–B–A–, where A represents the perfluoroalkyl-containing segment and B the hydrophilic segment. A typical example [104,107,116] is represented by structure 10.92, which is composed of alternating perfluorinated units of the type shown in structure 10.91 with hydrophilic poly(ethylene oxide) moieties derived from the thiol-terminated copolymer of tetraethylene glycol dimethacrylate and hydrogen sulphide (10.93).

$$\left[\begin{array}{cccc} R & R & R & R \\ | & | & | & | \\ C{=}O & C{=}O & C{=}O & C{=}O \\ | & | & | & | \\ {-}CH_2{-}CH{-}CH_2{-}CH{-}CH_2{-}CH{-}CH_2{-}CH{-} \end{array} \right]_n$$

$$R = OCH_2CH_2\underset{\underset{CH_3}{|}}{N}SO_2C_8F_{17}$$

10.91

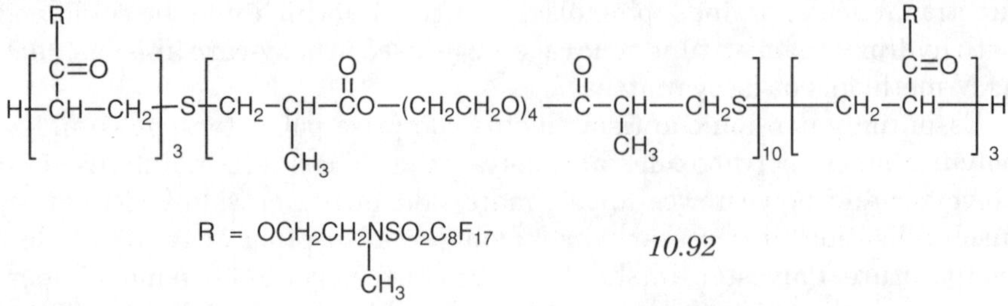

$$H\left[\begin{array}{c}R\\|\\C=O\\|\\CH-CH_2\end{array}\right]_3\left[S\begin{array}{c}O\\||\\CH_2-CH-CO-(CH_2CH_2O)_4\\|\\CH_3\end{array}\begin{array}{c}O\\||\\-C-CH-CH_2S\\|\\CH_3\end{array}\right]_{10}\left[\begin{array}{c}R\\|\\C=O\\|\\CH_2-CH\end{array}\right]_3H$$

$$R = OCH_2CH_2NSO_2C_8F_{17} \atop \qquad\qquad |\atop \qquad\qquad CH_3$$

10.92

$$HS\left[CH_2-\begin{array}{c}\\CH\\|\\CH_3\end{array}\begin{array}{c}O\\||\\-CO-(CH_2CH_2O)_4-\end{array}\begin{array}{c}O\\||\\C-CH-CH_2-\\|\\CH_3\end{array}S\right]_{10}H$$

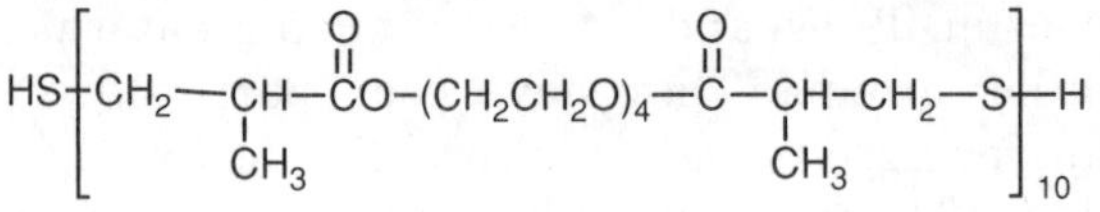

10.93

Once again these are only average schematic structures, in this case resulting in a block copolymer of alternating segments. The hydrophilic moieties in themselves show no significant oil repellency and are not very effective as soil-release agents, yet when incorporated into such hybrid structures they considerably improve the soil-release properties without inhibiting the inherent soil-repellency of the perfluorinated moieties. This is said [107] to result from the ability of these hybrid polymers to orient a specific moiety at the surface, depending on the polarity of the fibre–environment interface. Thus in air the fibre–air interface is dominated by the closely packed perfluoroalkyl moieties, promoting good repellency, whilst in aqueous wash liquors it is the hydrophilic moieties that orient at the fibre–liquid interface, thus enhancing soil release. In either case the non-active moiety is said to be collapsed below the surface. In this way, the lowest interfacial energy, with respect to the particular environment, is attained in both cases.

The example used here incorporated a polyacrylate 'backbone' and a poly(ethylene oxide) hydrophilic moiety. Other fluorochemical moieties, 'backbones' and hydrophiles can be used provided they display the alternating surface orientation characteristics with respect to air and water. The essential character of the hydrophilic unit is that it should have polar groups capable of strong interaction with water, preferably by hydrogen bonding; examples are hydroxy, carboxyl and ether oxygen. Usually C_5–C_{18} perfluoroalkyl groups are used, but individual products may contain a mixture of homologues. Thus there is tremendous scope for 'engineering' a great variety of these complex products.

These hybrid fluoropolymers, which have been known for some twenty years, have recently been incorporated in so-called stain blockers [117], especially in connection with nylon carpets. The fluorochemical is used in combination with an anionic syntan resist agent as described in section

10.7.1. The latter functions by blocking the cationic protonated amine sorption sites in the fibre. Thus the fluoropolymer repels oil-based soils and facilitates their removal during cleaning, whilst the syntan inhibits electrostatic interaction between the cationic sites and many coloured anionic substances in food, drinks and human/animal excretions. The two product types may be applied during fibre manufacture for maximum effect and durability, or they may be applied afterwards (in the dyehouse, for example), in which case the effect is less durable. For maximum efficacy the two component types must be carefully chosen after much empirical screening.

REFERENCES

1. T L Dawson, *J.S.D.C.*, **97** (1981) 115.
2. B C Burdett, *Rev. Prog. Coloration*, **13** (1983) 41.
3. Trevathan, *Advanced Instrum.*, **33** (1978) 69.
4. B C Burdett, C C Cook and J G Guthrie, *J.S.D.C.*, **93** (1977) 55.
5. J Park, *A practical introduction to yarn dyeing* (Bradford: SDC, 1981).
6. C L Bird, *The theory and practice of wool dyeing*, 4th Edn (Bradford: SDC, 1972).
7. R Nahta, *Amer. Dyestuff Rep.*, **68** (Mar 1979) 32.
8. R J Hannay and W H Major, *J.S.D.C.*, **69** (1953) 195.
9. S, German P 2 354 728 (1972).
10. S, German P 2 803 309 (1977).
11. O Annen, J Carbonell and E Engeler, *Textilveredlung*, **15** (1980) 296.
12. W Mosimann, *J.S.D.C.*, **100** (1984) 50.
13. J F Leuck, *Amer. Dyestuff Rep.*, **68** (Aug 1979) 49.
14. R Maurer, *Canadian Textile J.*, **99** (Aug 1982) 40.
15. A S Davidsohn and B Milwidsky, *Synthetic detergents*, 7th Edn (Harlow: Longman, 1987).
16. H Nijs, V Godecharles and B H May, *Seifen-Öle-Fette-Wachse*, **111** (1985) 149, 203.
17. *The dyeing of cellulosic fibres*, Ed. C Preston (Bradford: Dyers' Company Publications Trust, 1986).
18. L Sitver, *Amer. Dyestuff Rep.*, **67** (July 1978) 29.
19. J R McPhee and T Shaw, *Rev. Prog. Coloration*, **14** (1984) 58.
20. J T Marsh, *An introduction to textile bleaching*, 4th (revised) impression (London: Chapman and Hall, 1956).
21. M D Adams, *Amer. Dyestuff Rep.*, **67** (Jul 1978) 19.
22. K Dickinson, *Rev. Prog. Coloration*, **14** (1984) 1.
23. *The dyeing of synthetic-polymer and acetate fibres*, Ed. D M Nunn (Bradford: Dyers' Company Publications Trust, 1979).
24. R J Mann, *J.S.D.C.*, **76** (1960) 665.
25. D Haigh, *Dyeing and finishing knitted goods* (Leicester: Hosiery Trade Journal, 1971).
26. W S Hickman and H Andrianjafy, *J.S.D.C.*, **99** (1983) 86.
27. M J Palin, D C Teasdale and L Benisek, *J.S.D.C.*, **99** (1983) 261.
28. A M Schwartz and J W Perry, *Surface active agents* (New York: Robert E Krieger, 1949, reprinted 1978).
29. C Duckworth and L M Wrennal, *J.S.D.C.*, **93** (1977) 407.
30. R O Rutley, *J.S.D.C.*, **86** (1970) 337.
31. *Index to textile auxiliaries*, 11th Edn (Bradford: World Textile Publications, 1988).
32. S Heimann, *Rev. Prog. Coloration*, **11** (1981) 1.
33. P Dilling, Books of Papers, AATCC Nat. Tech. Conf. (1986) 148.

34. P H Elworthy, A T Florence and C B Macfarlane, *Solubilisation by surface-active agents* (London: Chapman and Hall, 1968) (especially chapter 2).
35. T L Dawson, *Text. J. Australia*, **42** (1967) 45.
36. E I Valkó, *Rev. Prog. Coloration*, **3** (1972) 50.
37. A Riva and J Cegarra, *J.S.D.C.*, **103** (1987) 32.
38. R H Beaumont, *Amer. Dyestuff Rep.*, **57** (1968) 777.
39. J A Hughes, H H Sumner and B Taylor, *J.S.D.C.*, **87** (1971) 463.
40. S Blackburn and T L Dawson, *J.S.D.C.*, **87** (1971) 473.
41. K A Hilton, *Dyer*, **139** (1968) 563.
42. H Barth, *Bayer Farben Rev.*, No. 15 (1969) 64; No. 16 (1969) 53.
43. O Schlösser, *Bayer Farben Rev.*, No. 17 (1969) 76; No. 18 (1970) 90.
44. J A Cooney, *Amer. Dyestuff Rep.*, **64** (1975) 20.
45. N J Christie, *Dyer*, **155** (1976) 19.
46. L T Holst, *Dyer*, **159** (1978) 60.
47. J Rosenbaum and J Shelso, *Text. Chem. Colorist*, **11** (1979) 220.
48. K Dunkerley, *Rev. Prog. Coloration*, **11** (1981) 74.
49. *Textile printing*, Ed. L W C Miles (Bradford: Dyers' Company Publications Trust, 1981) 232.
50. W Clarke and L W C Miles, *Rev. Prog. Coloration*, **13** (1983) 27.
51. G Rösch, *Melliand Textilber.*, **66** (1985) 66.
52. T L Dawson, *J.S.D.C.*, **75** (1959) 413.
53. *Ethylene–maleic anhydride resins*, Monsanto Technical Bulletin No. 1C/FP-7 .
54. *Speciality polymer data*, B F Goodrich Technical Leaflet SP1, Ref. 8001 EP.
55. *Textile printing grades of Carbopol resins*, B F Goodrich Technical Leaflet, Ref. 1278GL.
56. N A Barrett, lecture to SDC West Riding Region, Allied Colloids, Jan 1988.
57. C C Cook, *Rev. Prog. Coloration*, **12** (1982) 73.
58. J Shore, *J.S.D.C.*, **87** (1971) 3.
59. A R Smith, *J.S.D.C.*, **70** (1954) 381; **77** (1961) 416.
60. C C Wilcock and C P Tattersfield, *J.S.D.C.*, **59** (1943) 119.
61. T Robinson, *Melliand Textilber.*, **68** (1987) 137.
62. G Lützel, *J.S.D.C.*, **82** (1966) 293.
63. M Kamel, M M Kamel and M A El-Kashouti, *Amer. Dyestuff Rep.*, **60** (1971) 33.
64. J Hook and A C Welham, *Dyer*, **172** (1987) 10.
65. S, USP 4 410 652 (1983).
66. F M Rowe and K A J Chamberlain, *J.S.D.C.*, **53** (1937) 268.
67. V S Salvin, W D Paist and W J Myles, *Amer. Dyestuff Rep.*, **41** (1952) 297.
68. V S Salvin and R A Walker, *Text. Research J.*, **30** (1960) 381.
69. V S Salvin, *Amer. Dyestuff Rep.*, **53** (1964) 12.
70. A Murray and K Mortimer, *Rev. Prog. Coloration*, **2** (1971) 67.
71. J Park, *Rev. Prog. Coloration*, **10** (1979) 20.
72. J Park, *Rev. Prog. Coloration*, **11** (1981) 19.
73. B Milligan, *Rev. Prog. Coloration*, **16** (1986) 1.
74. S, BP 2 142 347 (1985).
75. W E Wood, *Rev. Prog. Coloration*, **7** (1976) 80.
76. G H Lister, *J.S.D.C.*, **88** (1972) 9.
77. S, BP 1 371 781 (1970).
78. M Capponi, A Flister, R Hasler, C Oschatz, G Robert, T Robinson, H P Stakelbeck, P Tschudin and J P Vierling, *Rev. Prog. Coloration*, **12** (1982) 48.
79. T L Dawson, Shirley Institute Publication S42 (1981) 29.
80. J G Roberts, Shirley Institute Publication S42 (1981) 1.
81. D W Heywood, Shirley Institute Publication S42 (1981) 9.
82. M Enger, Shirley Institute Publication S42 (1981) 15.
83. D Levy, Shirley Institute Publication S42 (1981) 19.
84. J H W Schaub, Shirley Institute Publication S42 (1981) 24.

85. AATCC Palmetto Section, *Text. Chem. Colorist*, **11** (1979) 270.
86. G F Clifford, *Amer. Dyestuff Rep.*, **69** (Apr 1980) 19.
87. R J Lyons, *Amer. Dyestuff Rep.*, **69** (Apr 1980) 22.
88. W Hartman, *Amer. Dyestuff Rep.*, **69** (June 1980) 21.
89. D Levy, *Dyer*, **164** (1980) 369.
90. W L Brown, *Amer. Dyestuff Rep.*, **70** (Feb 1981) 17.
91. J A Galek, Dyer, **165** (1981) 295.
92. G R Turner, *Text. Chem. Colorist*, **14** (Feb 1982) 23.
93. R S Gregorian, *Text. Chem. Colorist*, **19** (Apr 1987) 13.
94. D N Willig, *Amer. Dyestuff Rep.*, **69** (June 1980) 42.
95. J V Sinka and I A Lichtman, *Dyer*, **155** (1976) 489.
96. Diamond Shamrock, USP 3 207 698 (1965).
97. N V Dawson and K Mortimer, *Australasian Text.*, **4** (6) (Nov/Dec. 1984) 46.
98. W Mooney, *Textile Month* (Oct 1980) 32; *Dyers' Dygest* (July 1981) 3.
99. M M Joyner, *Text. Chem. Colorist*, **18** (3) (1986) 34.
100. R J Rooks, *Text. Chem. Colorist*, **4** (1) (1972) 47.
101. G C Johnson, AATCC Nat. Tech. Conf. (1977) 250.
102. J V Isharani, AATCC Nat. Tech. Conf. (1982) 144.
103. E Kissa in *Handbook of fibre science and technology*, Vol. 2, part B, Ed. M Lewin and S B Sello (New York: Marcel Dekker, 1984).
104. T F Cooke, *Text. Chem. Colorist*, **19** (1) (1987) 31.
105. M L Srivastava, *Textile Dyer and Printer* (July 1987) 17.
106. S Smith and P O Sherman, *Text. Research J.*, **39** (1969) 441.
107. P O Sherman, S Smith and B Johannessen, *Text. Research J.*, **39** (1969) 449.
108. H E Bille, A Eckell and G A Schmidt, *Text. Chem. Colorist*, **1** (1969) 600.
109. H E Bille and G A Schmidt, *Melliand Textilber.*, **50** (1969) 1481.
110. H E Bille, A Eckell and G A Schmidt, *Melliand Textilber.*, **51** (1970) 330.
111. C E Warburton Jnr and F J Parkhill, *Text. Chem. Colorist*, **5** (1973) 113.
112. ICI, BP 1 143 944 (1969).
113. Proctor and Gamble, USP 3 959 230 (1976); 3 985 923 (1976).
114. Deering Milliken, USP 3 649 165 (1972).
115. Kanebo, Japanese P 7 245 639 (1972).
116. Minnesota Mining and Manufacturing Co., USP 3 995 885 (1976).
117. G R Turner, *Text. Chem. Colorist*, **19** (9) (1987) 69.

CHAPTER 11

Fluorescent brightening agents

Alec V Mercer

11.1 INTRODUCTION

Partly from an association of whiteness with cleanliness and partly for aesthetic reasons, from the earliest times people have searched for methods of producing ever whiter textiles. The action of sunlight on wet fabric and the use of chemical bleaches to reduce the yellowish tinge of natural textile fabrics have been known for thousands of years. Blue pigments, applied in very small amounts, have also been used for many years to mask any residual yellowish colour remaining after bleaching, the overall greyish effect being perceived as 'white'. Today whiteness is achieved by a combination of chemical bleaching and the use of the so-called fluorescent brightening agents (FBAs).

In 1929, in the first recorded application of an FBA to textiles, Krais [1] used the naturally occurring glycoside aesculin (11.1) to brighten viscose and flax. The addition of blue-violet light to the total light reflected from the fabric produced a 'whiter than white' effect. Although aesculin is fugitive to light and washing, Krais's work stimulated research. In 1934 Paine and Radley [2] patented the use of 4,4'-bis(benzoylamino)stilbene-2,2'-disulphonic acid (11.2) in bank notes and in 1940 Bayer introduced Blankophor B (11.3) as a brightener for cotton.

11.1

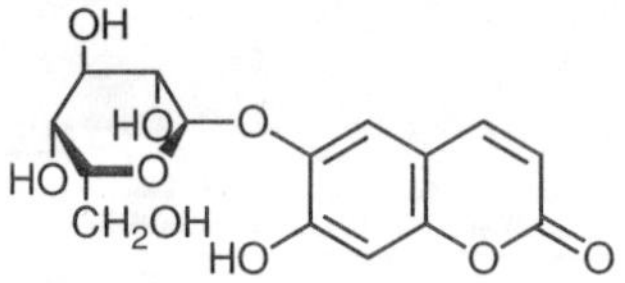

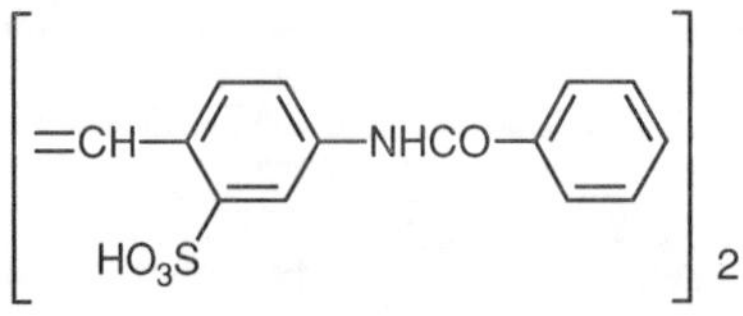

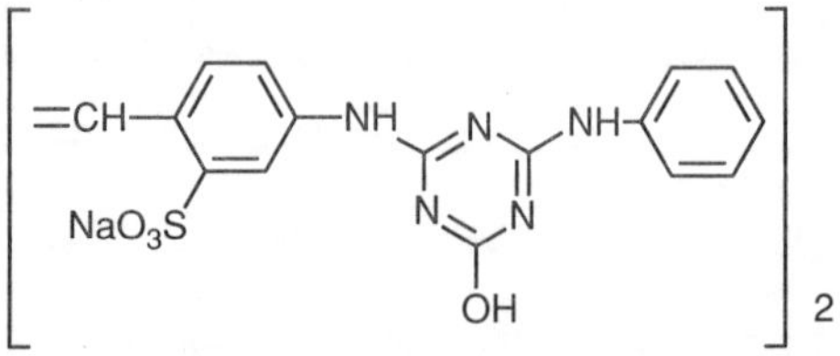

11.2

11.3

After the Second World War development of FBAs was very rapid. Reviews began to appear in the late 1940s [3,4]. Several hundred commercial products, representing a wide variety of chemical types, have now been marketed, with FBAs probably accounting for approximately 10% of world sales of dyestuffs. Several excellent books and reviews on the chemistry, application and properties of FBAs have appeared [5–13].

FBAs are used to brighten not only textiles but also paper, plastics and leather: they are important constituents of household detergents and have also been used in lasers and liquid crystals and as biological stains. By far the most important use for FBAs is, however, in application to textiles and paper and much of what follows will be concerned with these two substrates.

Names such as 'fluorescent whitening agent', 'optical brightener' and 'optical bleach' have all been used for the products described in this chapter as 'fluorescent brightening agents'. Many of these terms have a validity and the term 'fluorescent brightening agent' is preferred here only because it has been adopted in the indexes of *Chemical Abstracts*.

An FBA is a strongly fluorescent substance that emits light in the blue-violet region of the visible spectrum and is substantive to the substrate for which it is intended. The product should be applicable without undesirable side-effects, such as staining, on any other substrate that may be present. The treated material should retain its properties during its working life and under the conditions in which it will be found. For commercial success the product will also need to be priced attractively and be presented to the customer in a form that is convenient and practical to use. Neither active brightener nor the marketed product must present severe toxicity problems in use or create an environmental hazard.

11.2 MODE OF ACTION OF FBAs

All dyes absorb light. Fluorescent dyes re-emit the absorbed energy as light of longer wavelength. An FBA is a fluorescent chemical that absorbs in the ultra-violet region of the spectrum and emits blue-violet light. A typical FBA absorbs light with a maximum absorption at a wavelength between 340 and 380 nm and emits light at a maximum emission between 425 and 450 nm.

When present on a substrate an effective FBA increases the apparent reflectance of the article in the blue-violet region of the spectrum. The treated piece remits[1] more light in the visible region than does the untreated white article and thus appears 'whiter than white'. These effects

---

[1] In considering a substrate treated with an FBA, the terms 'remitted' (reflected plus emitted) and 'remission' (reflectance plus emission), which take into account the fluorescence emitted from the brightened substrate, are preferred to 'reflected' and 'reflectance'.

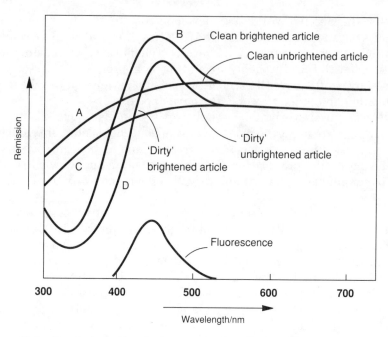

Figure 11.1 – Remission of brightened and unbrightened fabric

are illustrated in Figure 11.1, which shows the importance of a proper preparation of the substrate to be brightened. Curve C represents the remission of an unbleached and/or dirty article: on treatment with FBA this material is brightened but the treated piece (curve D) can still be less bright than the clean unbrightened article (curve A) and much less bright than the clean brightened article (curve B). The reader is referred elsewhere [14] for a discussion of bleaching and fabric preparation. In some cases brightening and bleaching can be carried out simultaneously and these possibilities will be discussed later in this chapter.

An efficient FBA must absorb strongly in the ultra-violet region and must also re-emit a large proportion of the absorbed energy as visible light, that is, it must have a high fluorescence efficiency. Although fluorescence can occur from the σ-bonds of organic compounds, strong fluorescence is associated with π-bonded electrons; all FBAs therefore contain a considerable number of conjugated bonds.

Processes occurring during absorption and fluorescence are shown in Figure 11.2, in which S_0, S_1 ... represent so-called singlet states in which all the electrons have paired spins, and T_1, T_2 ... represent triplet states in which two electrons have unpaired spins. The energy levels of both ground (S_0) and activated states (S_1, S_2 ...) are subdivided into vibrational and rotational energy levels. The vibrational energy levels are shown in Figure

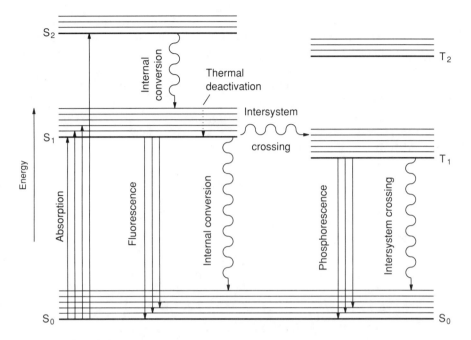

Figure 11.2 – Absorption and fluorescence processes

11.2. Differences in rotational levels are very small and can be ignored for the present discussion.

When an FBA absorbs a photon of light an electron is raised from the ground singlet state (S_0) of the molecule to one of its activated singlet states $(S_1, S_2...)$. Transitions from a singlet to triplet state are quantum-mechanically 'forbidden'. Absorption occurs from the ground state of the molecule, the vibrational level of the activated state entered being decided by the size of the quantum of energy involved (energy $= hc/\lambda$, where h is Planck's constant, c the velocity of light in a vacuum and λ the wavelength). Vibrational energy levels are very close to each other and vibrational energy is lost very rapidly (within about 10^{-12} s) before fluorescence occurs when the molecule returns from the lowest vibrational level of the activated state (S_1) to one of the vibrational levels of the ground state (S_0) whilst simultaneously emitting a photon of light. Fluorescence lifetime is typically about 10^{-9} s. Energy can also be lost from the S_1 state by non-radiative processes (internal conversion) and by the 'forbidden' intersystem crossing to give the triplet state, which in turn can lose energy, returning to the ground state by either phosphorescence or by a further radiationless intersystem crossing. Phosphorescence always occurs at a longer wavelength than fluorescence because the energy difference between T_1 and S_0 is less than that between S_1 and S_0. FBAs do not exhibit significant phosphorescence. For a more detailed discussion of the principles of fluorescence the reader is referred to books by Lumb [15] and Lakowicz [16].

Typical absorption and fluorescence spectra are shown in Figure 11.3. Since energy is lost in the activated state (S_1) before fluorescence, the emission maximum always occurs at a lower wavenumber than the absorption maximum. The difference, which is termed the Stokes shift, can be calculated approximately from the absorption spectrum using the Pestemer rule [17]; this states that the Stokes shift is 2.5 times the half-bandwidth at the absorption maximum.

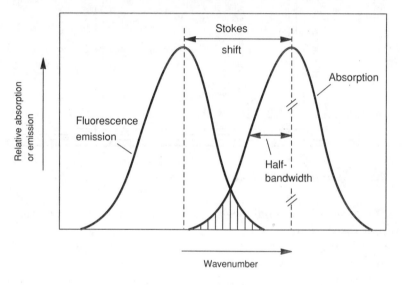

Figure 11.3 – Typical absorption and emission curves for an FBA (polar solvent)

For the following reasons the Stokes shift of an FBA should not be too large:

(a) The closer the maximum wavelength of light absorption of an FBA approaches the visible region, the greater is the energy content of sunlight, at the earth's surface, available for fluorescence excitation and the greater the potential fluorescence. An FBA with a Stokes shift of 60 nm or less would have a maximum absorption at 370 nm or longer and still show maximum fluorescence in the blue region of the spectrum.

(b) Although absorption and fluorescence spectra are not always (or even normally) symmetrical, a smaller Stokes shift reduces the chance of significant fluorescence in the green or yellow-green regions of the spectrum. Green or yellow-green fluorescence reduces whiteness.

The quantum efficiency of fluorescence of a molecule is decided by the relative rates of fluorescence, internal conversion and intersystem crossing to the triplet state. Up to the present time it has proved impossible to predict these relative rates. Thus, whilst it is now possible to calculate theoretically the maximum wavelength of light absorption of an organic molecule and thus its approximate maximum wavelength of fluorescence, it remains impossible to predict which molecules will be strong fluorescers. Design of new FBAs still relies on semi-empirical knowledge plus the instinct of the research chemist.

11.3 EVALUATION OF FBAs: MEASUREMENT OF WHITENESS

To evaluate an FBA it is necessary both to apply the product to the desired substrate and to measure the whiteness of the treated piece. Measurement of the fluorescence of the FBA on the substrate provides useful additional, although different, information.

Visual judgment of whiteness is highly subjective. Many factors, such as the observer's age and sex and even the hue of 'white' material normally found in the country in question, help to decide on individual preference for either a red-violet or a blue-green shade of white.

Instrumental measurement of whiteness (W) has been the subject of much research. Many whiteness formulae have been proposed. All are based on CIE colour space and X, Y and Z tristimulus values. Three of these formulae are those of Berger [18] (Eqn 11.1), Stensby [19] (Eqn 11.2) and the CIE (1982) (Eqn 11.3).

$$W = 3B + G - 3A \qquad (11.1)$$

$$W = L + 3a - 3b \qquad (11.2)$$

$$W = Y + 800(x_n - x) + 1700(y_n - y) \qquad (11.3)$$

The relationship between X, Y and Z, and A, G and B depends on the instrument in use; x_n and y_n are the chromaticity coordinates of the D_{65} ($2°$ or $10°$ observer) light source.

Information on the hue of whiteness is provided by dividing CIE colour space, in the neighbourhood of the D_{65} achromatic point, into a series of parallel strips corresponding to variations in hue of whiteness. The principle is illustrated in Figure 11.4. According to this system a neutral white has a nuance (NU) value of 0, greener shades having values between 0 and +5 and violet shades values between 0 and –5. The NU value can easily be calculated from chromaticity data. Typically $NU = -1132x + 725y + 115.45$. Very careful attention to the instrumentation and state of equipment is necessary if reliable data are to be obtained. The brightened piece under test must also, of course, be carefully prepared. The subject is

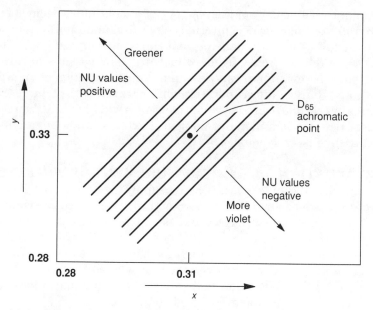

Figure 11.4 – Colour space and hue of whiteness

complex and has been well reviewed by Griesser [20].

To an average observer a piece of white material containing an FBA will have a dominant wavelength of approximately 467 nm. As the amount of FBA present in a substrate increases the hue changes. At first the piece may become slightly more violet but as the maximum possible whiteness is approached there is a distinct change in hue towards green until the piece becomes overloaded with FBA, whiteness falls and the material is perceived as coloured. Typical effects are illustrated in Figure 11.5.

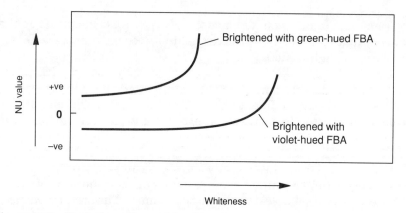

Figure 11.5 – Variation of hue with whiteness

In industry a single-strength comparison between two FBAs is frequently required. Where the two brighteners contain the same active component, or where both produce a very similar shade of white, such a comparison presents little difficulty. Where the two brighteners produce very different shades of white, however, such a comparison is usually meaningless. A typical situation is illustrated in Figure 11.6.

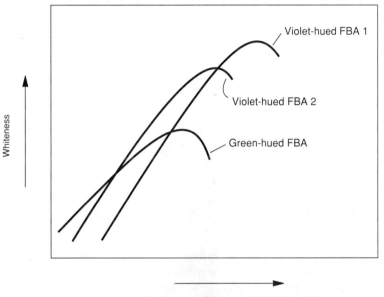

Figure 11.6 – Dependence of whiteness on concentration

At concentrations below that yielding the maximum whiteness achievable there is an approximately linear relationship between whiteness and the logarithm of the concentration of FBA present on the substrate. If two FBAs produce a similar hue the straight line portions of the graph are almost parallel and a single-strength relationship can readily be calculated. If, however, two FBAs produce different shades of whiteness their relative effectiveness changes with the level of white, the products giving greener hues generally being more effective at low concentrations.

Methods for the instrumental measurement of whiteness are well established but visual comparison remains important, even in sophisticated laboratories. Some degree of quantification is achieved by the method of paired comparisons, in which a panel of observers is presented with pairs of brightened pieces and asked to decide, without undue delay, which is the brighter. The total of positive scores can be used as a measure of whiteness and the results presented graphically as shown in Figure 11.7. Although

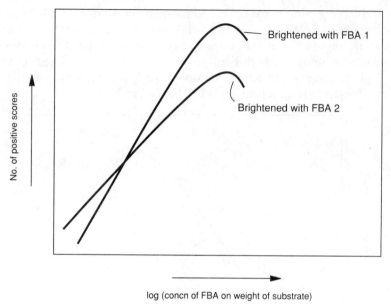

Figure 11.7 – Presentation of results of a paired comparison

time-consuming to carry out, a paired comparison produces results that can be regarded with considerable confidence and that usually agree well with a comparison based on Berger whiteness.

11.4 GENERAL FACTORS INFLUENCING FBA PERFORMANCE
Apart from being cost-effective, a good FBA needs to be capable of producing a high level of whiteness. As the amount of FBA on a substrate increases, whiteness increases until a maximum value is reached (Figure 11.6). Further application of FBA results in a reduction in whiteness. On polyester the fall in whiteness with increasing FBA concentration is apparently not accompanied by a fall in total fluorescence [21]. On cotton both whiteness and total fluorescence fall, the decrease in whiteness occurring before that in fluorescence [22]. In general the main cause of the fall in whiteness with increasing concentration of FBA is an increase in the aggregation of the FBA on the substrate, resulting in a shift in fluorescence hue. The effect is shown in Figure 11.8. Not surprisingly, FBAs that give a greenish hue of brightening below the maximum white tend to produce a lower maximum white than those exhibiting a violet hue. Other factors such as substantivity are, of course, of considerable importance.

The presence of salts and additives can have an important influence on the performance of an FBA. Traces of heavy-metal ions such as iron and copper have an adverse influence [23]. Other salts, even sodium sulphate

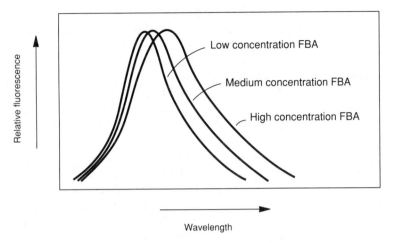

Figure 11.8 – Effect of FBA concentration on fluorescence hue

and sodium chloride, have been claimed to confer a positive effect on the solution fluorescence of FBAs [24]; apart from the normal salt effects in exhaust applications their influence on the whiteness of a brightened substrate is doubtful.

Surfactants, not surprisingly, can have a very significant influence on the fluorescence of FBAs in solution. The effect is associated with the critical micelle concentration of surfactant and can be considered as a type of special solvent effect. Anionic surfactants have almost no influence on the performance of anionic FBAs on cotton, but non-ionic surfactants can exert either a positive or negative influence on whiteness of the treated substrate [25]. Cationic surfactants would be expected to have a negative effect, but this is not always so [26]. No general rule can be formulated and each case has to be considered separately.

The influence of additives needs to be kept under constant consideration when formulating commercial brands of FBAs. Liquid formulations are of considerable commercial importance and it is often necessary to use solvents such as diethylene glycol, poly(ethylene glycol) and alkylphenol alkylene oxide adducts in order to achieve stable solutions. Surfactants can help to stabilise FBA–resin bath combinations but in other circumstances they can adversely affect the performance of the formulation, not only in its capacity to brighten but also in the desired end-use of the brightened fabric. For example, nylon brightened by the pad–Thermosol method using liquid formulations containing large amounts of alkylene oxide polymers cannot be used as a substrate for colour prints unless previously washed off; without a wash-off diffuse prints are obtained.

Violet or blue-violet dyes are sometimes used in combination with FBAs. These shading dyes are used in amounts of up to 2% of the weight of FBA and are of particular importance when the FBA is to be used to brighten slightly yellow material. The dyes convert the yellow background of the substrate to a perceived grey and enhance the effectiveness of the FBA. The effects can be considerable. Many types of violet or blue-violet dye can be used. Typical examples are crystal violet (C.I. Basic Violet 3), used in the brightening of paper stock or cotton, and C.I. Disperse Violet 28 and C.I. Acid Violet 43, used with cotton. Disperse dyes are also used for shading in combination with disperse FBAs on polyester and basic FBAs on acrylic fibres.

On slightly yellow cotton the use of shading dyes is particularly convenient, since the substrate becomes bleached during the wash/wear cycle. Detergent formulations contain FBAs that are substantive to cotton and loss of shading dye during washing is unlikely to have a noticeable effect on the perceived whiteness of the article. Shading dyes are of limited use with well-bleached and properly prepared cotton.

FBAs used in combination can show a synergistic effect. Synergism is, at present, of importance only with polyester brighteners and is discussed further in section 11.10. Conversely the presence of a trace impurity in an FBA may very much reduce its effectiveness. In industrial laboratories much time and effort can be spent in developing processes for the production of impurity-free products.

11.5 CHEMISTRY AND APPLICATIONS OF FBAs

FBAs are available for application to all types of substrate. Thus there are anionic FBAs for application to cellulose in the presence of added salts, anionic types for application to nylon or wool in the presence of acid, dispersed types for application to polyester, and so on. Brighteners such as C.I. Fluorescent Brightener 104 (11.4), capable in principle of being applied like a reactive dye, have been reported but are today of no commercial importance. Many reactive FBAs would need an aftertreatment to develop their full fluorescence [27] and there seems to be little sense in fixing products with only moderate light fastness to a fibre via a covalent link. Ingrain FBAs are unknown. The chemical structures of FBAs are many and varied although, of course, they all contain some sort of extended π-electron system. In the following discussion all the main chemical types are mentioned, but in terms of end application rather than chemistry of preparation.

11.4

11.6 BRIGHTENERS FOR CELLULOSIC SUBSTRATES

The earliest FBAs were developed for application to paper, and even today larger quantities of brightener are applied to cellulose than to any other substrate.

11.6.1 FBAs for cotton

Brighteners are applied to cotton in the manner of direct dyes. By far the most common are triazinyl derivatives of diaminostilbenedisulphonic acid (often called DAST types) of general formula 11.5, where M is an alkali-metal, an ammonium or a substituted ammonium cation. Most suppliers of FBAs market compounds of this type. Products have sometimes been introduced on to the market not for any real technological necessity but rather because the supplier, for commercial reasons, needed to have some-thing different to sell or needed to avoid infringing a competitor's patent.

11.5

It is impossible to give a comprehensive list of all the products of type 11.5 that have appeared on the market or been patented, but several important commercial products are shown in Table 11.1. The less water-soluble products are in general used to brighten cotton by exhaust appli-cation. The more soluble, less substantive types are used with large packages or applied by padding or other continuous processes. Application methods have been well described by Williamson [11].

Where the groups R_1 and R_2 mentioned in Table 11.1 are both derived from amines, variation of the amine has little influence on the hue of bright-ening. In general these products give slightly violet shades of white and the main technical justification for the existence of so many different products of this type is the need for different levels of substantivity. Compound 11.13, on the other hand, has a methoxy group in the R_2 position and gives a distinctly violet tone. All the products listed in Table 11.1 have light fastness values in the range 3–4 on cotton, and all the more substantive types can, in principle, be applied in conjunction with a hydrogen peroxide bleach. Their stability towards chlorine bleaches such as sodium hypo-chlorite varies, but they are all essentially unstable towards these reagents [6].

Triazinyl derivatives of diaminostilbenedisulphonic acid are also the types usually chosen for application to cotton in conjunction with an easy-care or durable-press finish. In these uses the FBA must show appreciable

TABLE 11.1

Important FBAs of type 11.5 used to brighten cotton

Compound	R_1	R_2	Substantivity	Use
11.6	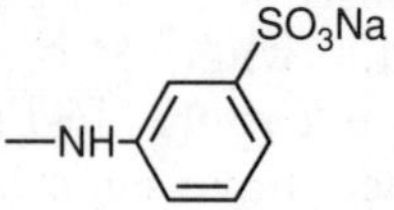 —NH— (phenyl with SO_3Na)	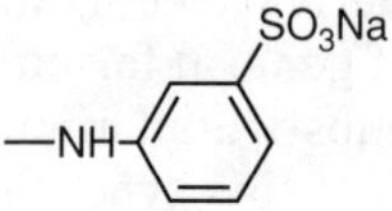 —NH— (phenyl with SO_3Na)	Lower	Towards continuous application
11.7	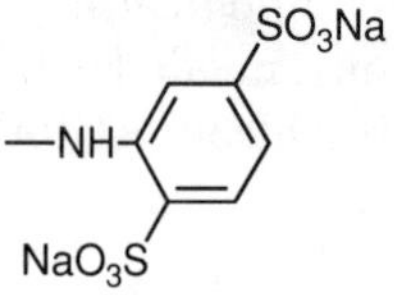 —NH— (phenyl with SO_3Na and NaO_3S)	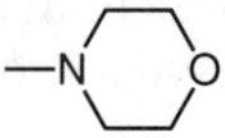 —N (morpholine)		
11.8	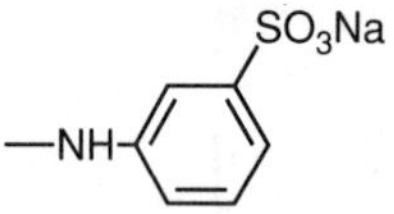 —NH— (phenyl with SO_3Na)	—N(CH_2CH_2OH)_2		
11.9	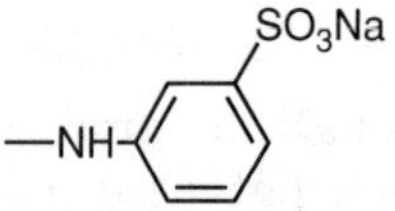 —NH— (phenyl with SO_3Na)	—NHCH_2CH_2OH		
11.10	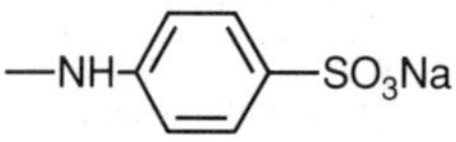 —NH— (phenyl)—SO_3Na	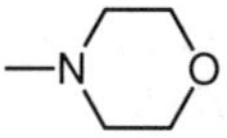 —N (morpholine)		
11.11	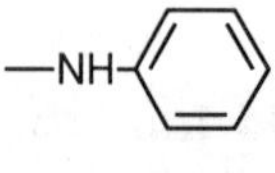 —NH— (phenyl)	—N(CH_2CH_2OH)_2		
11.12	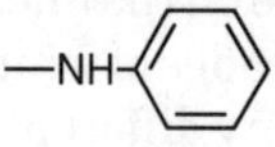 —NH— (phenyl)	—NCH_2CH_2OH with CH_3		
11.13	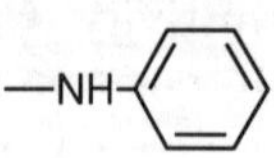 —NH— (phenyl)	—OCH_3	Higher	Towards exhaustion

resistance towards the catalyst (usually magnesium chloride) used to cure the resin and the mildly acid conditions (pH about 4) of the resin-containing pad bath. The less substantive types shown in Table 11.1 are important in this respect; so too are compounds 11.14 and 11.15.

The performance of an FBA applied in conjunction with a resin finish can be modified and improved by careful formulation of the pad bath but this

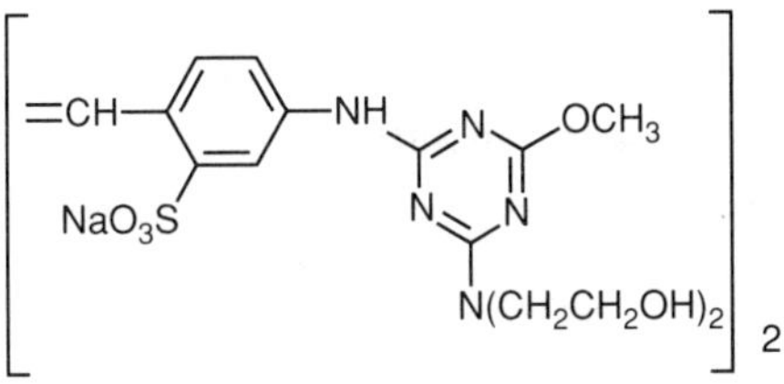

11.14

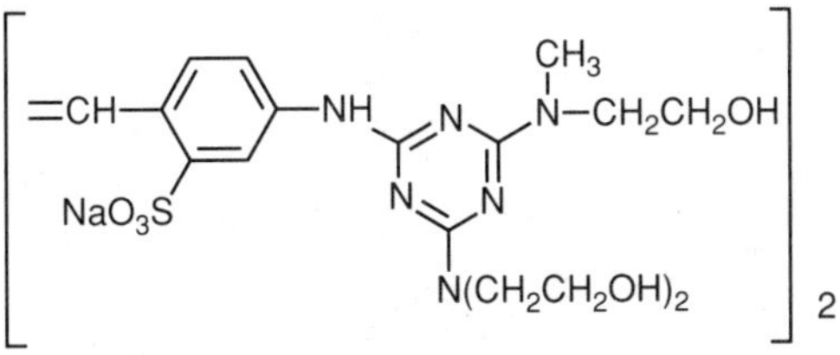

11.15

lies beyond the scope of the present chapter. Alternatively FBA and resin can be applied in two separate steps; most DAST brighteners would be suitable if applied in this way.

11.6.2 FBAs for paper

The paper industry is the second most important user of FBAs (after the detergent industry), most of the products consumed being of the DAST type.

Paper is brightened either during its preparation, the FBA being added to the pulp before the paper sheet is laid down (pre-bleached pulp must be used) or during a subsequent sizing operation. Approximately one-third of the total FBAs used are applied to pulp and two-thirds during sizing. An FBA applied by addition to the pulp must show good affinity for the cellulose and exhaust at low temperature, otherwise large amounts of brightener could be lost with the waste water from the process. Resistance towards acid conditions as low as pH 3 can also be important. Fillers used in paper making, such as alum, chalk and china clay, can cause loss of fluorescence and the type and quantity of the FBA employed may have to be adjusted accordingly.

For use from the size press it is necessary for the FBA to be compatible with the chosen size (starch, casein, urea–formaldehyde resin and so forth). Since sizes tend to be yellow and also absorb ultra-violet light, brighteners are in general less effective in sized paper.

The choice of type and method of application of FBAs to paper is very complex, being almost as much an art as a science. A useful short introduction can be found in a recent article [28]. Examples of important FBAs for use with paper are shown in Table 11.2. This list is far from exhaustive, however, and there are other important products of general type 11.5 used as FBAs for paper.

TABLE 11.2

Important FBAs of general formula 11.5 used on paper

Compound	R_1	R_2	Application
11.8	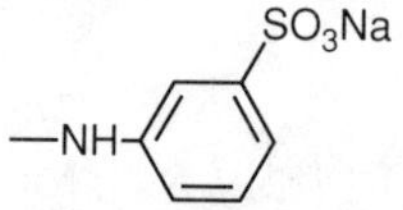 —NH—⟨benzene ring with SO$_3$Na⟩	—N(CH$_2$CH$_2$OH)$_2$	Pulp and size press
11.16	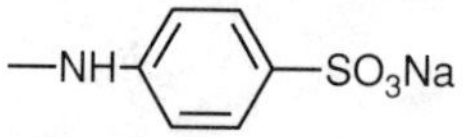 —NH—⟨benzene ring⟩—SO$_3$Na	—N⟨CH$_2$CH$_2$OH / CH$_2$CH$_2$CN⟩	Pulp and size press
11.11	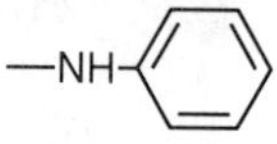 —NH—⟨benzene ring⟩	—N(CH$_2$CH$_2$OH)$_2$	Pulp
11.17	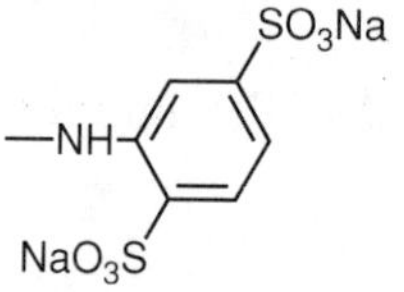 —NH—⟨benzene ring with SO$_3$Na and NaO$_3$S⟩	—N(C$_2$H$_5$)$_2$	Size press
11.18	—NH$_2$	—N(CH$_2$CH$_2$OH)$_2$	Size press

11.6.3 Preparation of DAST-type FBAs

A major reason for the importance of DAST brighteners is their essentially straightforward manufacture from readily available and inexpensive starting materials. Products with a variety of substituents, and consequently different properties, are easily prepared in a three-step, one-pot synthesis starting from diaminostilbenedisulphonic acid (DAS) (11.19). The method is illustrated in Scheme 11.1.

By suitable choice of reaction conditions the chlorine atoms of cyanuric chloride (11.20) can be replaced in a stepwise fashion. In the first step DAS reacts with cyanuric chloride between 0 and 20°C, ideally at pH 5–6. In the second step the amine or alcohol (R,H) reacts at 20–50°C under neutral or very slightly alkaline conditions. The third step is carried out at 50–100°C under alkaline conditions (pH 8–9). The exact conditions used in the second and third steps depend on the nature of the attacking nucleophile and that of the substituent already present in the intermediate dichlorotriazine.

Scheme 11.1 illustrates the 'normal' method for the manufacture of DAST brighteners. It is, however, not always necessary and may not be desirable for DAS to react in the first step. In principle the amines or alcohols can react in any order, but it is best for the most nucleophilic compound to react last to avoid forcing conditions during removal of the last chlorine atom.

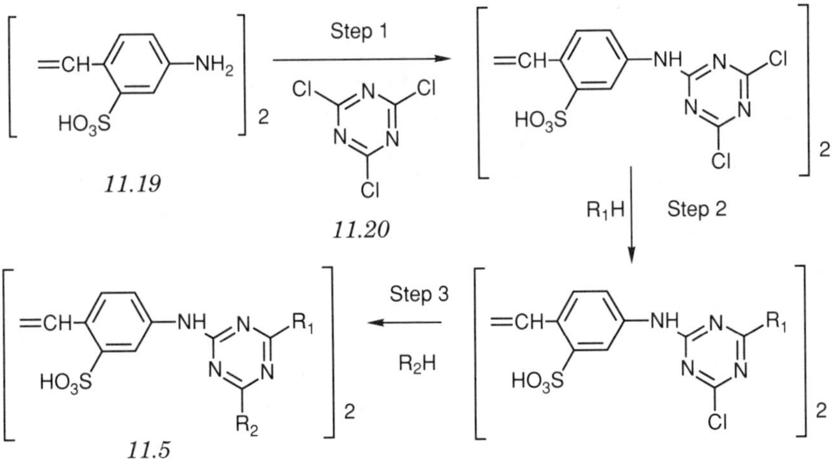

Scheme 11.1

The mechanism of these substitutions is shown in Scheme 11.2 for the reaction between a primary amine and the intermediate dichlorotriazine. A corresponding scheme can be drawn for reaction of a secondary amine, alcohol or other nucleophile at any of the replacement steps. It follows from this mechanism that the rate of reaction depends on:

(a) the nucleophilicity of the attacking species, the more nucleophilic reagents reacting faster or under milder conditions
(b) the electronegativity of the substituent R: the more electronegative the substituent, the faster the reaction or the milder the conditions required; thus the reaction rate decreases in the order $C_6H_5O > CH_3O > C_2H_5O > C_6H_5NH > NH_2 > CH_3NH > C_2H_5NH > (CH_3)_2N > OH$ [6].

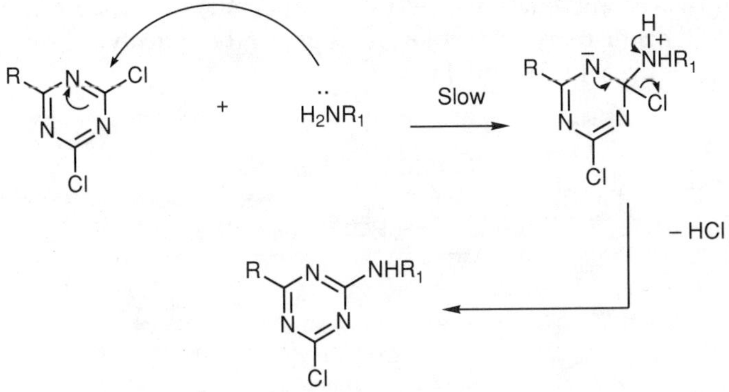

Scheme 11.2

It also follows that protonation of the triazine ring makes it more susceptible to attack by nucleophilic reagents unless the reagent itself is also protonated. If the triazine ring remains unprotonated when the nucleophile (an aliphatic amine, for example) is present as its acid salt the reaction is, of course, slower. Cyanuric chloride itself is a very weak base, only protonated under strongly acid conditions. Thus step 1 in Scheme 11.1 can be carried out in aqueous solution down to pH 2 without danger of unwanted hydrolysis of cyanuric chloride, water being a very weak nucleophile.

The manufacture of the important brightener 11.13 does not follow the 'normal' course. The first step involves reaction of cyanuric chloride with excess methanol and excess acid acceptor (usually sodium bicarbonate). Under acid conditions this reaction takes a different course and can become dangerously violent (Scheme 11.3).

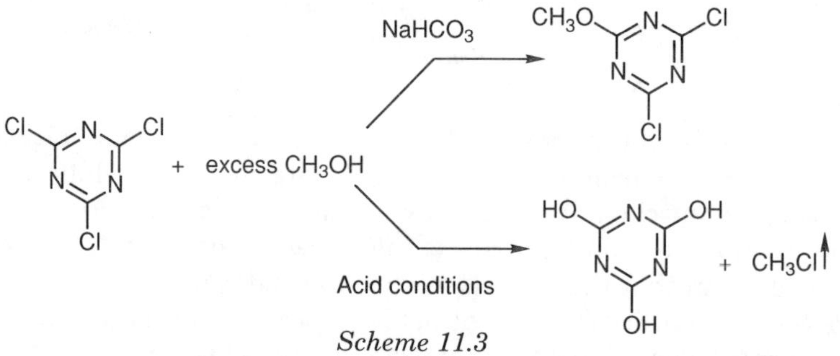

Scheme 11.3

It can also sometimes be advantageous in the preparation of other DAST brighteners if the reaction of cyanuric chloride with DAS is not made the first step. It is difficult completely to repress the reactivity of the second chlorine atom of the triazine, and undesirable by-products of the general type 11.21 can be eliminated if DAS is made to react at the second step. Very careful control of the reaction conditions, especially at steps 1 and 2, is also necessary in order to avoid formation of partially hydrolysed by-products such as structures 11.22 and 11.23.

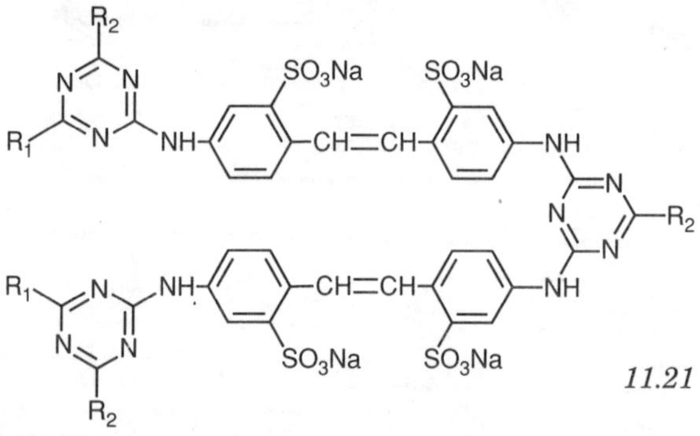

11.21

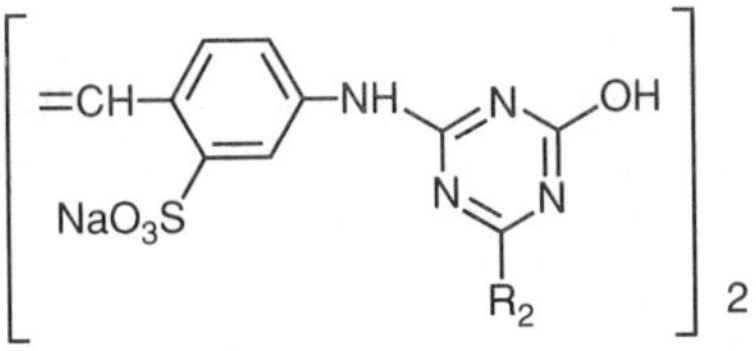

11.22

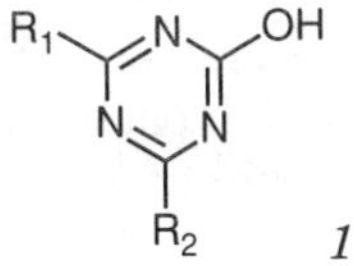

11.23

An important factor in the preparation of DAST brighteners of the purity necessary for good performance is the purity of the DAS used as starting material. DAS is prepared by the route shown in Scheme 11.4 and at one time it contained significant amounts of coloured azoxy compounds of the Sun Yellow family [29]. Today the major manufacturers supply DAS essentially free from these undesirable impurities.

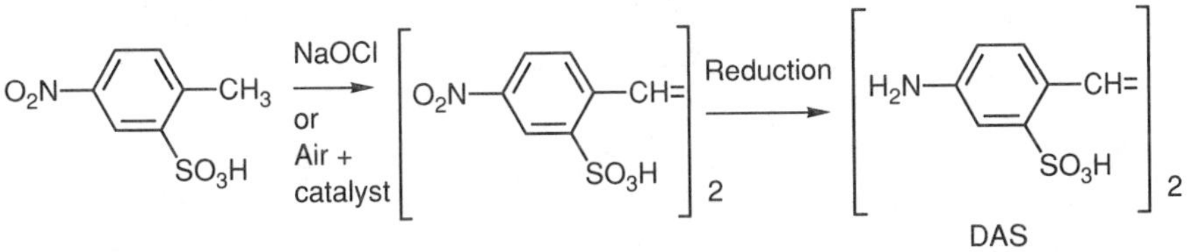

Scheme 11.4

Unsymmetrical products of type 11.24 derived from DAS have been described but are much more complicated and expensive to prepare than those with symmetrical structures. They have never become commercially important.

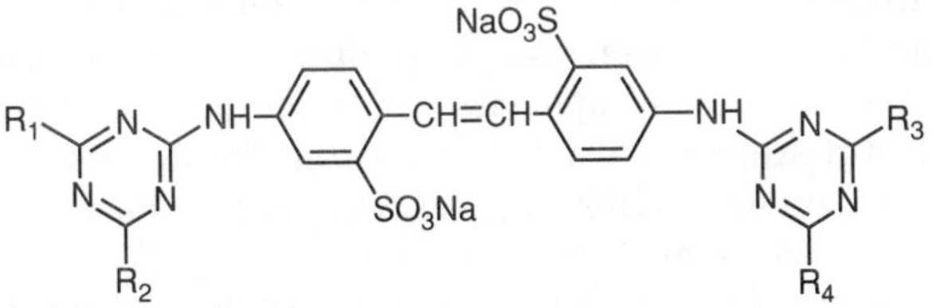

11.24

11.6.4 Speciality FBAs for cotton

Two commercially important brighteners for cotton are not of the DAST type.

The bis-stilbene 11.25 is mainly of value for brightening cotton during laundering, but can be used for brightening cotton by exhaustion. It has high aqueous solubility and has been recommended for use in combination with resin finishes, although its stability in the pad bath is suspect. It has also found uses in brightening nylon/cotton and polyester/cotton blend fabrics: both components of a nylon/cotton blend are brightened, whereas on polyester/cotton the cotton is brightened without any undesirable staining of the polyester. Its light fastness on cotton is 4, which is slightly superior to that of DAST brighteners. Compound 11.25 is also resistant to hypochlorite bleach but on cotton has limited fastness to washing in soft water. Its manufacture is shown in Scheme 11.5. The first chloromethylation stage can only be accomplished safely in a plant specially designed to ensure that the highly carcinogenic intermediate bis(chloromethyl) ether (formed from formaldehyde and hydrogen chloride) does not escape. Otherwise the preparation proceeds without undue difficulty.

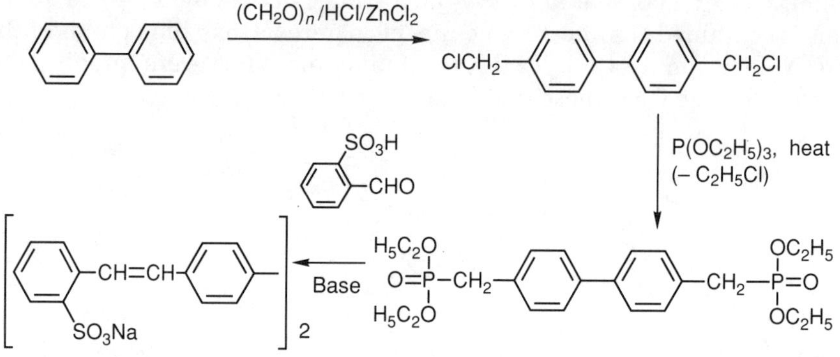

11.25

Scheme 11.5

The *vic*-triazole 11.26 is very much a premium product and cotton brightened with it has a light fastness of 5. The product is stable to hypochlorite and chlorite bleaching. It has adequate wash fastness and a liquid formulation has been marketed for use in combination with a resin finish. It is also of some importance as a component of household detergents. Unfortunately it is also expensive and its main use is probably as an FBA for nylon, on which fibre it gives better value for money. Its preparation is shown in Scheme 11.6.

A sulphonated derivative of compound 11.26, the tetrasulphonic acid 11.27, has been recommended for application to cotton in combination with a resin finish. Unlike DAST-type FBAs, compound 11.27 can be applied in the presence of a zinc nitrate-catalysed resin cure. The brightness achieved is not high, however.

Many other products of a variety of structures have been patented for use as cellulose brighteners. The reader is referred to the review articles mentioned earlier for further information.

11.7 BRIGHTENERS FOR CELLULOSE ACETATE AND CELLULOSE TRIACETATE

Cellulose acetate and triacetate are brightened with disperse-type FBAs,

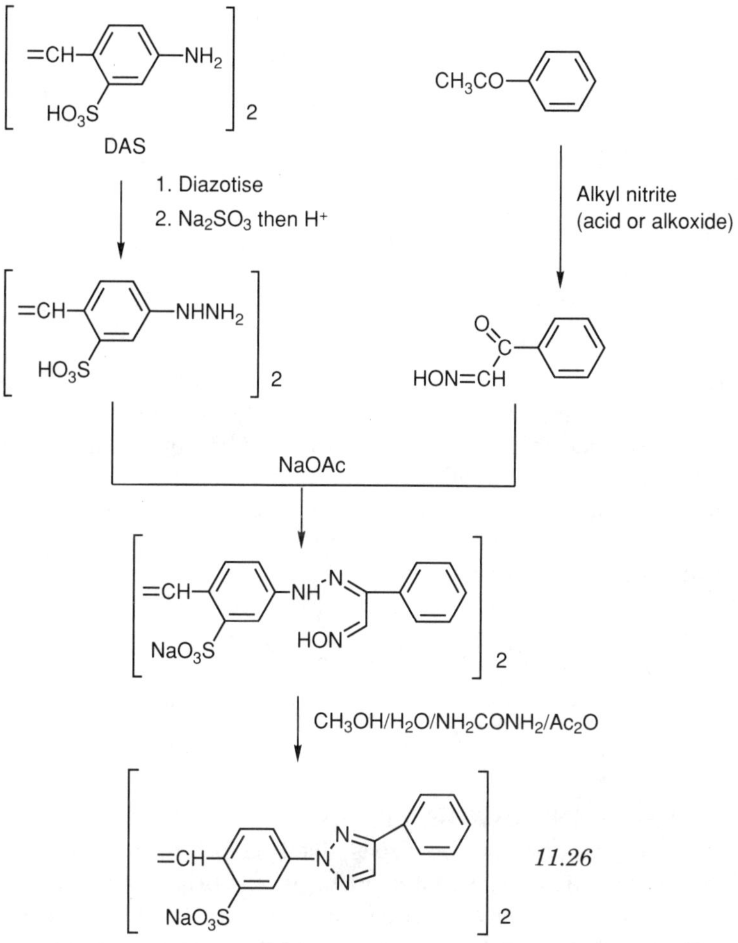

11.26

Scheme 11.6

11.27

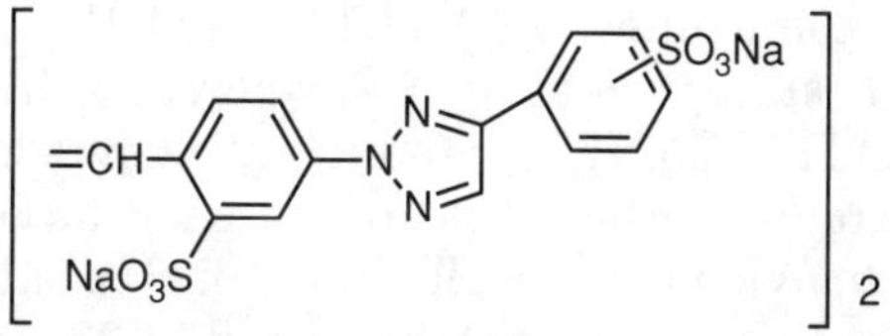

including derivatives of 1,3-diphenylpyrazoline (11.28). A pyrene derivative (11.29), a naphthalimide (11.30) and benzoxazoles of smaller molecular size are also used and are discussed in more detail in section 11.10. 1,3-Diphenylpyrazoline derivatives form a commercially important group

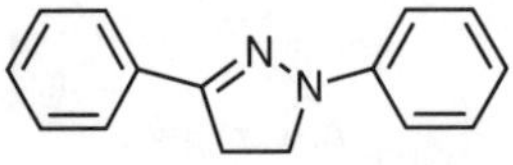

11.28 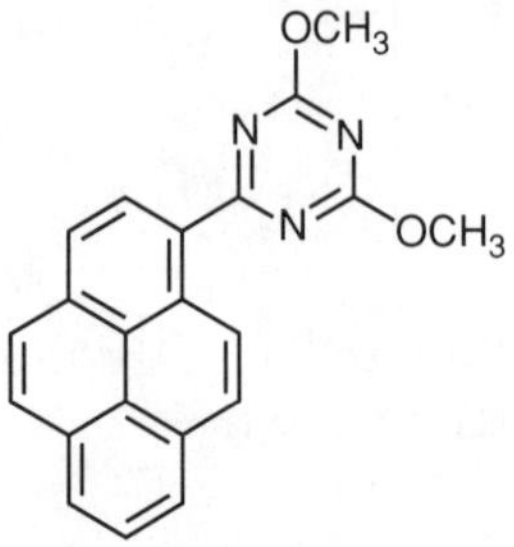   *11.29* 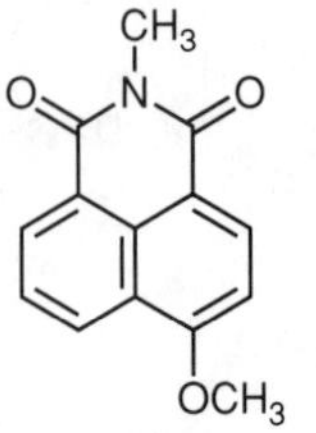   *11.30*

of FBAs. If suitably substituted they can be applied to substrates other than acetate and triacetate. The commercially more important products of this type are used to brighten nylon and acrylic fibres. Their preparation and other aspects of pyrazoline chemistry are discussed in section 11.8. Examples of pyrazolines used to brighten acetate and triacetate are the sulphonamide 11.31 and the sulphone 11.32, the former giving greenish and the latter violet effects.

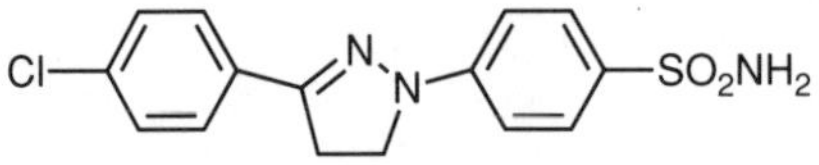

11.31 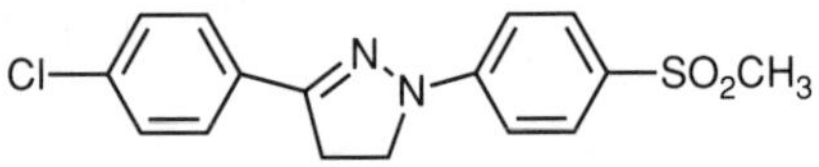   *11.32*

11.8 BRIGHTENERS FOR NYLON

Disperse brighteners of the types used to brighten cellulose acetate, cellulose triacetate and polyester can be used to brighten nylon. In practice, however, disperse types are little used and nylon is usually brightened by products akin to the acid dyes. Chief amongst these are FBAs of the DAST type discussed in section 11.6.3.

Exhaust brightening of nylon is usually combined with a reductive bleach based on sodium dithionite. Important DAST-type FBAs used in this process are compounds 11.10, 11.11 and 11.13 (Table 11.1). FBAs 11.10 and 11.11 are best applied at pH 4–5 whereas FBA 11.13 can be applied successfully at pH 6–6.5. These products all show a light fastness of *ca* 3 on polyamide. If a reductive bleach is unnecessary the DAST brightener 11.33 can be applied to nylon from an alkaline scouring bath. Good whites can be achieved but the light fastness of compound 11.33 is suspect on polyamide. Of importance on nylon are the premium FBAs 11.25 and 11.26 mentioned previously.

On nylon, as on cotton, the bis-stilbene 11.25 again has slightly superior light fastness to the DAST brighteners. In contrast to its properties on cotton it has excellent wash fastness on nylon.

11.33

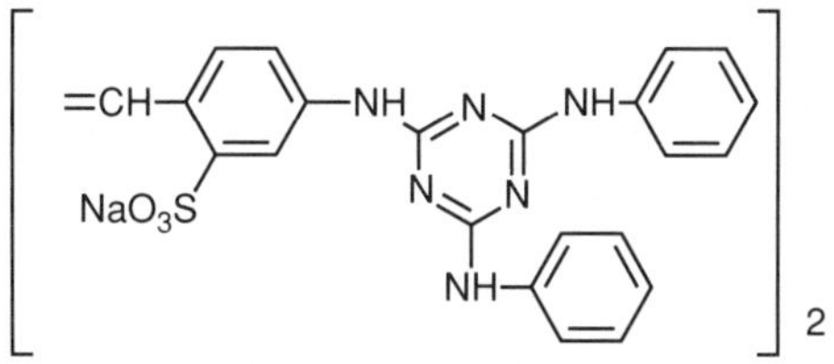

The light fastness of the *vic*-triazole 11.26 on nylon is 4–5, as on cotton significantly superior to that of the DAST types. Unlike the DAST types, the *vic*-triazole is also stable towards sodium chlorite bleach. Applied to nylon in combination with sodium chlorite, compound 11.26 can give very high whiteness and excellent fastness properties.

Nylon can also be brightened by anionic derivatives of 1,3-diphenylpyrazoline, such as FBAs 11.34, 11.35 and 11.36. Although these pyrazolines give excellent whites when applied to nylon by exhaustion they are usually more expensive than the DAST types. For continuous application by the pad–Thermosol or pad–acid shock methods the situation is reversed, however, and the pyrazolines are commercially important as FBAs.

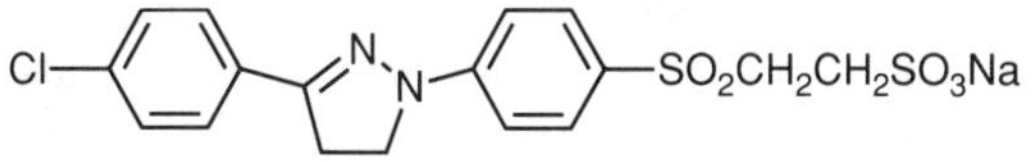

11.34

11.35

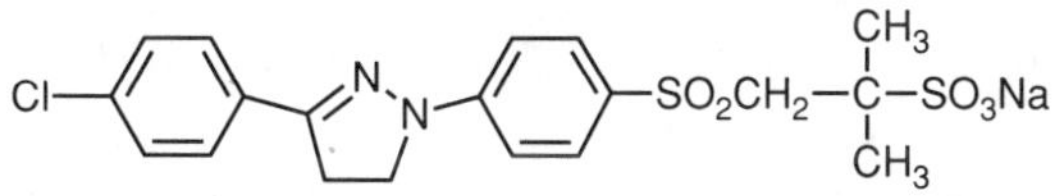

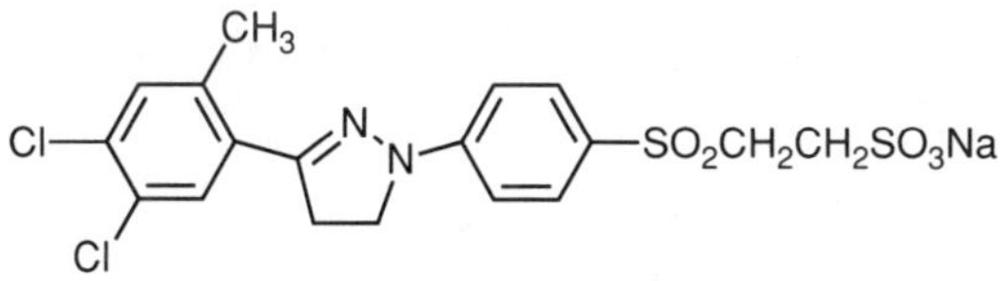

11.36

On nylon these three pyrazolines (11.34–11.36) have light fastness values in the range 3–4, somewhat superior to the DAST types. Light fastness in the wet state is generally lower, however, and the pyrazolines suffer more in this respect than the DAST types; pyrazolines 11.34 and 11.35 in particular have very poor light fastness values of 1–2 in the wet state. The extra substituents present in compound 11.36 have the effect of improving light fastness, especially in the wet state, but at the expense of loss in solubility, and slightly more difficult formulation and application. All three pyrazolines give violet brightening effects on nylon, compound 11.36 being slightly less violet than the other two.

Further increases in the number of substituents present in the diphenylpyrazoline molecule can improve light fastness in both the dry and wet states. For example, the light fastness of the pyrazoline 11.37 is slightly

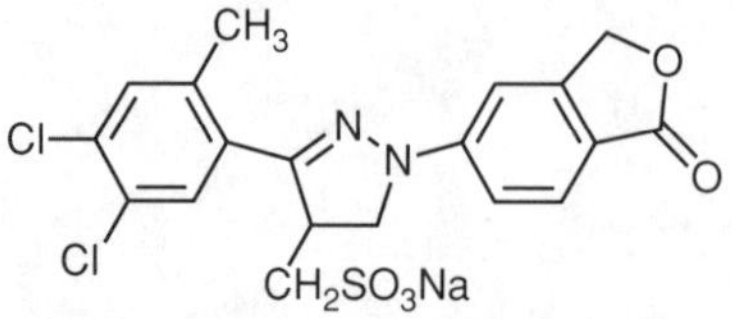

11.37

better than that of compounds 11.34–11.36 in the dry state and significantly better in the wet. Pyrazoline 11.37 is also capable of giving very high
whites of a pleasing bluish hue; it is complicated to manufacture, however.
Increasing substitution also reduces solubility and thus adversely affects
pad bath stability, although this problem can be solved by suitable
formulation. Pad bath formulation can be especially important in the
pad–Thermosol procedure, when the brightened material is often used,
before rinse-off, to produce coloured printed fabrics. Use of too much
surfactant in the pad bath can cause 'bleeding' during printing and lead to
diffuse printed effects.

The general method for the preparation of diphenylpyrazolines is shown
in Scheme 11.7, in which X is a suitable leaving group, usually chlorine but
sometimes dialkylamino. This reaction normally proceeds easily, although
pH control may be important. The preparation of the substituted ketone or
hydrazine needed as starting material may be lengthy and complicated.
Further reactions are often required to modify the substitution in ring B
after formation of the pyrazoline ring. The preparation of compound 11.34
shown in Scheme 11.8 illustrates one of the simpler cases.

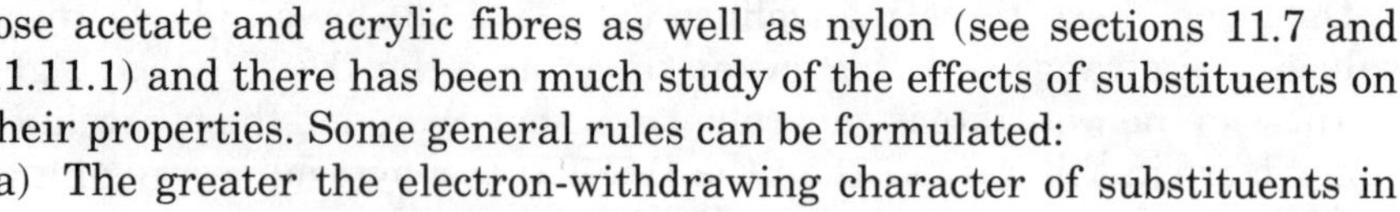

Scheme 11.7

Derivatives of 1,3-diphenylpyrazoline have been used to brighten cellulose acetate and acrylic fibres as well as nylon (see sections 11.7 and
11.11.1) and there has been much study of the effects of substituents on
their properties. Some general rules can be formulated:

(a) The greater the electron-withdrawing character of substituents in
     ring A, the greener the hue of brightening
(b) The greater the electron-withdrawing character of substituents in
     ring B, the more violet the hue of brightening
(c) An electron-donating group at position 4 of the pyrazoline ring has a
     slight hypsochromic effect, an electron-withdrawing group a batho-
     chromic effect
(d) Light fastness is improved by the introduction of electron-withdraw-
     ing substituents into ring A, but is adversely affected by electron-
     donating substituents.

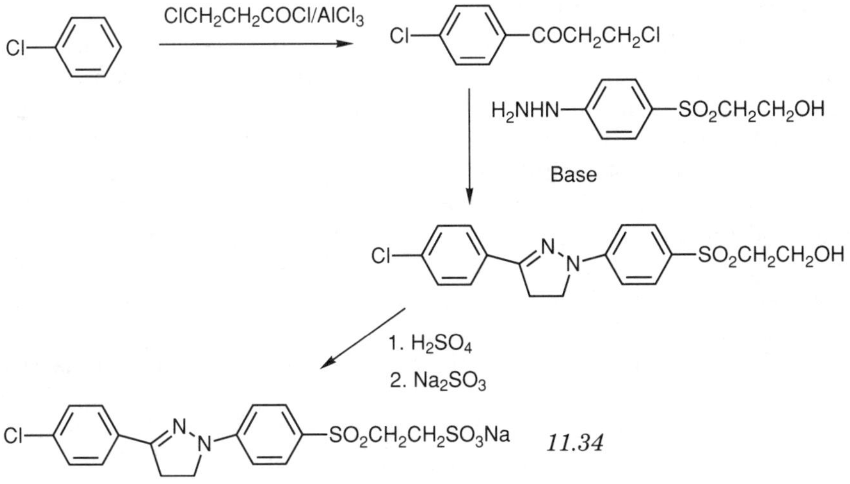

Scheme 11.8

Theoretical explanations for the effects of substituents on the hue of diphenylpyrazoline fluorescers have been published by Güsten and co-workers [30,31]. In practice almost all commercially important diphenyl-pyrazoline FBAs have the general structure 11.38, in which R is a sulphone or sulphonamide derivative.

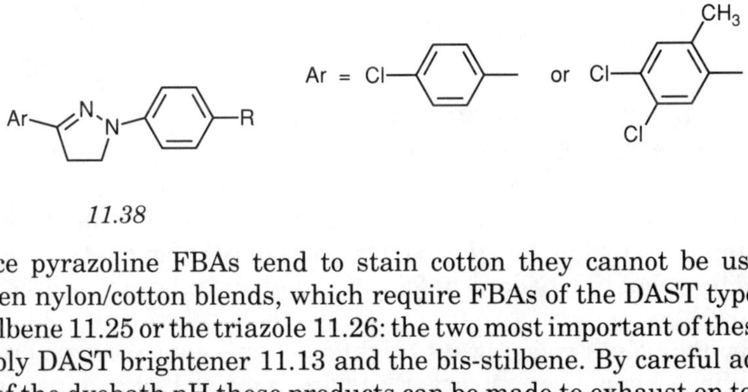

11.38

Since pyrazoline FBAs tend to stain cotton they cannot be used to brighten nylon/cotton blends, which require FBAs of the DAST type, the bis-stilbene 11.25 or the triazole 11.26: the two most important of these are probably DAST brightener 11.13 and the bis-stilbene. By careful adjustment of the dyebath pH these products can be made to exhaust on to both nylon and cotton to give a good solid white. Nylon can also be brightened by incorporation of an FBA in the melt, the FBA being added to the polymer before spinning or shaping. FBA 11.39 is typical of the compounds used for this purpose.

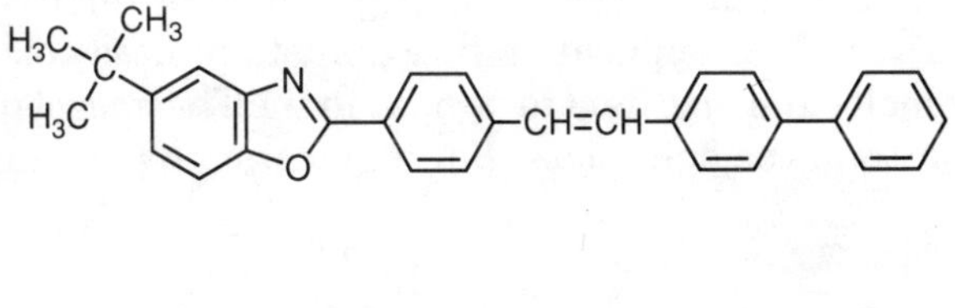

11.39

11.9 BRIGHTENERS FOR WOOL

Wool is naturally yellower than other textile substrates and is difficult to brighten. For a satisfactory result it is essential for the fibre to be well scoured and bleached, either with peroxide or with stabilised dithionite. Brightener is usually applied together with the dithionite bleach. For the best results the wool should first be scoured, then bleached with peroxide and finally treated with FBA during a second bleach with dithionite. Once bleached the wool will gradually become yellow again when exposed to light. Since FBAs absorb ultra-violet light they accelerate this photo-initiated yellowing, although a thiourea–formaldehyde aftertreatment of the brightened wool can help to retard it.

The FBAs used to brighten wool are mainly DAST types and pyrazolines of the acid-dyeing type discussed in section 11.8. Examples are the DAST brighteners 11.11 and 11.13, although on wool these have light fastness values of only approximately 2. The pyrazolines 11.34–11.36 have light fastness values of 3–4 on dry wool, but very poor light fastness in the wet state. The coumarin derivative 11.40 is sometimes used on wool and can give very bright results, but unfortunately its light fastness is only 1.

Silk and polyurethane fibres can also be brightened with FBAs used for nylon and wool.

11.40

11.10 BRIGHTENERS FOR POLYESTER

Much research has focused on the development of better brighteners for application to polyester. A very large number of patents has appeared and it is impossible to cover all the chemical types in this chapter. Most of the more important commercial products and many chemical types are discussed here, but the reader is referred to published reviews [7,8,12,13] for more detail.

Although polyester is always brightened with disperse-type products, the methods of application vary. FBAs are marketed for exhaust application with or without carrier, for use in the pad–Thermosol process at temperatures varying between 160 and 220°C and for mass brightening. Most products are applicable by more than one method, but none of them can be applied satisfactorily by all methods, and products introduced thirty or forty years ago remain important today.

In general, and as would be expected, brighteners of relatively small molecular size are used for application by exhaustion. Less volatile compounds of larger molecular size tend to be used in the Thermosol procedure or for application from the spin mass. For application by exhaustion the previously mentioned pyrene derivative 11.29, the naphthalimide 11.30 and compounds 11.41–11.44 are commercially important.

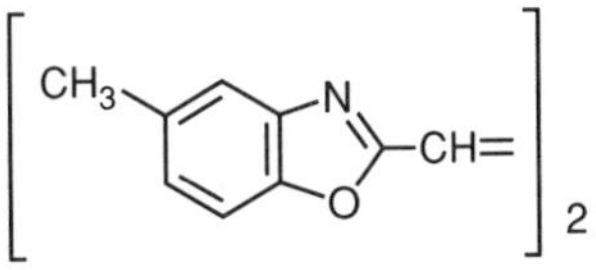

11.41

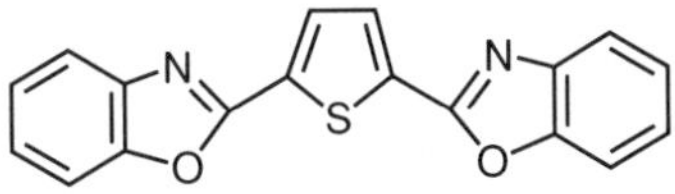

11.42

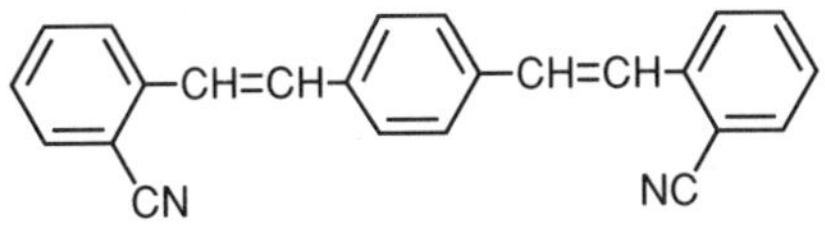

11.43

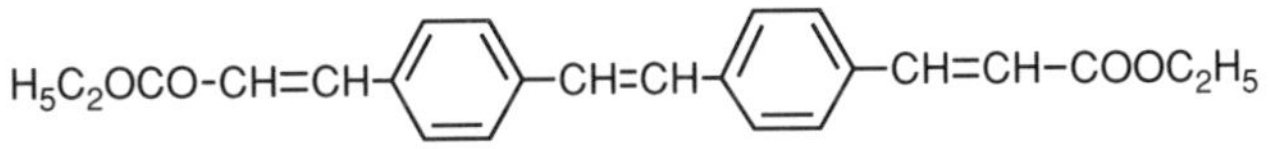

11.44

Polyester is brightened more effectively by exhaustion either by the high-temperature method at 125–130°C or at the boil in the presence of a carrier. Small amounts of carrier are also sometimes used in the high-temperature process. Commercially satisfactory results can be obtained at the boil in the absence of a carrier, however, using compounds 11.30, 11.41 and 11.42. Polyester FBAs that are suitable for application by exhaustion processes are normally also stable in sodium chlorite bleaching, although the pyrene derivative 11.29 and the ester 11.44 are exceptions.

Most of the FBAs used to brighten polyester by exhaustion can also be applied satisfactorily by the pad–Thermosol method at baking temperatures up to 190°C. At temperatures greater than this some brighteners sublime and are unsatisfactory, but compounds 11.29, 11.43 and 11.44 are suitable for use with a baking temperature above 190°C, as is the benzoxazole 11.39. The temperature used during the baking stage in the pad–Thermosol procedure depends largely on the equipment available to the finisher. Thus FBAs showing optimum performance at temperatures ranging from 160 to 220°C all have a place on the market. Shorter baking times, leading to greater throughput of brightened fabric, are possible at higher baking temperatures, although energy costs are greater. Products capable of giving good whiteness at a lower Thermosol temperature appear to be gaining in importance [32].

Many other compounds have been marketed as polyester brighteners for application by exhaustion processes or in the pad–Thermosol procedure. No account would be complete without mention of the important class of coumarin disperse FBAs, of which compound 11.45 is a typical example.

Many commercial polyester brighteners contain a benzoxazole group, and two such products have already been mentioned; compounds 11.46 and 11.47 are further examples.

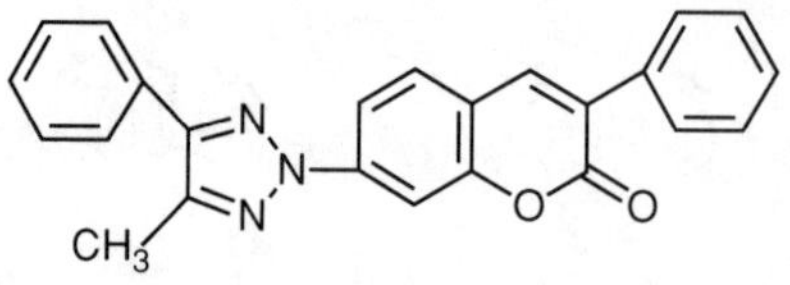

11.45

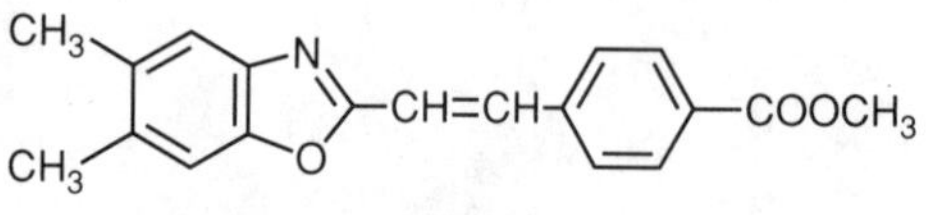

11.46

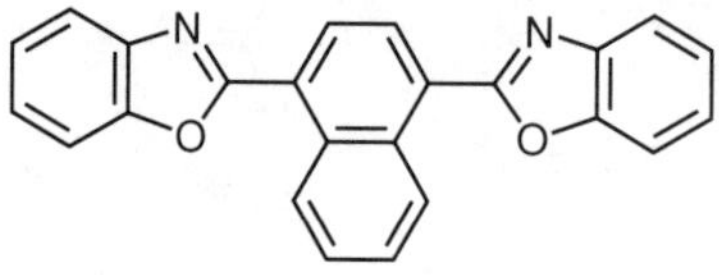

11.47

Polyester brighteners typically show excellent fastness properties. Light fastness is usually 5–6, the pyrene derivative 11.29 with a light fastness of only 2–3 being an exception. Although compound 11.29 also gives distinctly greenish brightening effects, it is capable of producing remarkably high whiteness and remains an important commercial product.

Yellowing of white textiles in the presence of gas fumes (nitrogen oxides) has become of importance in recent years. The yellowing is often caused by interactions between the nitrogen oxides and antioxidants present in packaging materials. Reinehr and Schmidt [33] have shown that several polyester FBAs yellow in the presence of very high concentrations of nitrogen oxide fumes, but they were unable to detect any yellowing at concentrations likely to be approached in practice.

Synergistic effects can often be observed with polyester brighteners, and mixtures of brighteners are increasing in importance: for example, mixtures of compounds 11.41 and 11.29 and of compounds 11.29 and 11.30 have been marketed. These effects may be to increase the maximum whiteness achievable and/or to enable a desired level of whiteness to be achieved with less FBA. The subject has been discussed by Martini and Probst [34], but the mechanism by which the synergy operates is not completely understood.

A large amount of polyester fibre is sold in pre-brightened form. The brightener is applied in the melt before or during extrusion. Two important FBAs used in this way are the coumarin 11.48 and the bis(benzoxazolyl)-stilbene 11.49; the latter gives brilliant brightening effects of a violet hue, more pleasing to most observers than the slightly greenish hue produced by compound 11.48. The coumarin is, however, stable under the conditions of preparation of the polyester and can be added before polymerisation whereas the benzoxazole is not entirely stable and has to be added to the polyester granules immediately before extrusion. Polyester brightened with the coumarin has a light fastness value greater than 7, making it commercially very important.

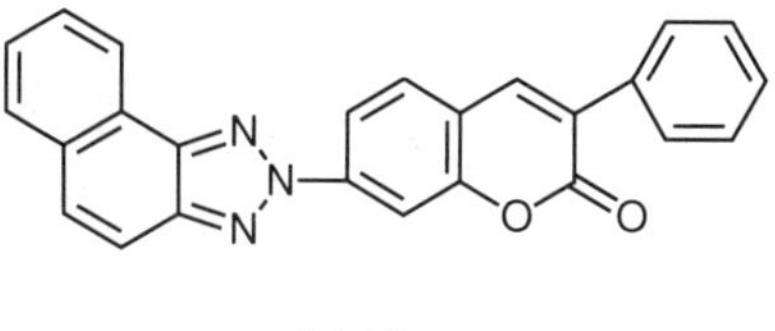

11.48 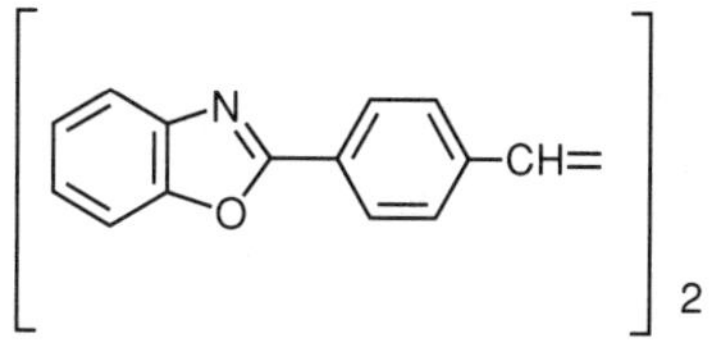   11.49

Since the structures of polyester FBAs are so varied, the methods used in their manufacture are also diverse. The organic chemistry can be complex and the intermediates required are often difficult to prepare. A full discussion is beyond the scope of this book. The reader is referred, in the first place, to the reviews mentioned in the introduction for further information. A summary of the more important methods of manufacture follows.

Those polyester FBAs that contain a benzoxazole group are usually prepared from the appropriate o-aminophenol and carboxylic acid (11.50; Y = OH) or one of its derivatives, as shown in Scheme 11.9. The reaction proceeds via an intermediate amide and it can be an advantage to start from an acid derivative such as the acyl chloride (11.50; Y = Cl) or ester (11.50; Y = OC_2H_5), which are better acylating agents. The preparation of compound 11.42, shown in Scheme 11.10, illustrates this process, but the optimum conditions for ring closure vary considerably from one product to another. The article by Gold [6] contains a valuable and detailed summary.

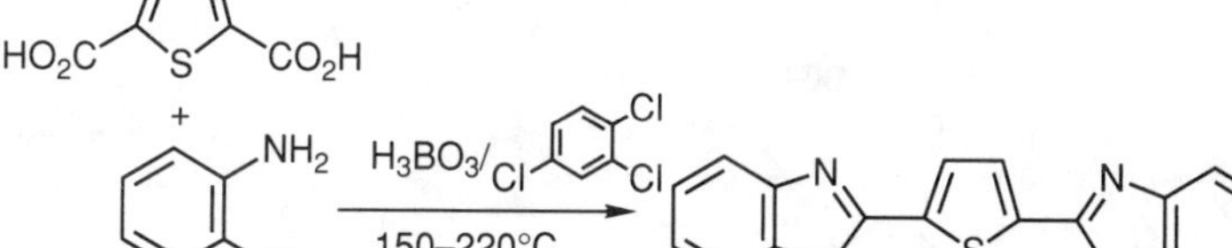

Scheme 11.9

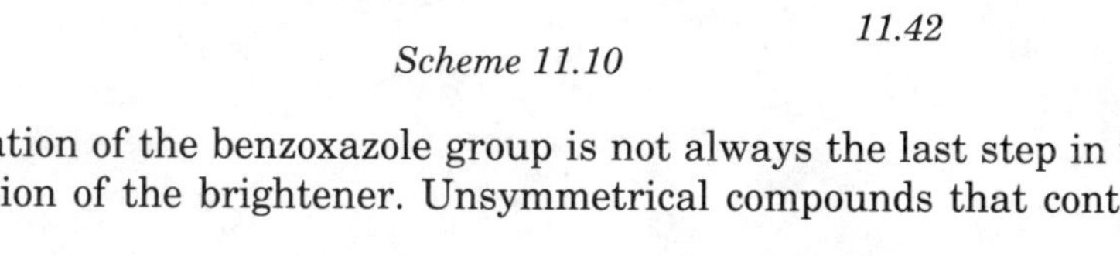

11.42

Scheme 11.10

Formation of the benzoxazole group is not always the last step in the preparation of the brightener. Unsymmetrical compounds that contain both a benzoxazole group and a C=C bond can be prepared using the 'Anil' synthesis, described by Siegrist [35], in which a compound possessing a reactive methyl group reacts with a Schiff's base. The preparation of compound 11.39) is an illustration of this method (Scheme 11.11).

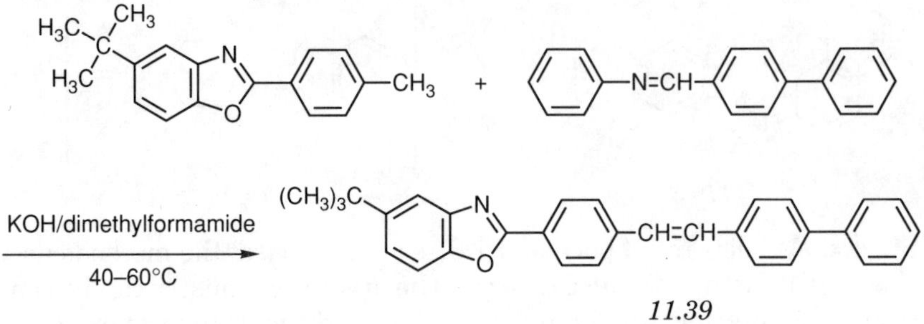

11.39

Scheme 11.11

Most of the important class of coumarins used as polyester FBAs are made via 7-amino-3-phenylcoumarin (11.51), which can be prepared by the Pechmann procedure from *m*-aminophenol. Conversion of compound 11.51 to the FBA is achieved in various ways, two examples of which are shown in Scheme 11.12.

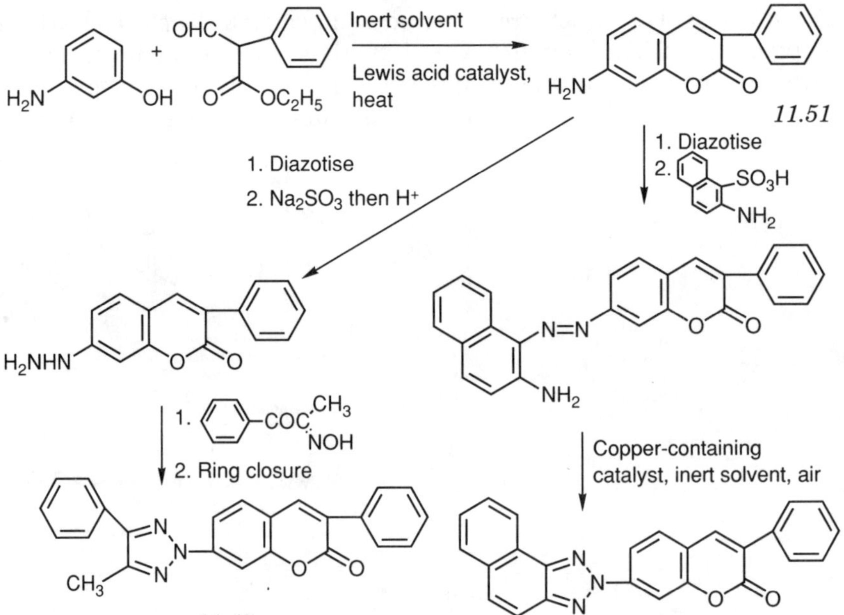

11.45

11.48

Scheme 11.12

The method used in the manufacture of the naphthalimide 11.30 is outlined in Scheme 11.13.

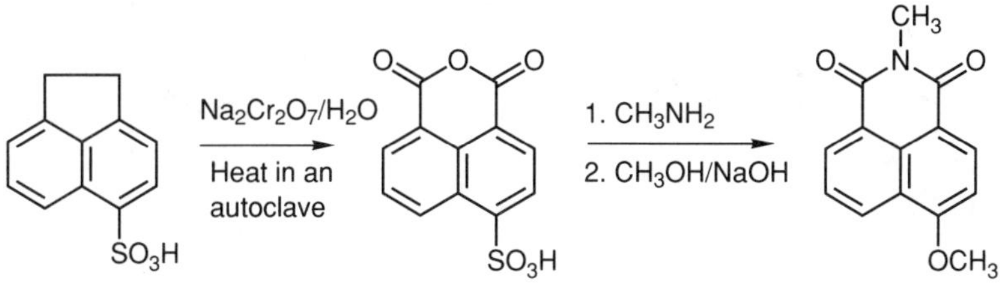

Scheme 11.13

A Michaelis–Arbusov rearrangement followed by a Wittig–Horner reaction is involved in the preparation of nitrile 11.43, shown in Scheme 11.14. The ester 11.44 can be made by a similar procedure, or altenatively by the reaction of ethyl acrylate with 4,4′-dibromostilbene in the presence of a palladium-based catalyst (Scheme 11.15), a procedure that yields the required *trans* form of the brightener.

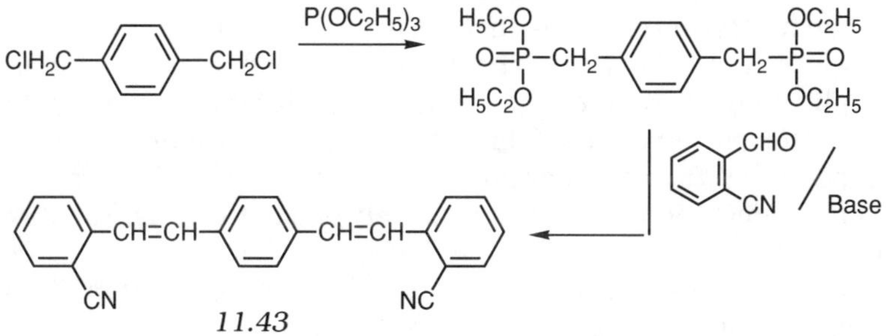

Scheme 11.14

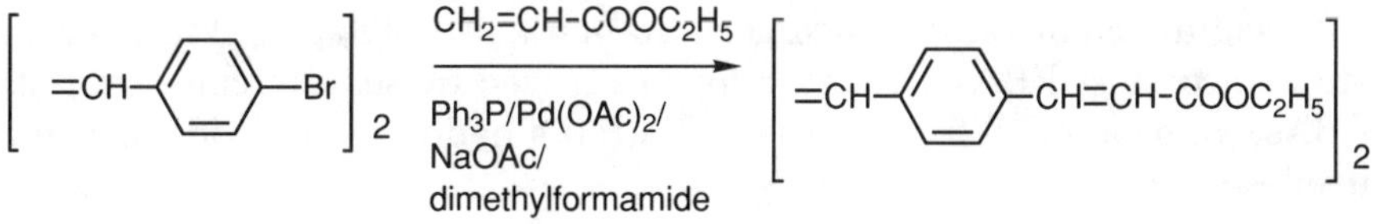

Scheme 11.15

The important brightener 11.29 is made by Friedel–Crafts acylation of pyrene (Scheme 11.16).

FBAs for incorporation in the melt are usually sold as the pure brightener without diluents. Most polyester FBAs are, however, supplied in the form of an aqueous dispersion. Considerable care is required in formulat-

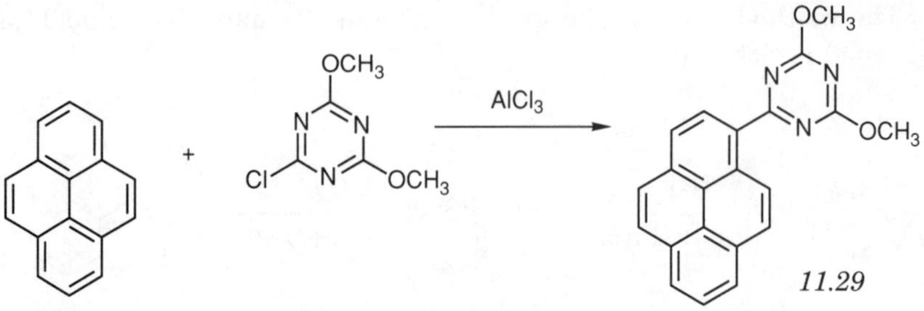

Scheme 11.16

ing these dispersions: not only must the dispersion be stable, but the dispersing agents must be of a type and in a concentration that does not negatively influence the properties (such as light fastness) of the article brightened with the product. A brightener must be properly formulated if it is to succeed commercially.

White polyester/cotton fabrics are important commercially. Such fibre blends can be brightened either by exhaustion or continuously by pad–Thermosol or pad–steam processes. Brighteners are selected from those used for polyester or cellulose. Most polyester/cotton fabrics are woven and it is essential to desize them before FBA application. Fabric for sale as whites would have to be chemically bleached before, during or after FBA application. In order to achieve the most solid white both the polyester and the cotton portions of the fabric must be brightened, in which case the chosen polyester and cotton brighteners must be compatible in hue; it is, however, common practice to brighten only one of the constituents of the blend.

If padding processes are used to brighten the polyester/cotton blend both polyester and cotton brighteners may be applied from the same pad bath, even when a resin finish is simultaneously applied to the cellulosic portion of the blend. Similarly, both types of FBA may be applied from the same bath by exhaustion. If the polyester portion of the blend is to be bleached with sodium chlorite, the cotton brightener is usually applied in a second step since most FBAs for cotton are destroyed by sodium chlorite. Both FBAs can be applied from the same bath if a hydrogen peroxide bleach is used.

11.11 BRIGHTENERS FOR ACRYLIC FIBRES
At one time disperse-type FBAs, such as pyrazoline, coumarin or naphthalimide derivatives, were commonly used to brighten acrylic fibres. Today all the important brighteners for these fibres are cationic in character and can be divided into two types:
– type A: products that are unstable towards sodium chlorite
– type B: products that are stable to sodium chlorite.

Type B brighteners can, of course, be applied in the absence of bleach but show the best results when applied simultaneously with sodium chlorite bleach, when they are capable of giving exceptionally high whiteness.

Acrylic fibres are usually brightened from an exhaust bath in the presence of acid. Application of brightener by padding methods, such as pad–roll and pad–steam, are also used but are uncommon. When these fibres are brightened from an exhaust bath careful control of dyebath conditions is necessary. Most acrylic fibres have a glass transition temperature of approximately 80°C and their dyeing characteristics are very different above and below this. Too rapid an increase in dyebath temperature can lead to unlevel results.

As an alternative to sodium chlorite, acrylic fibres are often bleached using sodium bisulphite in the presence of oxalic acid. This method is necessary with Courtelle (Courtaulds), which is damaged by sodium chlorite. Both types of acrylic brightener can be applied with bisulphite bleach.

11.11.1 Type A products

Products of this type are derivatives of 1,3-diphenylpyrazoline, such as compounds 11.52–11.54. The sulphones are marketed as aqueous solutions of their formate salts; they produce violet brightening effects of light fastness 4 and are capable of producing very high white effects. The sulphonamide 11.54 gives greener effects and will not produce the levels of white possible with either sulphone (11.52 or 11.53). In order to obtain less violet brightening effects, and also a higher visual level of whiteness for a given amount of FBA, the sulphones are sometimes formulated together with a shading dye.

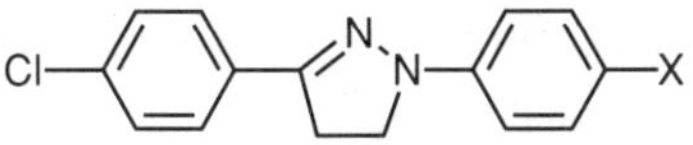

11.52   X = —SO$_2$CH$_2$CH$_2$OCHCH$_2$N(CH$_3$)$_2$

11.53   X = —SO$_2$CH$_2$CH$_2$CONHCH$_2$CH$_2$N(CH$_3$)$_2$

11.54   X = —SO$_2$NHCH$_2$CH$_2$CH$_2$N(CH$_3$)$_3$ Anion⁻

The general method for the preparation of diphenylpyrazoline derivatives has already been discussed (section 11.8). As a further illustration the preparation of compound 11.53 is shown in Scheme 11.17.

11.11.2 Type B products

In recent years several new products have been marketed for brightening acrylic fibres in combination with a sodium chlorite bleach. Formerly the benzimidazoles 11.55 and 11.56, both of which gave greenish brightening

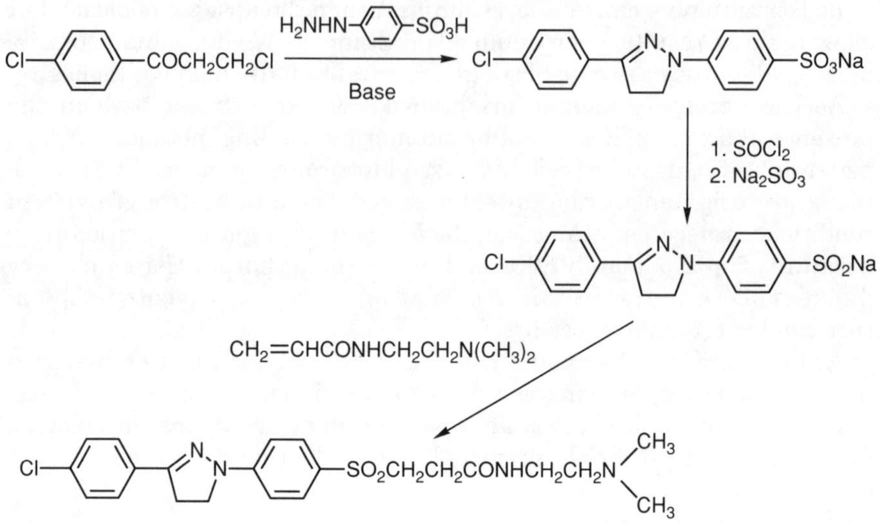

11.53

Scheme 11.17

effects, were commercially available. The older product (11.55) was especially important; it gave very good whites of light fastness 4, but a strongly acidic dyebath was recommended to give best results.

Both compounds 11.55 and 11.56 have been supplanted by products based on benzimidazoles 11.57 and 11.58, which give neutral shades of white with light fastness values slightly better than that of compound 11.55. They are easier to apply than compound 11.55 and are capable or producing a higher level of whiteness.

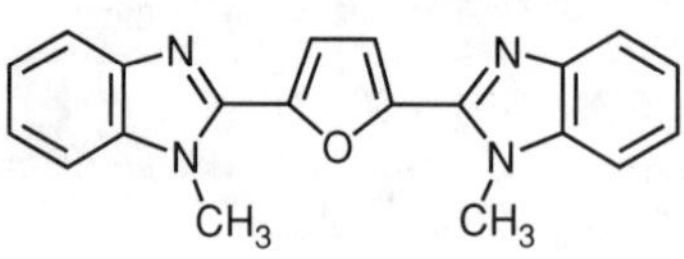

11.55

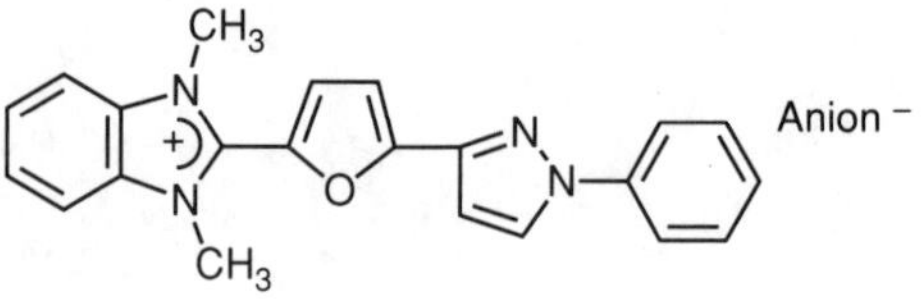

11.56

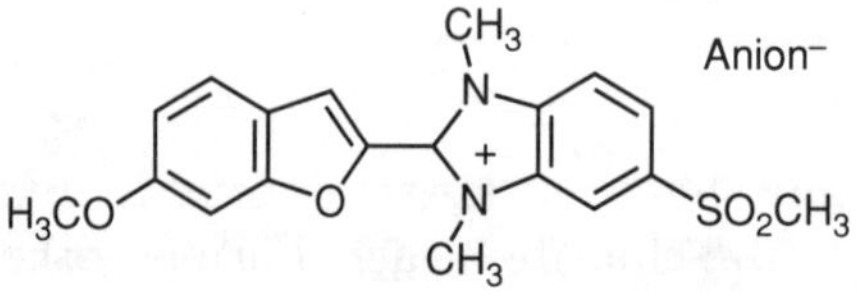

11.57

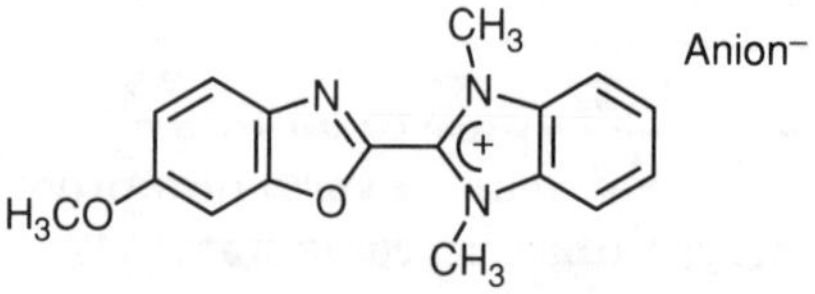

11.58

For a time compound 11.59, a similar product to compound 11.57 but easier to prepare, was also marketed. This was capable of producing very high levels of whiteness on acrylic fibres that were exceptionally violet in tone. If violet brightening effects are required they can be achieved in combination with sodium chlorite using the coumarin 11.60, which has been available for some years. Naphthalimide derivatives such as compound 11.61 can be used to give greenish shades of white on acrylic fibres in combination with sodium chlorite bleach, but the effects are generally inferior to those produced by benzimidazoles 11.57 and 11.58.

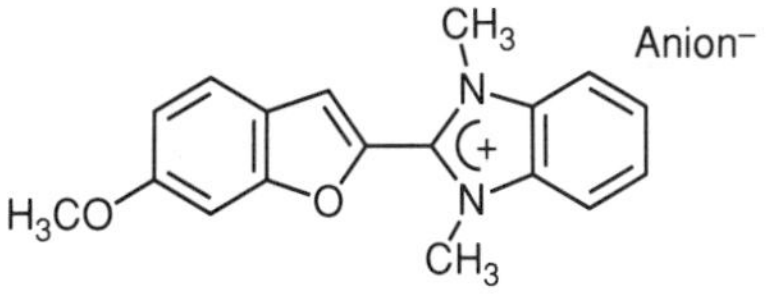

11.59 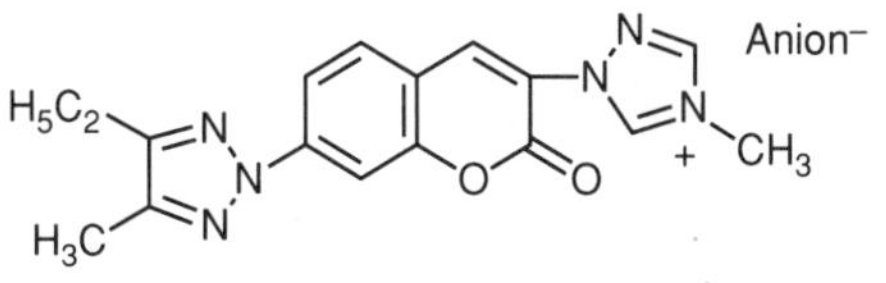   *11.60*

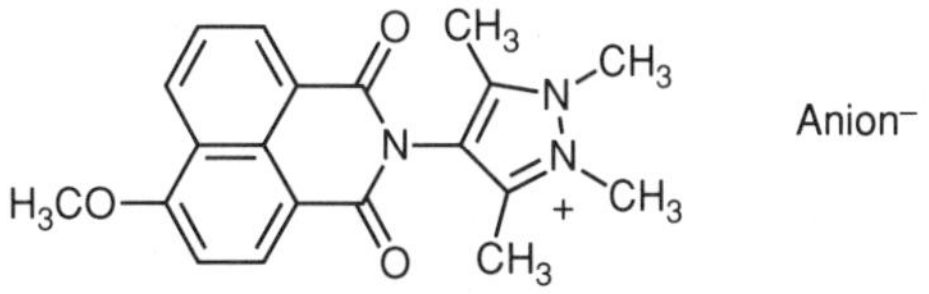

11.61

Acrylic fibres can also be brightened during their manufacture by the wet spinning process. Special FBAs have not been developed for this application and products such as compounds 11.52 and 11.57 have been used for this purpose.

Some interesting organic chemistry is involved in the preparation of chlorite-resistant brighteners for acrylic fibres. None of these compounds is easy to make and methods for the preparation of the starting materials can be complex. Much manufacturing 'know-how' is involved. One route for the preparation of benzofuran 11.57 is shown in Scheme 11.18. Preparation of the chemically somewhat simpler benzoxazole 11.58 is shown in Scheme 11.19.

The preparation of coumarin 11.60 is shown in Scheme 11.20. That of naphthalimides is described in section 11.10; similar procedures are used for the preparation of compound 11.61.

11.12 BRIGHTENERS IN DETERGENT FORMULATIONS
The largest single commercial use of FBAs is in domestic detergents. Detergent technology is continually changing and modified, improved or even chemically new FBAs are still appearing on the market. The combination of large sales volumes, limited numbers of large customers and several suppliers competing for the business ensures that prices remain low.

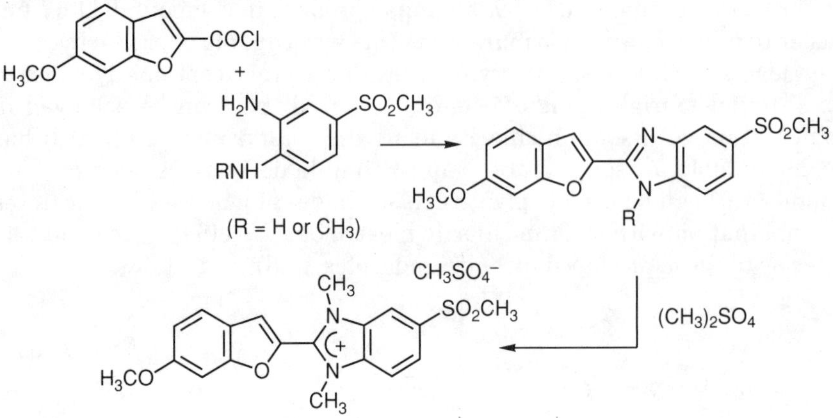

11.57

Scheme 11.18

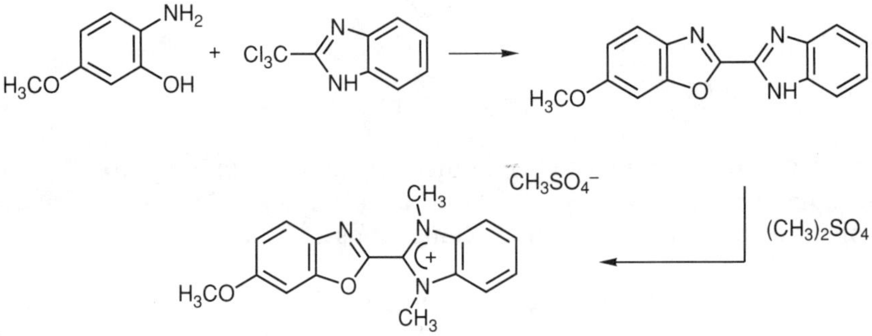

11.58

Scheme 11.19

Twenty years ago FBAs for both cotton and nylon were incorporated into household detergents; today FBAs for nylon are of little importance in detergents. FBAs that effectively brighten polyester from a household wash at acceptable wash temperatures (≤60°C) have not been developed. Other fibre types are largely ignored. FBAs incorporated into household detergents today are intended to brighten cotton.

There are basic differences between the reasons why FBAs are used by textile finishers and in household detergents. The former apply FBAs to unbrightened material; brighteners in household detergents are intended to preserve the whiteness of already brightened fabric during many successive wash and wear cycles. If too much FBA is present in the wash then it is wasted. Using far too much could even lead to deterioration in

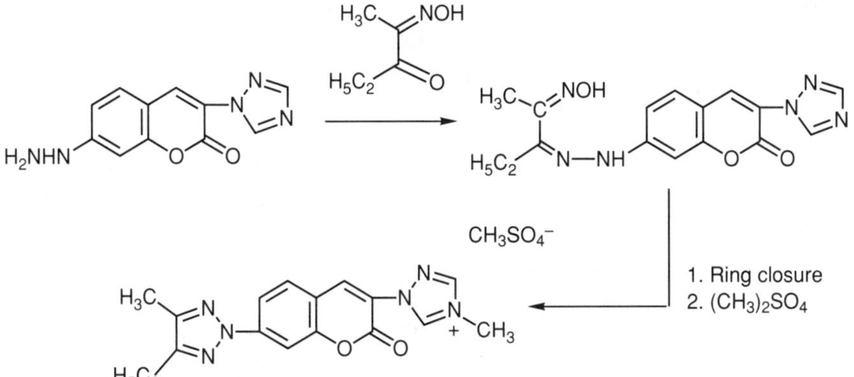

Scheme 11.20

whiteness in an article as an excess of FBA builds up after several washes. If too little is used then the article will gradually lose whiteness, although it could be several months before the loss of whiteness is noticed by the user. Typically a detergent powder contains 0.02–0.05% FBA, although the trend is probably towards the use of less FBA.

Both the type of surfactant in household detergents and the washing conditions vary from one part of the world to another. In some countries washing temperatures are as low as 30°C; in others they can be as high as 90°C. In some countries chlorine-containing bleaches are routinely used in the wash and in others very rarely, if ever. The intensity of the sunlight falling on the washed article during drying, and consequent fading of the FBA, obviously varies from place to place. Since a household detergent is sold as a consumer product, much attention has to be paid to its packaging and physical appearance; discoloration or development of odour in the powder, for example, would retard sales whatever the actual performance of the product in the wash. All these factors influence the choice of type and quantity of FBA to be incorporated in the formulation. In addition, wash loads often contain different types of fabric, so an FBA incorporated into the detergent to brighten cotton must not adversely affect other materials under the likely wash conditions.

Considerations of toxicity and environmental impact greatly influence selection of an FBA for use in household detergents. The effluent from a household wash is discharged directly into the waste system; there is no intermediate treatment as in factory conditions. The combined quantity of wash water from household washing is very large and the FBA must therefore be completely non-toxic and unobjectionable in the environment. Nor must the brightener contain any significant amounts of deleterious impurities.

Evaluation of an FBA for use in household detergents is a lengthy and expensive process. The information obtained from a standard one-wash procedure on unbrightened cotton is valuable, but it soon becomes necessary to test a product by measuring the build-up of whiteness in a series of successive washes from a detergent containing the very small amount of FBA usually found in practice. Tests continue on pre-brightened cotton in a wash cycle and in field tests. Extensive toxicity and environmental testing is necessary. Although many different FBAs have been used in household detergents, only four or perhaps five products are important today.

The structures of three of these (compounds 11.12, 11.25 and 11.26) have already been mentioned; the fourth product is the very important DAST brightener 11.62. Methods for the preparation of all these products are described in section 11.6. All four exist in both 'yellow' and 'white' crystalline forms. They are most easily prepared in the 'yellow' form, but incorporation of this form in a detergent leads to unacceptable discoloration of the powder. Today the products are usually supplied in their 'white' form, which can be obtained in various ways – for example, by heating an aqueous alkaline suspension of the 'yellow' form together with a co-solvent.

11.62

The DAST brightener 11.62 is the most important FBA for use in detergents, and is probably the cheapest to manufacture. It shows excellent performance at temperatures of 60°C and above but, relative to compounds 11.12 and 11.25, poor solubility in cold water: if it is to perform satisfactorily in low-temperature washing, it must be supplied in a finely divided form so that it can dissolve during normal household washing. The necessary particle size can be achieved in various ways; one method is to use wet milling in the presence of excess salt.

DAST-type FBAs can also contain by-products derived from hydrolysis of one or more of the chlorine atoms of cyanuric chloride. One such compound is the triazine 11.63. Not only is this compound environmentally undesirable, it also interacts with some bleaches and its presence can lead to the development of unpleasant odours in a detergent powder. The proportion of this triazine present as an impurity in a brightener such as compound 11.62 can be kept to a minimum by careful control of the reaction conditions during manufacture; alternatively it can be extracted from the FBA with hot alkali.

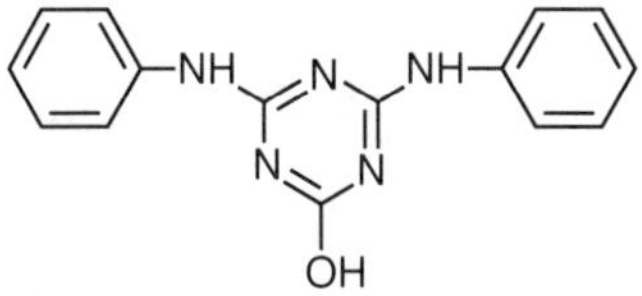

11.63

The instability of DAST-type brighteners towards chlorine-containing bleaches has already been mentioned. They also show limited stability towards per-acids. In recent years, as washing temperatures have tended to fall, a bleach consisting of sodium perborate activated by tetra-acetyl-ethylenediamine has become an important constituent of household detergents; this is effective at temperatures as low as 40–50°C. The active agent is a per-acid, however, and in some detergent formulations it is necessary to protect FBAs such as compound 11.62 by encapsulating either the brightener or the activator, if sufficient shelf life is to be achieved.

The so-called 'super brighteners' 11.25 and 11.26 are generally much more stable towards oxidising bleaches. Both of these, and especially the latter, also have better light fastness than the DAST brighteners. The bis-stilbene 11.25 is an effective FBA when applied from a wash bath at temperatures below 50°C, but very poor at higher temperatures; it has poor wash fastness in soft water. The triazole 11.26 is effective at all temperatures but is expensive, although in tropical countries, where washed articles can fade severely while drying, it may be cost-effective. The bis-stilbene 11.25 is particularly effective in brightening the detergent powder itself, although this in no way indicates its performance in the wash. Table 11.3 summarises the advantages and disadvantages of the four major products.

The poor performance of the bis-stilbene 11.25 at higher wash temperatures is a serious disadvantage in some countries. In an attempt to overcome this disadvantage it has been marketed in admixture with its chlorine-containing variant (11.64). This water-insoluble variant is by itself very effective at higher washing temperatures.

11.64

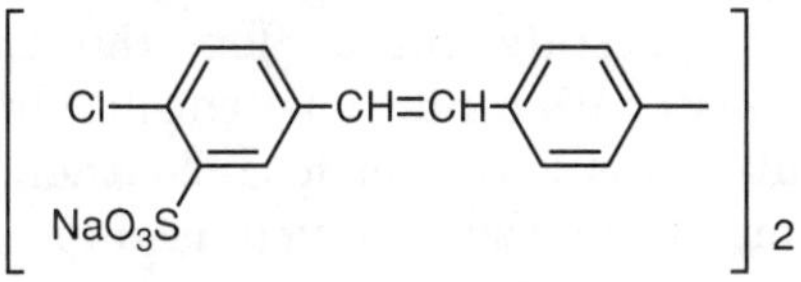

Where resistance to chlorine bleaches such as sodium hypochlorite is required, the naphthotriazole 11.65 can be used. Formerly this was an extremely important FBA for use in detergents, but today it is less so. It has the advantage of brightening both cotton and nylon from the wash bath.

In the absence of hypochlorite bleach pyrazolines such as compound 11.31 and the ester 11.66 give brighter results than compound 11.65 on the

TABLE 11.3

Advantages and disadvantages of FBAs in detergent formulations

Product	Advantages	Disadvantages
11.62	Price Effective at all temperatures	Unstable towards hypochlorite and activated perborates
11.12	Effective at all temperatures	Unstable towards hypochlorite and activated perborate
11.25	Stable in bleaching Good light fastness	Poor performance above 50°C Indifferent wash fastness
11.26	Effective at all temperatures Stable in bleaching Excellent light fastness	Price

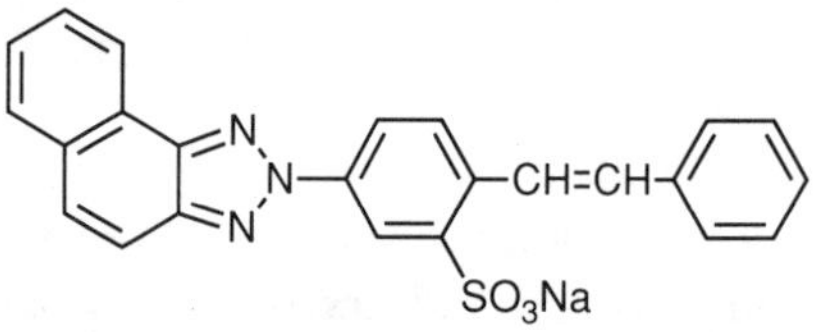

11.65 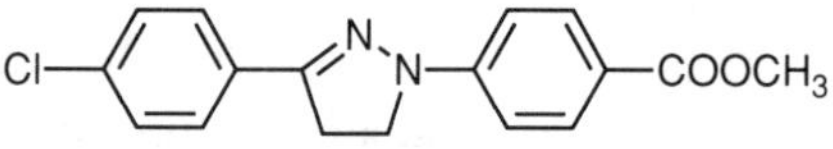   11.66

polyamide portion of the wash. Compound 11.66 gives especially bright if somewhat greenish results, but suffers the disadvantage of staining polyester under wash bath conditions. The sulphonamide 11.31 gives less bright effects but stains polyester less. Neither pyrazoline derivative is effective on cotton and neither is much used in detergents today.

In recent years domestic detergents in liquid form have become increasingly popular; this has created problems in the choice of FBAs as it is difficult to devise a stable liquid formulation. Liquid household detergents containing FBAs can cause yellow 'specking' on the wash goods, which can be a serious problem. It has been claimed [36] that use of FBAs such as compounds 11.65 and 11.67, which contain only one sulphonic acid group, ameliorates the 'specking' problem. It is possible that an FBA such as compound 11.67 could become important in liquid detergents. This compound is difficult to prepare, however, and like DAST brighteners is unstable towards important bleaches. With the trend towards lower washing temperatures increasingly active bleaches will be required. Some further developments in bleach-resistant non-specking FBAs for use in household detergents may be required.

11.67

11.13 ANALYSIS OF FBAs

Qualitative analysis of FBAs is best carried out by thin-layer chromatography (t.l.c.). Suitable standards are required. The plethora of possible brighteners of the DAST type, together with the impurities present in these products, can cause difficulties in their identification by t.l.c. The technique can also be used quantitatively, although expensive instrumentation is needed and considerable care must be taken in preparing and handling chromatograms. Silica gel is the usual stationary phase for both qualitative and quantitative t.l.c. of FBAs. Various eluents are available, and are chosen according to the chemical nature of the FBA. Chapters by Theidel and Anders in the book edited by Anliker and Müller [9] contain valuable information on the analysis of FBAs by t.l.c. More recently Lepri and Desideri [37] have described methods for the t.l.c. identification of FBAs in detergents.

If suitable standards are unavailable – for example, if the FBA is new – the active agent must first be isolated and purified. The pure material can be characterised by the usual methods such as elemental analysis, and infra-red, n.m.r. and mass spectroscopy. Difficulties may again be encountered with DAST-type compounds. Final proof of structure demands synthesis of the indicated FBA.

Once the FBA has been identified, ultra-violet absorption spectroscopy affords a rapid and accurate method of quantitative analysis. Care must be taken with stilbene-type brighteners, since *trans* to *cis* isomerisation is promoted by ultra-violet radiation. Usually, however, a spectrum can be obtained before any analytically significant isomerisation occurs. FBAs are often sold on the basis of their strength as determined by ultra-violet spectroscopy.

FBAs can also be estimated quantitatively by fluorescence spectroscopy, which is much more sensitive than the ultra-violet method but is more prone to error and is less convenient to use. Small quantities of impurities may lead to serious distortions in both emission and excitation spectra. Indeed, a comparison of ultra-violet absorption and fluorescence excitation spectra can yield useful information on the purity of an FBA: a pure FBA will show identical absorption and excitation spectra.

In recent years high-performance liquid chromatography (h.p.l.c.) has increasingly been used to identify FBAs, to investigate product purity and for process control. H.p.l.c. can present a convenient and rapid method of quantitative analysis, provided the constitution of the FBA is known and a pure sample is available for calibration, although an h.p.l.c. method may take time and effort to develop. Few details have been published, but the h.p.l.c. analysis of FBAs in detergents has been described [38,39].

REFERENCES

1. P Krais, *Melliand Textilber.*, **10** (1929) 468.
2. C Paine and J A Radley (ICI), BP 442 530 (1934).
3. A Landholt, *Textil-Rundschau*, **11** (1948) 376.
4. A Landholt, *Amer. Dyestuff Rep.*, **38** (1949) 353.
5. A K Sarkar, *Fluorescent whitening agents* (Watford: Merrow, 1971).
6. H Gold in *The chemistry of synthetic dyes*, Vol.5, Ed. K Venkataraman (New York: Academic Press, 1971).
7. D Barton and H Davidson, *Rev. Prog. Coloration*, **5** (1974) 3.
8. A Dorlars, C-W Schellhammer and J Schroeder, *Angew. Chem.* Internat. Edn, **14** (1975) 665.
9. *Fluorescent whitening agents*, Ed. R Anliker and G Müller (Stuttgart: Thieme, 1975).
10. R Zweidler and H Hefti, *Kirk–Othmer encyclopedia of chemical technology*, 3rd Edn, Vol. 4 (New York: Wiley Interscience, 1978) 213.
11. R Williamson, *Fluorescent brightening agents* (Amsterdam: Elsevier, 1980).
12. I H Leaver and B Milligan, *Dyes and Pigments*, **5** (1984) 109.
13. A E Siegrist, H Hefti, H R Meyer and E Schmidt, *Rev. Prog. Coloration*, **17** (1987) 39.
14. *The dyeing of cellulosic fibres*, Ed. C Preston (Bradford: Dyers' Company Publications Trust, 1986).
15. *Luminescence spectroscopy*, Ed. M D Lumb (New York: Academic Press, 1978).
16. J R Lakowicz, *Principles of fluorescence spectroscopy* (London: Plenum Press, 1983).
17. M Pestemer, A Berger and A Wagner, *Textilveredlung*, **19** (1964) 420.
18. A Berger, *Die Farbe*, **8** (1959) 187.
19. P S Stensby, *Soap Chem. Spec.*, **43** (1967) 80.
20. R Griesser, *Rev. Prog. Coloration*, **11** (1981) 26.
21. I Soljacic, A M Grancaric and K Weber, *Textilveredlung*, **10** (1975) 492.
22. A M Grancaric and I Soljacic, *Melliand Textilber.*, **62** (1981) 876.
23. I Soljacic and R Cenko, *Melliand Textilber.*, **60** (1979) 1032.
24. I Soljacic and K Weber, *Textilveredlung*, **9** (1974) 220.
25. I Sojacic, A M Grancaric and B Luburie, *Textil Praxis*, **39** (1984) 775.
26. K Seguchi, Y Ebara and S Hirota, *Yukagaku*, **34** (1985) 17.
27. R S Davidson, G M Ismail and D M Lewis, *J.S.D.C.*, **104** (1988) 86.
28. *Paper*, (June 1980) 33.
29. R Zweidler, *Textilveredlung*, **4** (1969) 78.
30. H Strahle, W Seitz and H Güsten, *Z. Naturforsch.*, **316** (1976) 1248.
31. H Güsten and G Heinrich, *Ber. Bunsen-Ges.*, **81** (1977) 810.
32. T Martini, *Textilveredlung*, **23** (1988) 2.
33. D Reinehr and E Schmidt, *J.S.D.C.*, **102** (1986) 258.
34. T Martini and H Probst, *Melliand Textilber.*, **65** (1984) 327.

35. A E Siegrist, *Helv. Chim. Acta*, **50** (1967) 906.
36. J Wevers, L A Halas and P R Peltre, USP 4 559 169 (1985).
37. L Lepri and P G Desideri, *J. Chromatog.*, **322** (1985) 363.
38. B P McPherson and N Omelczenko, *J. Amer. Oil. Chem. Soc.*, (1980) 388.
39. G Micali, P Curro and G Calabro, *Analyst*, **109** (1984) 155.

CHAPTER 12

Auxiliaries associated with main dye classes

Terence M Baldwinson

12.1 INTRODUCTION

The aim in this chapter is to summarise the auxiliaries normally used with each of the main dye classes. Where these have been dealt with earlier, the emphasis here is on application properties. Chemical details are included, however, for those auxiliaries that have not yet been mentioned; emphasis is given to the auxiliaries used rather than to processing details.

12.2 ACID AND MORDANT DYES

12.2.1 Acid dyes

Anionic acid dyes, applied principally to wool and nylon, vary widely in their fastness and level-dyeing properties (see Chapter 3); in general, the better the wet fastness properties of a dye the more difficult it is to apply evenly. Hence it is not surprising that the use of auxiliaries with acid dyes is related mainly to the level-dyeing properties. There are two basic aspects:

(a) controlling the pH to give a satisfactory dyeing rate and ultimate exhaustion

(b) using auxiliaries to give additional levelling, either through a competitive mechanism that exerts further control on absorption or through the promotion of migration and diffusion.

The control of pH is of particular importance, as the optimum pH varies with the different groups of acid dyes. This can be seen in Table 12.1 [1], which shows the pH values generally required to give 80–85% exhaustion.

Levelling acid and particularly 1:1 metal-complex dyes require an exceptionally low pH in order to promote exhaustion and levelling; up to 3% o.w.f. sulphuric acid is most commonly used for levelling dyes, although hydrochloric, formic and phosphoric acids are also effective. The 1:1 metal-complex dyes generally require as much as 8% o.w.f. sulphuric acid, as

TABLE 12.1

Dyebath pH for exhaustion of 80–85%

Dye class	pH
1:1 Metal-complex dyes	2.0–2.5
Levelling acid dyes	2.5–3.5
Chrome dyes	4.0–5.0
Milling acid dyes	4.5–5.5
Disulphonated 1:2 metal-complex dyes	4.5–5.5
'Super-milling' acid dyes	5.0–6.0
Monosulphonated 1:2 metal-complex dyes	5.0–6.0
Unsulphonated 1:2 metal-complex dyes	5.5–6.5

smaller amounts tend to give tippy dyeings and lower wet fastness [2]. With the so-called 'half-milling' or intermediate levelling dyes (those requiring an optimum pH of 4.0–5.5), such a low pH would lead to too high a rate of exhaustion with consequent risk of unlevel dyeing, and up to 2% o.w.f. acetic acid generally provides the optimum acidity. Milling and 1:2 metal-complex types are highly responsive to acid. Hence the tendency with these dyes is to use a pH-shift system (see section 10.1), starting from neutral or slightly alkaline and progressively decreasing the pH to the required level as dyeing proceeds. Latent-acid salts, such as ammonium sulphate or ammonium acetate, or a hydrolysable ester are used, often with ammonia to give a higher initial pH. Wool, however, is easily degraded by hot alkaline or neutral dyebaths. It suffers least damage at its isoelectric point of around pH 4.5 (see section 3.2.2). Hence in recent years the advantages of applying milling and 1:2 metal-complex dyes in this pH region have been promoted; an effective surfactant-type levelling/retarding agent must then be used to counteract the high rate of exhaustion promoted by this degree of acidity [1,3–7]. In general rather less acidity is required for the same dyes on nylon than on wool.

Neutral electrolytes, usually 10–20% o.w.f. sodium sulphate or sodium chloride, are widely used with acid dyes to aid levelling. Their action results from the competition for the dyeing sites in the fibre provided by this high concentration of inorganic anions. Ultimately these are replaced by the dye anions as a result of their higher affinity [2]. Electrolytes are less effective as levelling agents in near-neutral dyebaths, however, since under these conditions the ionisation of the fibre is too low to attract simple inorganic anions and dye sorption is generally through non-polar, rather than electrostatic, forces. Nevertheless, it is still common to add electrolyte when applying these dyes, but it then functions primarily to boost exhaustion through a common-ion mechanism, rather than as a levelling agent.

The use of surfactant-type levelling agents is of importance with acid dyes on wool and nylon, especially with dyes of higher wet fastness. Anionic surfactants act by competing for the dye sites and are mainly used to counteract fibre-oriented unlevelness due to physical and chemical irregularities in the fibre. Strongly cationic quaternary compounds readily form complexes with acid dyes, but may precipitate when used alone. Weakly cationic ethoxylated tertiary amines do not suffer from this disadvantage and are of great importance in minimising unlevelness associated with rapid dye uptake. Combinations of anionic and cationic types, carefully chosen according to the principles described in section 10.5, are of particular importance since they counteract both types of unlevelness. A well-chosen levelling agent, or combination of levelling agents, can effectively convert an incompatible combination of dyes (that is, one that does not build up on tone because of the sequential sorption of individual components) into a compatible one. In recent times amphoteric levelling agents, combining the properties of anionic and cationic agents, have been used [3–7]; originally developed for use with reactive dyes on wool, they are also being exploited with acid dyes, particularly for dyeing at pH 4.5. Ranges of 1:2 metal-complex dyes have recently been introduced that contain ionic solubilising groups (carboxyl or sulpho) rather than the non-ionised but polar groups (such as sulphonamide or sulphone) in the earlier dyes (see sections 3.2.2 and 5.4.2). These are often cheaper to manufacture and offer better wet fastness, but their growing popularity has owed much to the use of amphoteric betaine levelling agents [8,9].

By using more than the optimum amount of dye-complexing agent required for effective levelling some of these products can be used as stripping aids, either alone for partial non-destructive stripping or in combination with oxidising agents (such as sodium dichromate and sulphuric acid) or reducing agents (such as sodium formaldehyde–sulphoxylate or sodium dithionite) for more drastic destructive stripping.

Continuous dyeing with acid dyes is most frequently carried out at the pre-yarn stage, i.e. on loose fibre, tow or slubbing. Resilient fibres such as wool can cause problems at the padding stage and during subsequent steaming, leading to unlevel results characterised chiefly by tippy or frosty effects. Similar effects can be observed with pile fabrics such as carpets owing to differing degrees of penetration of the pile. These defects are usually overcome by using a hydrotrope, such as urea, with surfactant auxiliary agents [8,10–12]. Certain anionic surfactants are claimed to be effective, particularly sodium dioctylsulphosuccinate and its 2-ethylhexyl and 1-methylheptyl isomers [10,11]. The object is to form an agent–dye complex that wets the fibres evenly and forms a uniform film around them. The surfactant creates a foam during steam fixation, thus assisting the uniform transport of the dye throughout the fibre; the complex subsequently breaks down and the dye is then uniformly fixed. Another method [13] used a coacervate phase system to bring about a similar effect, but this has now been superseded by the foam transport system.

Printing processes also use hydrotropes such as urea or thiourea, particularly for the less soluble dyes; additional solvents, such as thiodiethylene glycol, may also be added [13]. Locust bean or guar derivatives are used as thickening agents, either alone or in combination with water-soluble British gum; high solids content is preferred for fine effects and low solids content for larger-area prints, because of better levelling and freedom from crack marks. Acid-generating products are also needed (except with metal-complex dyes); ammonium sulphate, ammonium tartrate or ammonium oxalate are usually used. Wool or the thickeners used may tend to promote reduction of certain sensitive dyes; to counteract this small amounts of sodium chlorate may be added to the print paste. Defoamers and surfactant auxiliaries to prevent frosting may also be used.

Similar considerations also apply to the production of discharge prints, with the addition of zinc formaldehyde–sulphoxylate (C.I. Reducing Agent 6) and, in the case of white discharges, titanium dioxide [13].

The washing-off of prints is best carried out with anionic polycondensation products of aromatic sulphonic acids [13].

Under some processing conditions – for example, when dyeing polyester/wool blends at temperatures above 100°C – fibre-protection agents are sometimes used to limit damage to the wool. Protective colloids such as lignin sulphonates offer some (minimal) protection. The most effective protection is obtained with formaldehyde [14,15] or with a formaldehyde precursor such as NN'-dimethylolethyleneurea [16]. The mechanisms involved with these protecting agents have been summarised [17].

12.2.2 Mordant dyes

The principles of metal–dye chelate formation have been fully described in Chapter 5 in connection with metal-complex dyes. The same essential principles are inherent in the chroming of mordant dyes, but clearly additional factors are involved due to the conditions under which the reactions are carried out on the fibre. The chromium compound may be applied before (mordant method), with (metachrome method) or after (afterchrome method) the dye, although only the afterchrome method is now of significance. Despite the growth in recent years in the use of metal-complex and reactive dyes, together with restrictions on the discharge of chromium-containing effluent to the environment, chrome dyes are still the most widely used class of dye on wool because of their coloristic and economic advantages [18].

The theoretical aspects of chroming have been reviewed by Hartley [19] and a full account of the chemistry and application of these dyes up to 1972 has been given by Bird [2]. Recent developments concerned with reducing the amount of chromium in the exhaust liquor have been summarised [8,20,21].

The most widely used chroming agent is sodium dichromate. Potassium dichromate is occasionally used, and chromium(III) fluoride ($CrF_3.4H_2O$) is preferred in many steam-fixing processes in printing and continuous dyeing. The mechanism of chroming is complex and only partially understood; it is generally represented as follows [2].

1   Dichromate (chromium (VI)) anions interact with protonated basic groups in wool, the sorption proceeding most rapidly in acidic media:

$$2\,\text{F}{-}\overset{+}{N}H_3\,\bar{O}OC{-}\text{F} + Cr_2O_7^{2-} + 2H^+ \longrightarrow \text{F}{-}\overset{+}{N}H_3\,Cr_2O_7^{2-}\,\overset{+}{N}H_3{-}\text{F} + 2\,\text{F}{-}COOH$$

2   The absorbed dichromate ions are gradually reduced by cysteine and other groups in the wool to cationic trivalent chromium:

$$Cr(VI) \xrightarrow{\;100^\circ C\;} Cr(III)$$

3   The cationic trivalent chromium then combines with the carboxylic groups in the wool:

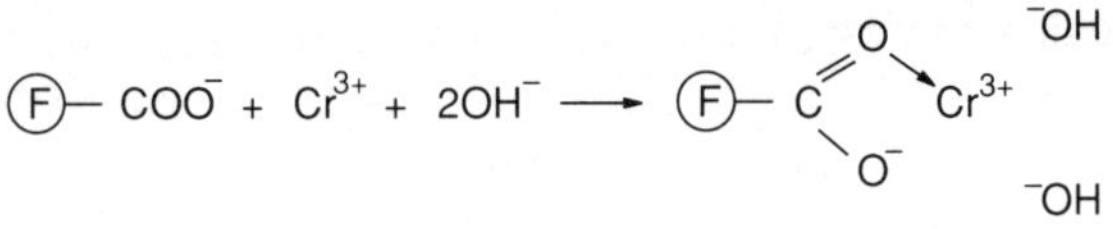

$$\text{F}{-}COO^- + Cr^{3+} + 2OH^- \longrightarrow \text{F}{-}C\underset{O^-}{\overset{O}{<}}Cr^{3+}\;\begin{smallmatrix}{}^-OH\\[4pt]{}^-OH\end{smallmatrix}$$

4   The dye then interacts with the trivalent chromium to yield mainly the 1:2 metal-complex, the complex being bound to the wool mainly through van der Waals and electrostatic forces:

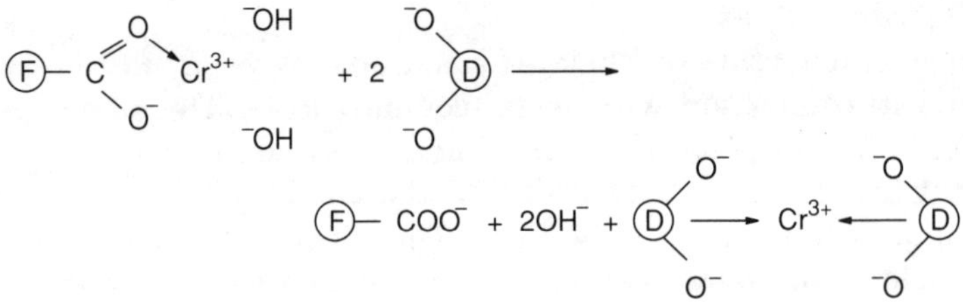

An excellent schematic representation (Figure 12.1) has been given by Meier [22], which indicates that in the ideal final state some of the chromium is complexed only with the dye, although any excess will tend to be linked with the wool.

In the chrome mordant method the wool is first treated with sodium

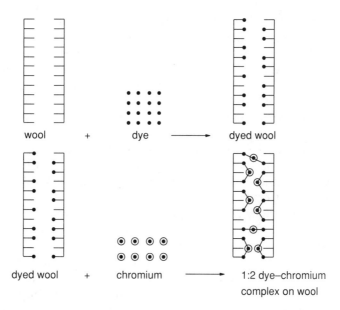

Figure 12.1 – The mechanism of chroming

dichromate in a bath made slightly acidic with acetic acid (to neutralise any alkali carried over in the wool from scouring and any developed in the chroming process itself). Certain sensitive dyes are oxidised by this so-called 'sweet' chrome mordant. Such dyes are therefore applied to a reduced chrome mordant produced by incorporating a reducing acid or salt into the mordanting bath, typical agents being potassium hydrogen tartrate, formic acid, oxalic acid or lactic acid with a little sulphuric acid. The dye application sequence is generally carried out in a slightly acidic medium, such as 0.3–1.5% o.w.f. acetic acid.

The metachrome method has the advantage of being a single-bath method but, as in most combined processes, care needs to be exercised to ensure that all components are fully compatible. The chemical reactions taking place are basically the same as described above but the processes take place simultaneously rather than sequentially. The bath generally contains up to 8% o.w.f. of the metachrome mordant (sodium chromate:ammonium sulphate 1:2 by mass), although variants, summarised by Bird [2], have also been used.

In the commercially much more important afterchrome process a conventional dyeing is carried out first, usually in the presence of acetic acid. Sodium dichromate is then added to the cooled (70°C) well-exhausted dyebath to give simultaneous chroming of the wool and formation of the chromium–dye complex as outlined above, when the temperature is again raised to near the boil.

Originally the amount of dichromate used varied in the range between 25 and 50% of the mass of dye, with the lower and upper limits set at 0.25% and 2.5% of the mass of wool. This quantity of chromium was usually well in excess of the stoichiometric amount required for complex formation. This tended to leave excess chromium in the bath for discharge to effluent and also on the fibre, where it could affect workability in subsequent processes such as spinning, weaving and knitting. Meier [22] has given an excellent account of the limitations of this method in relation to the stoichiometric requirements of the system. Legislation now restricts the amount of chromium for discharge to effluent to 0.2–0.5 mg/l for the more potent dichromate and 2–4 mg/l for the chromium(III) ion, depending on the water authority.

All the methods so far proposed for reducing excess chromium recommend an afterchroming pH of 3.0–3.9, as the mordant is used most efficiently at around pH 3.5. Chroming in a fresh bath also tends to give lower residual chrome contents [21], and this is recommended for use wherever possible. Every effort should be made to exhaust the dyebath completely, since any residual dye will complex with chromium(III) ions in the dye liquor, thus giving rise to increased residual chromium as well as the possibility of lower fastness through surface adsorption of the complex. Methods that give lower residual chromium tend to produce unlevel chroming, which can be effectively counteracted by using surfactant levelling agents; the amphoteric products developed originally for reactive dye application are particularly useful in this respect, although non-ionic products such as alkylaryl ethoxylates can also be used. Products that tend to form chromium complexes should be avoided, as should products that decrease the activity of dichromate such as sodium sulphate, ammonium sulphate and sulphuric acid. Thus any levelling agents used should be free from sequestering agents such as EDTA, DTPA and the phosphates; water free from iron and copper is much preferred [23]. An aftertreatment in ammonia (pH 8.5) for 20 minutes at 80°C, followed by acidification to pH 5, helps development of maximum fastness properties, especially on shrink-resist wool.

In one method [22] the wool is initially dyed at the boil to effect maximum penetration and levelling; the temperature is then lowered to 75°C, since maximum exhaustion of chrome dyes takes place below the boil. After adjusting to pH 3.5–3.9 by addition of formic acid the near-stoichiometric quantity of dichromate, calculated from the relative molecular mass and purity of each dye in relation to the formation of 1:2 complexes, is added and the temperature again raised to near the boil. About 7.5% o.w.f. sodium sulphate is added after about 15 minutes chroming, and boiling is continued for some 30 minutes: sodium sulphate displaces adsorbed chromium from wool, thus making it more readily available for interaction with the dye so that less chrome is needed. Clearly this method can only be used effectively if the r.m.m. and purity of the dyes are known, factors which are rarely available to the dyer; hence Bayer, who developed this method, has made the necessary details known for its range of Diamond chrome dyes.

Another method [24], developed by Ciba–Geigy, uses a lower dyeing and chroming temperature (92°C) and dispenses with the need to lower dyebath temperature before chroming. This lower temperature clearly helps obviate wool damage. After dyeing at 92°C and exhausting the bath with a small amount of formic acid, dichromate is added, the amount being calculated from Eqn 12.1:

$$C = 0.2 + 0.15D \qquad (12.1)$$

where C is the percentage of dichromate required and D is the percentage of dye used. Chroming is allowed to continue for some 10 minutes at this relatively high pH to help levelness of chroming with this reduced quantity of dichromate. The pH is then lowered to around 3.5 to bring about maximum utilisation of the chromium, and treatment at 92°C is continued for some 45 minutes.

A third approach involves the use of reducing agents, which are best added to the chroming bath after about 10 minutes at or near the boil. Their exact mode of action is not fully understood, but clearly the increased rate and extent of reduction of hexavalent to trivalent chromium plays an important part. The first technique of this type [25] used lactic acid (for example, at 1–3% o.w.f.), which was found to be the most effective of the α-hydroxymonocarboxylic acids evaluated in assisting rapid conversion of hexavalent to trivalent chromium and increasing the adsorption of the latter. The method needs to be used in conjunction with reduced amounts of dichromate if the subsequent advantages to be gained from a lack of fixed chromium in the fibre are to be attained. The lactic acid method, however, appears to have given way to a technique using sodium thiosulph- ate (1.1 times the amount of dichromate) [26,27]. A modification of this method, developed by Sandoz [18], employs a glucose-based proprietary product as the reducing agent. The use of thiosulphate will enable many dyes to be effectively chromed at temperatures as low as 80°C with con- sequent advantages in respect of fibre damage; some dyes are inadequately chromed at 80°C, however, and a minimum temperature of 90°C is recommended [21].

It should be noted that Hercosett-treated wool generally requires more dichromate than does untreated wool, since some of the dichromate is taken up by the cationic Hercosett polymer layer [21].

A practical comparison of these methods and some modifications has been carried out [21], from which it was concluded that methods are avail- able to enable the requirements of almost any water authority to be met. The attractions of these low-chrome, low-temperature methods do not rely on expensive equipment or chemicals; in fact, the hazards of heavy-metal residues from exhausted metal-complex dyebaths may often be greater than those from afterchrome dyebaths using low-chrome methods [18].

12.3 AZOIC DYES

There are three main areas for consideration in the use of auxiliaries in the application of azoic combinations [28]:

(a) the composition of the naphthol solution
(b) the composition of the diazo solution (developing bath)
(c) aftertreatments to develop hue and maximum fastness.

These will be considered first in relation to batchwise application, after which any variations pertinent to continuous dyeing and to printing will be dealt with. The discussion relates solely to cotton, which is by far the most important substrate for these dyes; application to other substrates follows generally similar principles, the main difference being in the concentrations of the products used.

12.3.1 Composition of the naphtholate solution

A primary requirement for the preparation of the naphtholate solution is soft water; otherwise insoluble calcium or magnesium naphtholates will be formed. If soft water is not available then a sequestering agent must be used, the sodium hexametaphosphate, EDTA or NTA types being suitable. A little alcohol is generally used in the initial pasting and dissolving of the naphthol. Given water of suitable quality, the naphtholate bath in batchwise dyeing then generally contains the following additions:

– alkali, invariably sodium hydroxide
– a protective colloid (dispersing agent) and perhaps a wetting agent
– formaldehyde
– electrolyte, either sodium chloride or sodium sulphate.

The purpose of the alkali is to convert the insoluble free naphthol into the colloidally soluble sodium salt. An excess of sodium hydroxide is generally needed but too much will tend to promote hydrolysis. The actual amount used varies with the naphthol and processing conditions, and the naphthol manufacturer's detailed literature must be consulted.

The protective colloid/wetting agent may be a single product; Turkey Red Oil, for example, combines both functions but is prone to form a precipitate in hard water. Most protective colloids are of the following types:

(a) lignosulphonates
(b) protein–fatty acid condensates (such as Ofna-pon ASN (HOE))
(c) sulphonated condensates of aromatic compounds, especially of phenols and naphthols with formaldehyde.

This type of chemistry has been described previously (see section 10.4.1). The colloid helps to stabilise the colloidal solution of the naphtholate, through a mechanism similar to that already described. Where the protective colloid itself does not give adequate wetting of the fabric a suitable wetting agent, which in batchwise dyeing must function well in the cold, should be added; the alkylnaphthalenesulphonates and non-ionic types are suitable.

The formaldehyde plays an important role in counteracting the tendency of the naphtholate to hydrolyse at high pH values to BON acid, which couples to give coloured by-products of inferior fastness. Its protective action is in addition to that provided by the excess alkali and its use is recommended with most naphthols, exceptions being yellow naphthols where coupling is inhibited. It works through the reversible formation of a 1-methylol derivative at 40–50°C, but at temperatures above 50°C this derivative reacts with a second molecule of naphtholate to give a non-coupling dinaphthylmethane compound [28] (Scheme 12.1).

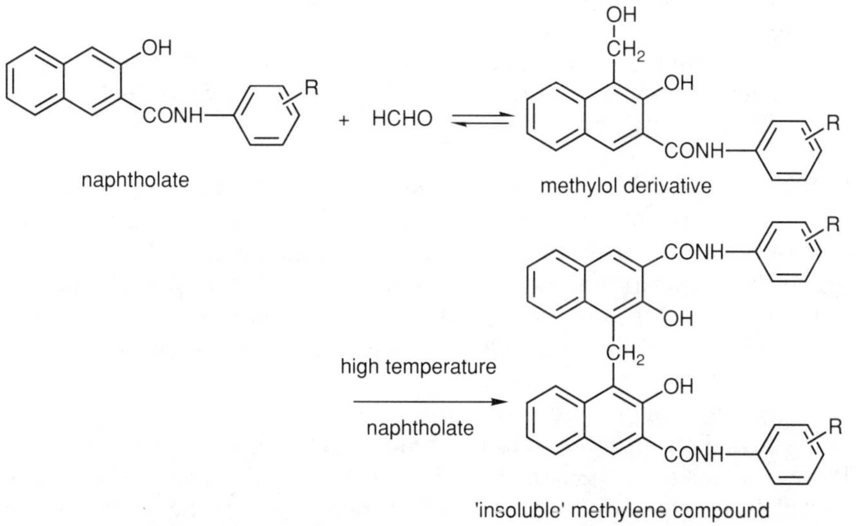

Scheme 12.1

The naphthols used in batchwise dyeing are moderately substantive and their exhaustion is improved by electrolytes, with consequent improvement in depth of shade and fastness properties. The amount of electrolyte required varies with the substantivity of the naphthol, the depth applied, liquor ratio and substrate quality, but generally ranges from 10 to 40 g/l sodium chloride or sodium sulphate – for example, higher amounts will be required for heavier depths of low-substantivity naphthols in long liquors. In some cases treatment with the naphtholate solution is begun without electrolyte, which is added later (for example, with high-substantivity naphthols, substrates that are difficult to penetrate and short liquors). After application of naphthol by batchwise techniques, excess surface naphthol is usually minimised or removed by hydroextraction, suction, squeezing or by rinsing in 10–50 g/l electrolyte and 0.3–0.6 g/l sodium hydroxide solution.

Batchwise application of naphthols is generally carried out at 20–30°C. Although a higher temperature may be permitted to improve the penetration of difficult substrates, it should not be allowed to rise above 50°C; substantivity decreases with increasing temperature. In continuous dyeing, however, in order to ensure levelness of uptake from the pad bath, the requirement is for minimum substantivity. Hence application temperatures are generally high (80–95°C) and naphthols of low to medium inherent substantivity are used. These factors indicate a need for the following modifications to the auxiliary formulations used:

(a) formaldehyde should be omitted due to formation of the methylene derivative at temperatures higher than 50°C
(b) electrolyte should be omitted
(c) the amount of wetting agent can be reduced, or it may be omitted if the higher temperature together with the protective colloid promote sufficient wetting.

12.3.2 Composition of the diazo solution or developing bath
This bath is essentially a dilute solution of a diazonium salt produced either by the diazotisation of an aromatic amine (Fast Colour Base) or by simply dissolving a stabilised diazonium compound (Fast Colour Salt). Soft water is desirable but not essential. General additions for batchwise dyeing with Fast Colour Bases include acid, sodium nitrite and possibly ice, together with a dispersing agent.

Hydrochloric acid is the most widely used acid to effect dissolution of the base and activation of the sodium nitrite so as to bring about diazotisation. Temperatures must be kept low (5–15°C) to avoid decomposition of the relatively unstable diazonium salt (see section 4.3.1); hence ice is often added to the solution. Non-ionic fatty alcohol ethoxylates (see section 9.6) are widely used as dispersing agents to aid the fine and uniform dispersion of the azoic dye as it is formed.

Once diazotisation is complete the excess hydrochloric acid must be neutralised before the diazonium salt is coupled with the naphthol, usually by addition of an 'alkali-binding agent'. The agent most commonly used is sodium acetate, which by reaction with the hydrochloric acid produces acetic acid, so that the resultant mixture of acetic acid and sodium acetate acts as a buffer. The acetic acid/sodium acetate balance must be adjusted to suit specific needs related to the reactivity or coupling energy of the system (see Chapter 4), giving a pH varying from 4–5.5 for those having high coupling energy to 6–7 for those with low coupling energy. Sometimes sodium dihydrogen orthophosphate and disodium hydrogen orthophosphate buffers or sodium bicarbonate are used.

When Fast Colour Salts are used hydrochloric acid and sodium nitrite are obviously not needed, although some Fast Colour Salts do require an addition of acetic or formic acid. The non-ionic dispersing agent is still needed, however, but as most Fast Colour Salts contain an alkali-binding agent (aluminium sulphate, zinc sulphate, magnesium sulphate or, in a few cases, chromium acetate) to give the required pH, it is not normally necessary to make additions of this type to the developing bath except to correct any local variations in pH.

In some cases, as in the batchwise application of diazo components, it may be advisable to add electrolyte to the developing bath to inhibit bleed-off of low-substantivity naphthols. Otherwise the auxiliaries for batchwise and continuous application of diazo components are essentially the same.

12.3.3 Aftertreatments to develop hue and maximum fastness
After the coupling (development) process is complete the goods are rinsed, acidified and given an alkaline soaping treatment, which not only substantially removes surface dye but also brings about a process of aggregation of dye molecules within the fibre, thus developing the full potential of hue and fastness. A combination of Marseilles (olive oil) soap (3–5 g/l) with sodium carbonate (batchwise 1–2 g/l, continuous 2–3 g/l) is particularly recommended. A polyphosphate sequestering agent is needed if the water is hard. A second wash with a non-ionic surfactant is also required.

The main technique in printing is to apply the naphthol by padding as described for continuous dyeing, followed by the printed application of the diazo component using cellulose ether, locust bean or guar derivatives as thickening agents. In other respects the auxiliaries and general processing requirements are similar to those described above. Another method involves the application of naphthol coupling component and a stabilised diazonium salt in a single printing paste followed by steaming to effect development; a starch ether thickening agent is recommended for this process [13]. In certain resist styles aluminium sulphate is applied by printing on to naphthol-treated material; this brings about a localised reduction in pH that inhibits coupling during subsequent application of the diazo component, thus giving rise to a resist effect [13].

The stripping of fully developed azoic dyeings can often be carried out using a hot solution of sodium hydroxide (1.5–3 g/l), sodium dithionite (3–5 g/l) and a surfactant; addition of anthraquinone (0.5–1 g/l) generally increases the effectiveness of the process. Yellow azoic dyeings are resistant, however, and can only be partially stripped [28]. On the other hand, stripping of naphtholated material before it has been coupled to the diazo component can be done quite effectively in boiling alkali.

12.4 BASIC DYES

There are two major characteristics of basic dyes applied by exhaustion techniques to acrylic fibres:

(a) below the glass transition temperature (about 80°C) exhaustion is very slight, becoming much more rapid at temperatures only a little above this

(b) very little, if any, migration occurs at temperatures up to 100°C.

Consequently the rate of dyeing, and hence levelness, are very difficult to control; the degree of difficulty varies from fibre to fibre, generally tending to a maximum for readily dyeable fibres with a high glass transition temperature. Owing to the sensitivity of some basic dyes to alkaline hydrolysis, these dyes vary in their response to dyebath pH, again depending on fibre type (see section 3.2.4). The pH needs to be controlled to within 4.0 to 5.5 in order to obtain reliable, reproducible results across the range of dyes and fibres. Hence in the conventional batchwise application of basic dyes to acrylic fibres auxiliaries have a twofold function:

(a) to give the required pH

(b) to control the rate of sorption in the critical temperature region and, as far as possible, to promote migration.

A buffer system is preferred for the control of pH, the most common one being the relatively cheap acetic acid–sodium acetate system, although a simple addition of acetic acid may be adequate with water that does not show a significant pH shift on heating.

The major variables are undoubtedly the rate of temperature rise and the use of retarding agents to control level dyeing. General accounts, within the context of acrylic dyeing as a whole, are available [29–32], but we are concerned here mainly with the essential chemistry of retarding agents.

Cationic types of retarding agent are principally used nowadays; these function essentially as colourless dyes competing for the anionic sorption sites in the fibre. Quaternary ammonium compounds (see section 9.5) largely predominate; their fundamental structure (9.25) posits the possibility of varying up to four substituent groups around a quaternary nitrogen atom, and hence the variety of possible structures is enormous. A range of these compounds examined for their retarding effect in the application of basic dyes [33] gives some idea of the possibilities (Table 12.2). The selection of a retarder depends on several factors, however, of which the most important are the rate and extent of sorption of the retarder compared with that of the dyes. The dyeing kinetics of basic dyes in mixtures are now universally denoted by compatibility values covering the range from 1 to 5 [34–38]; simply varying the substituents in otherwise structurally similar dyes can change their compatibility values [37]. The sorption properties of quaternary ammonium compounds can be similarly characterised and varied, as can be seen from the examples shown in Table 12.3 [39], which were obtained using a titration–spectrophotometric method [40].

TABLE 12.2

Structures of some retarding agents

Substituents in quaternary ammonium compound

R	R_1	R_2	R_3	Anion
$C_{12}H_{25}$ (dodecyl)	CH_3	CH_3	CH_3	Cl
Coco*	CH_3	CH_3	CH_3	Cl
$C_{16}H_{33}$ (hexadecyl)	CH_3	CH_3	CH_3	Cl
$C_{18}H_{37}$ (octadecyl)	CH_3	CH_3	CH_3	Cl
Tallow**	CH_3	CH_3	CH_3	Cl
Coco*	CH_3	CH_3	CH_3	CH_3SO_4
Coco*	CH_3	C_2H_5	CH_3	CH_3SO_4
Coco*	CH_3	$C_6H_5CH_2$	CH_3	Cl

* Consisted of approximately 47% C_{12}, 18% C_{14} with lesser amounts of C_8, C_{10}, C_{16} and C_{18} hydrophobes.

** Consisted of approximately 48% oleyl, 13% stearyl, 27% cetyl, with minor quantities of others.

TABLE 12.3

Compatibility values of retarding agents

Substituents in quaternary ammonium compound				Compatibility value assigned by experiment
R	R_1	R_2	R_3	
$C_{14}H_{29}$	CH_3	$C_{14}H_{29}$	CH_3	1.0
$C_6H_5CH_2$	CH_3	$C_{14}H_{29}$	CH_3	2.5
CH_3	CH_3	CH_3	$C_{14}H_{29}$	3.0
$C_6H_5CH_2$	CH_3	$C_{7-9}H_{15-19}$	CH_3	5.0
$C_6H_5CH_2$	CH_3	$C_6H_5CH_2$	CH_3	>5.0

The type of anion has only a minor effect on the properties of the retarder. General practical experience [39,41] suggests that optimum control is achieved if the retarder has a compatibility value equal to or slightly lower than that of the dyes, so that it will tend to be adsorbed by the fibre either at the same rate as the dyes, or somewhat more quickly. If the compatibility value of the retarder is significantly lower than that of the dyes, then there is a very real tendency for it to act as a blocking agent (with the attendent problems), whilst if its compatibility value is much higher its efficacy is impaired.

Once the substituents in the quaternary ammonium compound have been selected, consideration must be given to the concentration of the retarder to use. Acrylic fibres vary significantly in the number of anionic sites available for sorption of cations [30] but it is generally assumed that maximum likelihood of level dyeing accrues when the number of cations in the system (retarder as well as dyes) is just enough to saturate the anionic sites in the fibre. Thus the amount of retarder needed to achieve this theoretical saturation will vary from fibre to fibre, and also depends on the concentrations of the dyes. More retarder will be needed for fibres of high saturation value and for paler shades; the actual quantities required to satisfy the given conditions are generally specified by the dye manufacturers. However, the use of these theoretical quantities can lead to lower degrees of dye exhaustion within normal dyeing times. In any case level dyeing is not just simply a function of the ionic dye–fibre system but involves many other aspects, especially physical factors such as substrate form and machinery efficiency. It may well be that in a given practical situation there may be little or no level dyeing problem, so why use any more retarder than is necessary to ensure a level dyeing under practical conditions? Experience suggests that much less than the theoretical amount of retarder will often be adequate, and this will help to alleviate any problems due to saturation if subsequent reprocessing (correction of shade) is needed.

In addition to having an effect on the rate of dyeing, cationic retarders also assist migration to an extent that depends on the fibre and the substantivity of the dyes. They tend to have higher diffusion rates than dyes and to be adsorbed at lower temperatures (perhaps 65–70°C, compared with 80–85°C), although the magnitude of these effects will depend on the structure and properties of both the retarders and dyes. In some cases, such as hank dyeing on machines with poor circulation or inadequate temperature control [42], it may be preferable to use a retarder that almost totally restrains the uptake of dye until the top temperature has been reached, after which dye sorption takes place gradually.

A useful general classification of cationic retarders according to their properties has been given [43]:

(a) strongly cationic with a strong blocking effect

(b) medium cationic activity with a low blocking effect
(c) weakly cationic with no blocking effect
(d) products with little or no retarding effect but giving some levelling.

Products in groups (b) and (c) allow for greater safety margins and give optimum exhaustion curves in bulk practice, although they may be more expensive than products in group (a). The main need for retarding activity arises during the critical exhaustion phase as the temperature increases from about 80°C to the boil. Some cationic retarders have therefore been designed to hydrolyse progressively in this temperature region, so reducing the retarding activity in the later stages of dyeing and safeguarding against blocking effects. Subsequent shading and redyeing are then less problematical. Also the amounts of hydrolysing retarder used are perhaps less critical than with their non-hydrolysing counterparts, although more may initially be needed to obtain an equivalent retarding effect. A combination of hydrolysing and non-hydrolysing types has been recommended [29,44].

On 100% acrylic materials the quaternary ammonium retarders are used almost exclusively nowadays [42]. Other types have been tried, however. For example, a range of saturated alkylamines (RNH_2; R = C_{10}, C_{12}, C_{14} and C_{16} hydrophobes) were found to be just as effective as the quaternary types although other factors, such as aqueous solubility at the optimum dyebath pH and resistance to subsequent discoloration, favour the quaternaries [33]. On the other hand, bis(hydroxyethyl)cocoamine (12.1) had relatively little effect and the amphoteric carboxymethyl-dimethylcocoamine (12.2) none at all, although dimethylcocoamine oxide (12.3) was quite an effective retarder [33]. Other cationic compounds used [31,45,46] have included alkylpyridinium salts, imidazole and imidazolium salts, alkyldiamines, alkylpolyamines and sulphonium and phosphonium derivatives.

$$12.1 \quad R_{coco}-N \begin{array}{c} CH_2CH_2OH \\ CH_2CH_2OH \end{array} \qquad 12.2 \quad R_{coco}-\overset{\overset{CH_3}{|}}{\underset{\underset{CH_3}{|}}{N^+}}-CH_2COO^-$$

$$12.3 \quad R_{coco}-\overset{\overset{CH_3}{|}}{\underset{\underset{CH_3}{|}}{N}}\rightarrow O$$

A more recent development has been the introduction of cationic polymer retarders that contain up to several hundred cationic groups per molecule [47,48]. These are said to be quaternised polyamines (cf. section 9.5) of relative molecular mass 1000–20 000 as compared with 300–500 for conventional quaternary ammonium compounds. These agents, because of their large molecular size, do not diffuse into the fibre but are strongly adsorbed at the fibre surface, reducing its anionic potential. They retard the dyeing rate far more than does an equal amount of a conventional quaternary agent, but do not assist migration. Some of these products can adversely affect the compatibility of dyes as a result of selective behaviour [30], but are said to be free from blocking effects, not to interfere with crimp development as conventional retarders sometimes do, and to be particularly useful in giving superior coverage of bicomponent fibres. Despite the claimed advantages and the prediction that they would rapidly become the preferred way of dyeing acrylic fibres with a high content of dye sites [47], they do not appear to have developed significantly in the market.

It is also possible to use retarders of opposite ionic charge to the dyes. Anionic retarders [30–32,35,49–52] function by forming a thermally labile complex with the dye, lowering the substantivity of the dye for the fibre. Undesirable precipitation of this complex, which is one of the drawbacks of the system, can be inhibited by using excess anionic agent, by using an anionic agent that contains two or more sulphonate groups so that the resultant 1:1 complex retains solubility, or by incorporating a non-ionic agent as an anti-precipitant. Examples include sodium dinaphthylmethanesulphonates and polyethoxylated alkylarylsulphates (see Chapter 9). Polymeric types, such as polystyrene sulphonate [53], have also been tried but do not seem to have any advantages over the more conventional systems [47]. The advantages and disadvantages of anionic retarders have been summarised by Beckmann [30]. The advantages include:

(a)   the system is compatible with anionic dyes and anionic dispersing agents
(b)   there is no blocking of the fibre
(c)   they have no adverse effects on the 'bulk' of certain bicomponent fibres
(d)   they promote good dye migration
(e)   they can be used as stripping agents to reduce depth of colour in reprocessing.

The disadvantages include:

(a)   to prevent precipitation the quantity of anionic retarder should increase with increasing quantity of dye (i.e. the opposite of the situation with cationic dyes) and this conflicts with requirements for promoting exhaustion; hence exhaustion of dye when applying medium and heavy depths is poor
(b)   they show less levelling during the exhaustion stage
(c)   the use of cationic softeners in the dyebath is not possible.

Thus in practical terms the disadvantages outweigh the advantages, limiting the importance of anionic retarders nowadays. A current index of commercially available auxiliaries [54] lists many cationic retarders but only one declared anionic product.

Electrolytes such as sodium chloride and sodium sulphate [30,35,55,56] also tend to retard dyeing through preferential adsorption and subsequent displacement by the dye of the more mobile sodium ions, although the effect is relatively weak compared with even the weaker cationic retarders. Nevertheless, the use of up to 10% o.w.f. sodium sulphate in combination with cationic retarder may enable the amount of the latter to be reduced by up to 20–30% [35]. The limitations of electrolytes, apart from their lower effectiveness, are that they reduce final uptake of dye, their effectiveness decreases with increase in temperature and their effect is greatest with fibres containing weak anionic groups such as carboxylate, rather than strong ones such as sulphonate. Cationic softeners for acrylic fibres are also sensitive to the presence of electrolytes, although sulphate-tolerant softeners may be used.

Continuous dyeing [30,51,57,58] with basic dyes generally requires the use of saturated steam for fixation. As in batchwise dyeing there is a need to maintain an optimum pH of 4.5–5.0. If a sodium acetate/acetic acid buffer is used the acetic acid may volatilise in the steam, leading to development of alkalinity; hence it is usual to add a non-volatile acid such as citric acid or tartaric acid. The thickening agent for use with basic dyes must not be anionic, a useful choice being galactomannan-based locust bean gum. Hydrotropes and fibre-swelling agents assist dye solubilisation and fixation; compounds used include thiodiethylene glycol, dicyanoethylformamide and potassium thiocyanate. A non-ionic wetting and solubilising agent may also be useful.

Similar considerations apply in direct printing where a typical stock print paste [13] may contain the following components (by mass): 3% thiodiethylene glycol, 7% acetic acid (30%), 0.5% citric acid, 50–60% locust bean thickener and 1–2% dicyanoethylformamide. Dioctyl phthalate, caprolactam, and urea together with resorcinol are also said to act as fixation assistants [59]. The extra addition of an anionic thickening agent such as carboxymethylcellulose [13] can act as a levelling agent when printing large blotches. A wash-off with anionic surfactant is usually given.

Discharge white styles are obtained with either formaldehyde–sulphoxylate or the weaker tin(II) chloride as reducing agent; crystal gum or British gum are recommended thickening agents, together with potassium thiocyanate as a fibre-swelling agent [13]. For coloured discharges tin(II) chloride is the recommended reducing agent, since formaldehyde–sulphoxylate reduces the illuminant basic dyes; other additions are generally as for direct printing. Discharge styles, after steaming and rinsing, are given a clearing treatment at 40°C in 1 ml/l ammonia (25%) and 1 g/l sodium dithionite [13], followed by rinsing and soaping with anionic detergent at 60–70°C.

Non-destructive partial stripping techniques for basic dyes on acrylic fibres employ a bath at 100°C (or higher if possible) containing, for example, 1–10% anionic retarder on the weight of goods and 1 g/l acetic acid

(60%), or 1–5 g/l Marseilles (olive oil) soap [30]. Destructive stripping uses acidified (pH 5.5–6.0) sodium hypochlorite followed by an antichlor in sodium dithionite or sodium bisulphite. In some cases a boiling treatment in 5 g/l monoethanolamine and 5 g/l sodium chloride, before the stripping process, is said to improve the effect of the stripping treatment [30].

12.5 DIRECT DYES

Direct dyes represent one of the simplest dyeing systems, usually requiring only electrolyte as an essential auxiliary for their application. Nevertheless surfactants may sometimes be used to aid wetting and levelling, as well as sequestering agents, since many direct dyes are overtly sensitive to hard water. Control of pH may also be desirable. Some dyes also require aftercoppering as part of their application procedure, whilst the aftertreatment of direct dyes to improve their fastness properties is quite usual. The recent popularity of polyester/cellulose blends has required the application of direct dyes at temperatures higher than 100°C.

An up-to-date account of the application of direct dyes is available [28]. The main area to be considered in the batchwise application of these dyes is the use of electrolyte, either sodium chloride or sodium sulphate, to promote exhaustion although the sulphate can give rise to calcium sulphate deposits in hard water. Direct dyes vary enormously in their response to electrolyte; in general the more highly sulphonated dyes require greater amounts of salt. This is in line with the behaviour of dyes according to the universally used SDC classification scheme [28,60,61] whereby dyes are classified into three application classes. Class A dyes are generally the most soluble and least sensitive to salt, hence necessitating quite large additions of electrolyte to boost their low degrees of exhaustion. It is even advisable with this class of dye to add electrolyte to the rinsing water to inhibit the otherwise copious bleed-off of dye into the water. For this purpose magnesium sulphate may be more efficient than sodium salts since it can form the less soluble dye–magnesium salt, but the acceptability of this will depend on whether magnesium can be tolerated in subsequent processing. Dyes in classes B and C are generally less soluble and are so responsive to electrolyte that salt must be added gradually over the dyeing cycle as otherwise the rate of strike will be so rapid as to give unlevel, unpenetrated dyeings and there may even be salting out of the dye in the dyebath. More salt is needed in longer liquors, and for heavier depths.

Dyes having the same C.I. generic name but made by different manufacturers may also require different amounts of electrolyte to be added to the dyebath, according on the amount of electrolyte present in the commercial formulation. A typical instruction is to use from 0 to 20 g/l salt depending on the factors described above.

Electrolyte may influence migration as well as exhaustion [62], an optimum concentration of electrolyte being found for maximum migration of class A and B dyes, whilst the migration of class C dyes decreases with increasing amounts of salt.

A sequestering agent will be needed in hard water to prevent the formation of sparingly soluble calcium and/or magnesium salts, which can lead to loose deposits of lower fastness on the surface of the fabric as well as reduced yields due to precipitation in the dyebath. Polyphosphates are particularly useful in this respect. Organic sequestering agents such as EDTA must be avoided with metal-complex direct dyes as they tend to scavenge the metal from the dye, resulting in a change in hue and a significant lowering of fastness, although they may be used with non-metallised dyes.

Some direct dyes are sensitive to reduction or hydrolysis under alkaline conditions, particularly if temperatures above 100°C are used (see section 3.1.3); pH 6 is frequently favoured for stability and can usually be achieved with ammonium sulphate [28]. A few dyes give best results under somewhat alkaline conditions, using sodium carbonate or soap; C.I. Direct Black 22 is an example. Whether or not an addition is needed will depend on whether alkali is already present in the commercial brand.

Levelling and wetting agents, if needed, are mostly poly(oxyethylene) adducts, although anionic types such as alkylaryl sulphonates, phosphate esters and alkylbenzimidazoles are also marketed, as well as non-ionic alkylaryl ethoxylates [28].

Copperable dyes are normally applied in the same way as conventional dyes. They are then rinsed and aftertreated in an acidified solution of copper(II) sulphate, beginning cold and raising the temperature to 60–70°C to bring about *in situ* chelation. Copper(II) sulphate (1–3% o.w.f., depending on the depth of shade) is used together with acetic or formic acid to give a pH of about 3.5.

The aftertreatment of conventional direct dyes to improve fastness to light and particularly to wet treatments, using copper(II) sulphate, formaldehyde, diazotisation and coupling techniques or cationic fixing agents, has been described in section 10.7 and will not be discussed further here.

Various techniques are available for the application of direct dyes by semi-continuous and continuous methods, such as pad–jig, pad–batch, pad–roll, pad–steam, pad–dry and pad–Thermofix. The major problem arises from the high substantivity of direct dyes for cellulosic substrates, making it very difficult to avoid tailing problems. Hence concentrated brands of dyes having minimum electrolyte content are preferred; of these, the class B dyes offer better operating properties [28]. The main methods of controlling even uptake remain careful selection of dyes for compatibility, speed of padding and the rate of supply of pad-liquor. Low solubility of the dyes may also be a problem; use of a hydrotrope such as urea improves the solubility of certain dyes and may also improve fixation, particularly in dry fixation processes. The wash-off process after fixation may need to be combined with an aftertreatment to improve the wet fastness and avoid undesirable bleeding of dye. Treatment with durable-press resins and with cationic products, particularly of the multi-functional reactant type, is especially useful here. An interesting, if little-used, method of overcoming dye substantivity problems at the padding stage involved the use of certain amines, particularly those containing carboxyl or hydroxy groups (for example, structure 12.4) [63] in combination with copper-complex direct dyes. The amine forms a loose complex with the dye. The complex diffuses readily into the fibre and reverts to dye and amine during steam fixation, the amine being subsequently removed in the wash-off. Careful selection of the amine, or mixture of amines, is required to obtain the desirable balance of properties. It is interesting to compare this use of an amine and metal-complex direct dyes with the similar requirement for such dyes in the much more recent Indosol (S) process (see section 10.7.2).

$$HOCH_2CH_2NHCH_2CH_2NHCH_2CH_2OH \qquad 12.4$$

Direct dyes are of limited interest for printing because of their restricted wet fastness, which easily results in cross-staining of adjacent areas when the prints are subsequently washed. Somewhat better results can be obtained by treating the prints after steam fixation with, for example, a cationic compound, durable-press resin or, in the case of chelatable dyes, copper(II) sulphate as already described (see section 10.7.2). Most azo direct dyes will discharge easily with reducing agents and can therefore be used for discharge print styles, although the limitations described above in regard to wet fastness are especially pertinent here.

Partial non-destructive stripping of untreated direct dyes can be accomplished with an alkaline solution of soap or synthetic detergent. Destructive stripping using a reducing agent such as sodium dithionite is also effective except with stilbene-type dyes. Aftertreated dyeings may additionally require a treatment to counteract the aftertreatment; for example, coppered dyeings can be treated with a sequestering agent such as EDTA and dyeings treated with a simple, non-reactive cationic agent may respond to treatment with an anionic agent.

12.6 DISPERSE DYES

Disperse dyes as a class are peculiarly sensitive to the influence of auxiliary agents, both as regards the quality and stability of the dispersion and the response of the dyes during the various coloration processes. Essential auxiliaries in batchwise dyeing include dispersing agents and chemicals to control the pH. Supplementary auxiliaries termed 'carriers' are needed under certain circumstances to accelerate the otherwise inadequate rate of dyeing. The aftertreatment of the dyeings to remove surface dye is also important in many cases, as are also the conditions of drying and finishing since these can have a bearing on fastness properties.

12.6.1 Dispersing agents

The essential chemistry of dispersing agents has been discussed in section 10.4.1, where it was also mentioned that different considerations may apply at the comminution stage of dye manufacture compared with maintaining the stability of the dispersion during subsequent coloration processes. The dyeing of polyester at temperatures in the region of 120–140°C in beam and package dyeing machines has placed especially great demands on aspects of both initial dispersion quality and on subsequent stability under adverse conditions. Jig dyeing with large amounts of dye in a very short liquor (as for navy blues and blacks) can also be the source of dispersion stability problems.

The crux of the problem lies in the inherent thermodynamic instability of all dye dispersions, there being an overall tendency of fine particles to undergo Ostwald ripening with the consequent formation of larger particles. Although disperse dyes are generally considered to be substantially insoluble in water they are, in colloidal terms, sparingly soluble; indeed some degree of solubility, albeit limited, seems to be a necessary prerequisite for dyeing to take place from an aqueous medium [64]. It is this sparing solubility that favours Ostwald ripening. The detailed colloid chemistry of dispersions with particular reference to these phenomena has been well argued by Braun [65]. The solubility of disperse dyes normally increases with temperature and dispersing agent concentration, although these effects vary enormously from agent to agent and from dye to dye.

Most dispersing agents are of the anionic polyelectrolyte type, comprising various sulphonated condensation products of aromatic compounds and ligninsulphonates (see section 10.4.1). Increasing understanding of lignin chemistry with consequent improvements in manufacture, enabling lignins to be more economically and reliably 'tailored' for specific end uses, currently favours the use of these products, although by no means exclusively. Powder brands of disperse dyes contain a significant proportion of dispersing agent added during manufacture; liquid brands contain rather less as they do not have to withstand the thermal and mechanical rigours of spray drying [66] and do not require redispersing at the dyebath preparation stage. Despite this, it is still advisable to add extra dispersing agent at the dyeing stage, more being required when liquid dyes are used so as to compensate for their lower intrinsic content. At the grinding stage of dye manufacture ligninsulphonates with a high degree of sulphonation generally perform better. Products with a smaller proportion of sulphonate groups tend to give better stability at high dyeing temperatures [67] since they are more readily adsorbed on to and retained by the hydrophobic surfaces of the dye particles.

Some azo dyes are susceptible to reduction under certain conditions [68,69]. The least stable dyes tend to be those containing electron-withdrawing groups, such as nitro, chloro, bromo and cyano, adjacent to the azo

linkage. This instability to reduction is minimised by dyeing at the optimum pH, usually pH 4–5, in the presence of air, and by keeping the dyeing time at high temperature to a minimum. Hence, under appropriate conditions, instability is not a serious problem. Decomposition can be favoured, however, by various factors:
- pH values greater than 6
- the absence of air (anaerobic dyeing conditions)
- the presence of reducing fibres such as cellulose and wool
- the presence of catalysing metals, such as copper or iron, in the water
- certain dispersing agents containing phenolic groups
- conditions that tend to maintain the dye for longer periods in the liquor, such as slower-dyeing substrates (low-porosity sewing threads, for example) and auxiliaries that tend to solubilise the dye.

Lignin dispersing agents tend to promote this reduction of sensitive dyes, much more so than the naphthalenesulphonic acid condensation types, probably owing to the presence in lignin of catechol residues and other easily oxidised functional groups [69] (see structures 10.35 and 10.36). Commercial lignins vary considerably in their detailed constitution, however, and consequently in their reducing power. In certain cases the effects can be minimised by adding an oxidising agent (such as sodium dichromate) to the dyebath, but the effects can be variable and difficult to control. In printing applications, where steam fixation can have a pronounced reductive effect, stronger oxidising agents such as sodium chlorate are often added to the print paste. In theory the reductive tendency of lignins can be counteracted by chemical blocking of the active phenolic groups, but this also damages the dispersing properties of the product [69]. Significant improvements can be obtained by replacing the conventional sodium ion in the lignin salts by other cations [70]; lithium is effective in this respect, but the most promising salt appears to be that of triethanolamine which additionally acts as a chelating agent and so protects against the catalytic influence of iron and copper.

Since high concentrations of electrolyte can reduce stability, low-electrolyte dispersing agents have been favoured recently [71]. These also help to minimise viscosity reduction by electrolytes with certain synthetic thickening agents in printing applications.

In some cases it is necessary to choose dispersing agents that give minimum staining. This particularly applies when dyeing nylon since anionic dispersing agents can have significant substantivity for this fibre under acidic conditions. In general lignins have a greater propensity to stain than have the naphthalenesulphonic acid condensation products.

12.6.2 pH control and sequestering agents
Although many disperse dyes give good results over a wide pH range (pH

2–9 for example), some will only give satisfactory results over a narrower acidic range (pH 2–6) and a few require control to within pH 4 to 5.5. Since practically all of them give good results in the last-named region, this range tends to be regarded as the standard for most dyeing conditions. A simple addition of acetic acid will be satisfactory where water quality permits; otherwise a buffered system is preferred.

EDTA is widely used to counteract the effects of metallic impurities, which not only affect the shade and fastness of a few susceptible dyes but can also catalyse dye reduction and promote deterioration of dispersion properties, as described above.

12.6.3 Levelling agents

It is necessary to distinguish between levelling agents and dispersing agents. The primary function of a dispersing agent is to maintain a stable dispersion. Since these agents usually enhance the low solubility of disperse dyes they sometimes also improve level dyeing, although they vary significantly in this effect. Maximum dispersion stability is usually obtained with agents that maintain dye particles of constant size and minimum solubility. Hence primary dispersing agents nowadays seldom enhance levelling; additional auxiliaries are used where some levelling action is needed. These are invariably anionic or non-ionic surfactants and tend to solubilise the dye much more effectively. Some such levelling agents additionally promote dispersion stability whilst others in fact debase it, and great care is therefore required in selection.

It is useful to consider how such agents can adversely affect dispersion stability. As dyebath temperature increases, thermal effects tend to cleave the film of agent protecting the dye particles. High shear rates in certain dyeing machines and additives such as electrolytes, fibre lubricants and sizes, as well as oligomers from the fibre, can contribute to this effect; commercial batches of the same dye brand may behave differently according to the initial dispersion quality of the dye. A dispersion of a vulnerable dye then tends to deteriorate, and precipitation begins. Biedermann has described the types of precipitation that occur [72]. Suspended dye particles may aggregate to form agglomerates. The small proportion of dissolved dye molecules should diffuse into the fibre, but under adverse conditions crystals may be formed. Once seeded, the crystals may grow in size whilst retaining their original form, or they may undergo a transformation from the original thermodynamically metastable form to a more stable but less soluble form. On the other hand, such crystals may not form until the incompletely exhausted dyebath is cooled after the dyeing process; this problem may be avoided by blowing off the dye liquor at 125–130°C. The former type of precipitation (agglomeration) tends to dominate with those dispersing agents that have minimum dye-solubilising power, whilst crystallisation is more prevalent with levelling agents or dispersing agents having greater solubilising power. It is interesting that surfactant additions may be used during dye synthesis in order to obtain the dye in the optimum form for isolation and subsequent milling; for example, very fine crystals may clog filters, and thin needle-like crystals tend to mill more easily than platelets.

Anionic levelling agents, especially the polyelectrolyte dispersing agents previously described, are generally preferred as the primary addition [73], particularly where it is desired to promote level dyeing by control of exhaustion during the heating phase of dyeing; higher concentrations have a greater restraining effect. Most of these anionic products have relatively little effect on dye migration, however, a characteristic that is useful if more powerful levelling is required.

Non-ionic surfactants, on the other hand, tend to have much more pronounced dye-solubilising effects and may thus contribute to level dyeing both by a restraining effect and through the promotion of migration. Consequently they are generally more powerful levelling agents than anionic products although their effects are much more dye-specific. The major problem with non-ionic agents arises principally from their inverse solubility. Thus low-cloud-point types may increase dye precipitation, although once again the effect is dye-specific. Examples given by Murray and Mortimer [68] suggest that a nonylphenol ethoxylate of low degree of ethoxylation, having a cloud point of about 40°C, should be avoided as a disperse dye levelling agent. A product of the type 12.5, having a cloud point of about 105°C, may be satisfactory for dyeing at temperatures up to 100°C but should be avoided at higher temperatures. On the other hand, a carefully selected non-ionic agent may be mixed with an anionic agent to raise its cloud point; for example, a mixture of the fatty acid ethoxylate 12.6 with some 7–10% sodium dodecylbenzenesulphonate [68] has a cloud point of about 150°C, and is more suitable for use at high dyeing temperatures. Since non-ionic surfactants tend to restrain dye uptake, amounts used should be carefully monitored.

$$CH_3(CH_2)_{15}(OCH_2CH_2)_nOH \ (n = \text{approx. } 17) \qquad \textit{12.5}$$

$$CH_3(CH_2)_7CH=CH(CH_2)_7CO(OCH_2CH_2)_nOH \quad (n = \text{approx. } 14) \qquad \textit{12.6}$$

Schlaeppi et al. [74], however, were unable to confirm the adverse effect of non-ionic surfactants of low cloud point in the high-temperature dyeing of polyester, even in the presence of electrolytes. This was probably because of the rather low concentrations used. They found adducts containing a C_{18}–C_{20} hydrophobe and a decaoxyethylene hydrophile, as well as sorbitan ester ethoxylates, to be particularly effective levelling agents, and proposed the use of 'a balanced composition of ethylene oxide adducts'. They did find, however, that certain dyes were sensitive to non-ionic additives under the stringent conditions of the laboratory dispersion tests carried out in the absence of fibre, but pointed out that these systems performed satisfactorily in actual dyeing.

Another type of levelling system contains a mixture of ethoxylates with aliphatic esters [75]. This combination exerts a retarding effect on many dyes whilst heating up to about 100–110°C, especially if the dyes are present in low concentration; at higher temperatures this retarding effect is said to be increasingly offset by the accelerating component of the auxiliary. This temperature-dependent interaction is said to improve the compatibility of combinations of dyes.

The adverse effect of non-ionic adducts of low cloud point can be avoided by the use of hybrid agents of the ethoxylated anionic type, variously and confusingly referred to as 'modified non-ionics', 'modified anionics' or 'weakly anionic types'. Thus Mortimer [76] has proposed the use of products of the ethoxylated phosphate type (12.7). In this structure, R, as well as the degree of ethoxylation, may be varied to optimise the overall HLB value. The numerous ether groups are said to enhance the dye-solubilising and levelling capacity whilst the phosphate group has several useful effects [76]:

(a) the compound is sufficiently anionic to avoid most of the disadvantages of non-ionic agents with regard to high-temperature tolerance and the lack of an electrical double layer of value in dispersion stability
(b) its behaviour is analogous to that of more orthodox polyphosphate sequestrants, thus offering some protection from hard water and other metallic impurities
(c) it has increased stability to high concentrations of electrolytes
(d) varying the nature of M leads to possibilities for pH control
(e) it is fully effective at pH 4–5, the most useful pH range for application of disperse dyes, whereas conventional non-ionic types are said to become less effective as levelling agents at pH values less than 7.

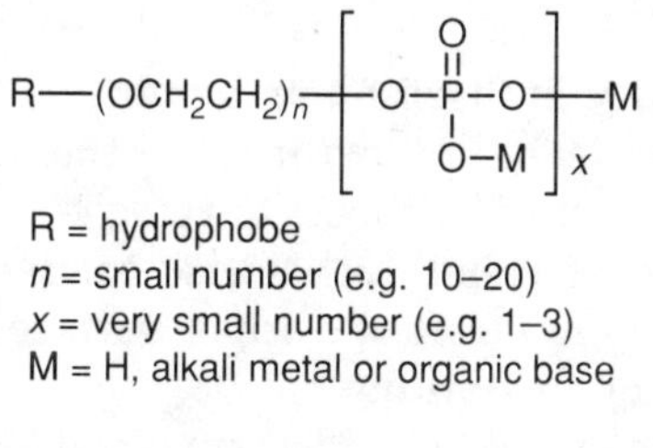

$$R\text{---}(OCH_2CH_2)_n \left[O\text{--}\overset{\overset{O}{\|}}{\underset{\underset{O\text{--}M}{|}}{P}}\text{--}O \right]_x M$$

R = hydrophobe
n = small number (e.g. 10–20)
x = very small number (e.g. 1–3)   12.7
M = H, alkali metal or organic base

Hence this is a sophisticated 'multifunctional auxiliary', which can take the place of separate additions of levelling agent, sequestering agent and products to control the pH. Non-ionic surfactants can also be beneficial in minimising the redeposition of the sparingly soluble polyester oligomers that are released from polyester fibres during high-temperature dyeing.

12.6.4 Carriers

Although polyester and triacetate fibres are normally dyed at high temperatures, some are still dyed at the boil at atmospheric pressure. In such cases an auxiliary termed a carrier must be used to promote adequate exhaustion of disperse dyes within commercial dyeing times. Even in high-temperature dyeing, there are occasions when the usual maximum temperature (around 130°C for polyester) cannot be used, as when dyeing polyester/wool blends or qualities of texturised polyester that suffer loss of crimp at 130°C. Carriers may then be employed to assist more rapid and complete exhaustion, usually using smaller amounts than at the atmospheric boil. Carriers are sometimes employed to promote migration.

The active component of a carrier is generally a non-ionised aryl compound of r.m.m. 150–200. A useful review of the types of compound used, their general properties, and the mechanisms proposed for carrier action is available [77]. Waters [78] concluded in 1950 that the most effective compounds fell into four main groups: phenols, primary amines, hydrocarbons and esters, and this remains substantially true to the present day [77,79], although arylamines are too hazardous to feature in commercial carriers. Carrier compounds used in recent years include o-phenylphenol, biphenyl, methylnaphthalene, di- and tri-chlorobenzene, methyl cresotinate, methyl salicylate (sometimes mixed with phenyl salicylate), butyl benzoate, methyl dichlorophenoxyacetate, ethers of 2,4-dichlorophenol, diethyl and diallyl phthalate and N-alkylphthalimide derivatives. In addition benzaldehyde has been used for the dyeing of aromatic polyamides such as Nomex (DuP) [80,81].

None of these compounds possesses all the characteristics of the ideal carrier [77]:

(a) readily available at an economic price
(b) sufficiently effective to enable all depths up to blacks to be readily obtained without the need to use an excessive amount
(c) compatible with all disperse dyes and other auxiliaries likely to be used
(d) of good emulsion stability (if insoluble in water), as emulsion breakdown will give rise to carrier stains on the fabric that take up more dye than the normal fabric and are difficult to remove
(e) reasonably non-volatile in steam, otherwise condensed droplets of concentrated carrier may fall from the upper surfaces of the machine on to the fabric, resulting in staining
(f) unlikely to cause undue shrinkage of the material
(g) unlikely to affect the handle of the material adversely
(h) free from unpleasant odour
(i) readily removable from the material by a simple aftertreatment or in finishing
(j) unlikely to affect adversely the fastness to light or other fastness

properties of the dyes used
(k) non-toxic in use
(l) unlikely to cause dermatitis to dyehouse operatives or to the subsequent wearers of garments
(m) preferably biodegradable, to facilitate effluent disposal
(n) non-toxic to plant life when discharged to the atmosphere.

It is necessary therefore to choose the carrier that as far as possible optimally satisfies the requirements of the job in hand. Space here permits only a general description of the properties of carrier compounds; more detail is available elsewhere [77].

The degree or power of carrier action is obviously very important and varies considerably. For example, the phthalates have little action on polyester but are very efficient on triacetate, for which they are the most widely used compounds. o-Phenylphenol and the chlorinated benzenes are generally powerful carriers for polyester, whilst methylnaphthalene and particularly butyl benzoate are less powerful. Although all carriers tend to promote the exhaustion of dyes, some degree of dye-specific behaviour will result from the respective hydrophobic/hydrophilic balance of dye and carrier [68].

Some carriers, such as o-phenylphenol, tend to lower the light fastness of many dyes if carrier residues remain in the dyed fibre; others, such as the chlorobenzenes, have no effect on this property. Similarly, carrier residues differ considerably in odour. A dry heat treatment at 160–180°C after dyeing, to volatilise the residual carrier, is the best method of minimising light fastness and odour problems. The steam volatility of a carrier and its toxicity to human and plant life need careful consideration. For example, o-phenylphenol has relatively low volatility in steam and may thus be used in machines open to the atmosphere. The chlorinated benzenes, on the other hand, are readily steam-volatile and are toxic, so should not be used in open machines or in machines where volatilised carrier is likely to condense (for example, on a cooler lid) since drops of condensate may cause 'carrier spots' if they fall on to the fabric. Biphenyl is relatively non-toxic to river life but is not readily biodegradable; methylnaphthalene, also of low toxicity, is fairly biodegradable, but halogenated benzenes are both toxic and difficult to biodegrade. Some carriers such as chlorinated benzenes and butyl benzoate are relatively efficient at promoting migration; others, such as o-phenylphenol, are less so. When dyeing a blend such as polyester/wool it is useful to consider the extent to which the carrier will promote migration of dye to polyester so as to minimise staining of the wool.

All the carrier compounds mentioned above have little or no solubility in cold water. They are therefore used in the form of emulsions, many being marketed as 'self-emulsifiable' liquids (they form emulsions on dilution in the dyebath). The choice of emulsifying system is very important, not only from the viewpoint of emulsifying the active carrier component, but also in regard to stability of the emulsion under dyebath conditions and its compatibility with dyes and dispersing agents; it must also permit efficacy of carrier action. Thus two carriers of identical active components but with different emulsifying systems may well differ appreciably in behaviour. Two typical formulations [82] are given in Figure 12.2, both being completely solubilised concentrates which when diluted in the dyebath give stable emulsions of good dyebath compatibility. The weakly anionic ethoxy-sulphates and ethoxyphosphates are especially useful emulsion bases for carriers. A small amount of a simple organic solvent such as ethanol may also be added to improve stability.

Formulation 1	Formulation 2
90% Diethyl phthalate	40% Phenyl salicylate
10% Ethoxylated castor oil	40% Methyl salicylate
(40 mol ethylene oxide)	20% Ethoxylated nonylphenol
	(20 mol ethylene oxide)

Figure 12.2 – Typical examples of carrier emulsions

Most commercial carriers are used in the dyebath at concentrations of 1–8 g/l depending on active strength of the carrier concentrate, depth of shade, liquor ratio and other dyeing conditions. Although carriers to some extent exhibit dye-specific properties, a particular carrier will generally have an optimum concentration in the dyebath to give maximum dye yield; higher concentrations will tend to solubilise the dye to such an extent that colour yield is depressed.

12.6.5 Antifoams
In dyeing with disperse dyes the choice of antifoam needs very careful thought to avoid incompatibility with, and perhaps breakdown of, dispersions; antifoams should be used only when necessary. A few years ago silicone types were highly suspect in high-temperature dyeing, but recent improvements (see section 10.8.2) have produced satisfactory forms when used carefully in most disperse dyeing systems.

12.6.6 Aftertreatments and thermomigration
Secondary acetate and nylon dyed with disperse dyes are usually given a simple rinse with or without a synthetic detergent (anionic or non-ionic) after dyeing. Most triacetate is similarly treated; however, some full depths are given a clearing treatment to remove surface dye so as to improve the fastness properties. Such a clearing treatment is more generally

important with polyester dyeings. It most frequently takes the form of a reduction clear using 1–2 g/l sodium dithionite in alkali. For triacetate the preferred alkali is ammonia (1–2 ml/l of sp. gr. 0.800) at temperatures up to 60°C. Polyester will tolerate more severe conditions; hence the alkali is usually 1–2 g/l sodium hydroxide used at temperatures up to 70°C, or even higher in continuous 'short dwell' processes. This treatment works mostly by reductive fission of azo dyes and by converting anthraquinone dyes to their soluble leuco forms. It is also advantageous to use 1–2 g/l of a non-ionic surfactant in the reduction clear to assist solubilisation of the reduction products and in some cases their thorough removal is ensured by a subsequent treatment with a non-ionic detergent alone. Fatty acid ethoxylates of the type mentioned earlier (structure 12.6) are excellent non-ionic agents for use in reduction clearing which, however, is an expensive process.

Polyester dyed with disperse dyes generally shows excellent fastness to wet treatments and rubbing after thorough reduction clearing and drying at low temperature (that is, below 120°C), irrespective of the dyes used. However, nowadays production speeds and the requirements for fabric dimensional stability demand the use of a combined drying and heat-setting treatment at temperatures in the range 150–210°C, most frequently at 180°C. This causes some dyes to migrate from the core of the fibre to the surface, thus tending to negate the effect of reduction clearing. This surface dye is a potential source of lower fastness to rubbing and wet treatments [83,85], although the extent to which this occurs depends greatly on the dye and its applied depth. This phenomenon has been termed 'thermomigration', its effect on fastness varying considerably because of the generally adverse influence of surfactants, lubricants, softeners, antistats and so on. It also occurs on triacetate, although there it is less commercially and technically significant than on polyester. It is best avoided by selecting dyes with acceptable fastness after heat setting, and by careful choice of finishing agents and finishing conditions. In heat setting and curing, for example, temperature has a greater effect than time in promoting thermomigration [86]. Thus improved fastness to rubbing and wet treatments may be obtained by using a selected durable-press/softener finish (one with a faster-reacting synthetic resin/catalyst system) giving the required finish effect at, say, 140–160°C, since the longer curing time required at this lower temperature has a less deleterious effect than a higher temperature (such as 180°C) for a shorter time. Another means of minimising the effects of thermomigration is to apply certain chemicals after dyeing; for example, the application by padding of polysiloxanes with an organotin catalyst along with any other finishing agents [86,87] gives rise to a reducing effect during subsequent dry heat treatment, thus decomposing many dyes brought to the surface by thermomigration. Such products do not work successfully with all dyes and finishes, however, and can confer a degree of water repellency that is not always acceptable.

The presence in polyester fibres of polymerisation by-products (oligomers) can give rise to problems, particularly if their concentration is greater than normal. With polyesters based on ethylene glycol and terephthalic acid, the amount of oligomer is normally between 1.4 and 1.7% [30] and consists mainly of the cyclic trimer of ethylene terephthalate with smaller amounts of a pentamer, a dimer containing diethylene glycol residues and traces of other compounds. Significant migration of such oligomers from within the fibre can occur at dyeing temperatures of 110–135°C, leading to deposits on the fibre and/or machine surfaces and sometimes also to interference with dispersion stability, since oligomers form potential nuclei for the crystallisation and agglomeration of disperse dyes. Discharge of the spent hot dye liquors without prior cooling is the best way of avoiding oligomer problems. Reduction clearing will normally remove any deposits from the fibre surface. Deposits on machine surfaces must be removed by regular cleaning at high temperature with strong solutions (5 g/l) of sodium hydroxide together with stable surfactants and solvents.

12.6.7 Continuous dyeing

The customary method of continuous dyeing with disperse dyes is the pad–Thermosol process [88–91], most frequently used for polyester/cellulosic blends although it can be used with 100% polyester (or triacetate) materials. The normal auxiliaries used at the padding stage include a thickening agent or migration inhibitor and a wetting agent. Alginates and other polyelectrolytes such as polyacrylamides are popular as migration inhibitors. Anionic sulphosuccinates are suitable wetting agents; since cloud point problems do not arise in continuous dyeing to the same extent as in batch processes, non-ionic adducts may also be used, often fulfilling a dual role as wetting and levelling agents. An addition of acetic acid to give pH 5–6 is usually adequate when applying disperse dyes alone, although certain processes may demand selection of dyes stable at higher pH, as in the combined alkaline application of disperse and reactive dyes to polyester/cellulosic blends. In some processes, too, the use of hydrotropes such as polyglycols and their esters, as well as of urea and related compounds, can be useful to enhance the degree of fixation.

12.6.8 Printing

Printing with disperse dyes is generally carried out with a thickening agent and an acid donor to maintain a low pH during steam fixation. High-solids thickeners such as crystal gum or British gum give optimum sharpness of outline but suffer from the disadvantage of forming brittle films [13]. Hence low-solids thickeners such as alginates and locust bean ethers, which form more elastic films and are more easily removed in subsequent washing-off, are preferred. Other additions may include a fixation accelerator (hydrotropes such as urea, thiodiethylene glycol, cyclohexanol, dicyanoethylformamide) or a carrier and an oxidising agent, such as sodium chlorate or sodium m-nitrobenzenesulphonate, to inhibit the steam reduction of susceptible dyes.

For polyester, the washing-off process to remove unfixed dye and thickening agent is generally a reduction clear as described in section 12.6.6. A simple wash-off with non-ionic surfactant must be used on acetate fibres, although a mild reduction clear may be useful on triacetate.

Discharge effects on the acetate fibres are carried out by overprinting dyed grounds with a thickened paste containing the reducing agent thiourea dioxide and thiodiethylene glycol; a disperse dye stable to these reducing conditions may be added to this paste to give a contrasting illuminant effect. Similar effects may be produced on polyester by printing a discharge (reducing) paste on to fabric that has been padded with dye; reduction of the discharge areas and simultaneous fixation of dye in the non-discharge areas then takes place during subsequent steaming. The discharge paste may contain a reducing agent such as zinc formaldehyde–sulphoxylate or tin(II) chloride, although special ranges of alkali-dischargeable dyes are available that require only alkali. Reduction-stable dyes may be added to the discharge paste to create illuminant effects. More detailed recipes are available [13].

12.6.9 Stripping

Non-destructive stripping can be carried out at dyeing temperature with surfactants, the non-ionic types with high cloud points being particularly effective. In the case of polyester the stripping effect can be increased markedly by adding a carrier that has migration-promoting properties, the chlorobenzenes and butyl benzoate being particularly effective. The efficiency of destructive stripping depends on the fibre and dye types. The most usual method is to use a reduction process (alkaline sodium dithionite) together with non-ionic surfactant and, where possible, a carrier, the temperature being varied to suit the fibre. In some cases, particularly with anthraquinone dyes, an oxidation treatment (hypochlorite, chlorite or permanganate) may be more efficient. Occasionally a sequential combination of oxidation and reduction treatments may have to be used.

12.7 REACTIVE DYES

12.7.1 Cellulosic fibres

As described in Chapter 7, the various types of reactive dye for cellulosic fibres differ considerably in their reactivity and the number of application procedures appropriate to the various ranges is bewilderingly large, including numerous variants within each group of batch, continuous, semi-continuous and printing methods. Even a specific method may require modifications to suit a particular quality or form of substrate, dyeing machine or the specific dyes culled from a given range. Fortunately certain general principles are applicable to the great majority, if not all, of these methods; more details of application procedures are available elsewhere [28,92], but in the working situation it is especially important with reactive dyes to consult the dye manufacturer's literature.

The critical importance of substantivity and its overriding influence on the application properties has been described in sections 3.2.1, 3.3.2 and 7.5, as well as elsewhere [28,92]. The essential auxiliaries used to control reactive dyes in batchwise dyeing are electrolyte and alkali. Secondary auxiliaries may include sequestering agents, oxidising agents to prevent reduction of certain sensitive dyes, and wetting or levelling agents.

The classic procedure for dyeing with reactive dyes involves application of dye in a substantially non-reactive form by exhaustion with electrolyte at a temperature to suit the reactivity of the particular dyes used, followed by addition of alkali to enhance absorption and, more particularly, to create the conditions through which the dyes can covalently react with the fibre. In the so-called 'all-in' process electrolyte and alkali are present together throughout to bring about simultaneous sorption and reaction, though this inevitably increases the opportunity for hydrolysis of the dye in the dyebath. Application temperatures vary from room temperature to the boil or even higher.

Sodium chloride is undoubtedly the most widely used electrolyte, a particular advantage being its ease of dissolution. Certain dyes, such as brilliant blue phthalocyanines and anthraquinones, are susceptible to aggregation and sometimes even precipitation in its presence, however, and in these cases sodium sulphate, which has a lesser aggregating effect, is preferred. The electrolyte should be free from calcium and magnesium salts and from alkali (to avoid premature fixation in a two-stage process). The electrolyte functions with reactive dyes in a manner similar to that with direct dyes, but as reactive dyes are more highly sulphonated, and hence less substantive than direct dyes, more salt is required to produce equivalent exhaustion. Beech [92] quotes, as a typical example, using a liquor ratio of 30:1: 3–7 g/l salt for direct dyes and 30–60 g/l for reactives. As with direct dyes, the higher the concentration of salt, the greater the uptake of dye, provided over-aggregation and precipitation do not occur. The primary objective is to obtain maximum exhaustion over an optimum dyeing period, taking care to ensure level uptake since this is the only phase during which the rapidly diffusing reactive dyes can migrate. Hence electrolyte may be added in portions over the whole dyeing period. The amount used rarely exceeds 40–60 g/l, since beyond this the slightly improved exhaustion tends to be outweighed by the cost of the salt. As might be expected with highly soluble dyes, liquor ratio itself has a pronounced effect on exhaustion, especially with dyes of low substantivity, and thus on the amount of electrolyte needed. Decreasing the liquor ratio from 30:1 to 5:1 would justify lowering the electrolyte concentration to one-sixth (5–10 g/l) but in fact even less than this can be used because of the marked effect of the reduction in liquor ratio itself [92].

There is another important effect of electrolyte: initially the internal pH of the fibre is lower than that of the dyebath, a state that would tend to favour hydrolysis of the absorbed dyes; electrolyte tends to equalise these pH values, thus protecting against hydrolysis. In general, the longer the liquor ratio, the lower the dye substantivity and the greater the depth of shade, then the higher is the concentration of electrolyte required.

Depending on the reactivity of the dyes used and the depth of shade, the pH required for reaction with the fibre varies from 8 to 12, and in practice falls mainly between 9 and 11. The most widely used alkali is sodium carbonate, although sodium bicarbonate and sodium hydroxide are also used; these reagents may be used singly or in mixtures. Sodium bicarbonate, for example, can be used as a 'pH-shift' agent, since the pH slowly increases on heating as sodium carbonate is formed (Scheme 12.2).

$$2NaHCO_3 \longrightarrow Na_2CO_3 + CO_2 + H_2O$$

Scheme 12.2

In certain applications sodium silicate is used. The alkali induces ionisation of the cellulosic hydroxy groups, enabling the dye to form a covalent bond with the fibre (see Chapter 7). It might be thought therefore that increasing quantities of alkali would favour maximum reaction between dye and fibre, but in practice an optimum level of alkali, rather than a maximum, has to be sought. This is because the cellulosate anion tends to repel the anionic reactive dye, thus decreasing the efficiency of dye uptake and so increasing the tendency towards hydrolysis of the dye. Consequently the aim must be to keep the pH as low as possible consistent with maintaining complete reaction in a commercially acceptable dyeing time. With a liquor ratio of 30:1 (as used in the previous example in relation to electrolyte) a typical quantity of alkali in the batchwise application of monochlorotriazine dyes would be 10 g/l sodium carbonate; however, fixation conditions vary widely according to the dye type and process used.

Reactive dyes as a group are not overtly sensitive to hard water. Nevertheless, the alkali used in most reactive dyeing processes may precipitate calcium or magnesium salts on the substrate, to cause problems in later processes. Ideally, soft water with a pH not greater than 7 is preferred. Where the use of hard water is unavoidable, a sodium hexametaphosphate sequestering agent may be used in the minimum amount needed to overcome the hardness, since excessive quantities may bring about a significant reduction in dye yield. Organic sequestering agents of the EDTA type are generally best avoided because they often result in colour changes and reduced light fastness, although they can occasionally be used successfully in minimal quantities [28].

Of course, once reactive dyes have reacted with the fibre no levelling is possible; hence any levelling must be achieved before reaction takes place. The most usual means is by controlled additions of electrolyte rather than with a surfactant-type levelling agent; the latter causes restraining, although it may be used in minimal amounts to aid wetting and to safeguard against rope marks through its lubricating action. Non-ionic types are also occasionally used as disaggregating agents with certain phthalocyanine dyes and other dyes of low solubility, in the presence of electrolyte [28].

Certain dyes are susceptible to reduction, particularly under anaerobic dyeing conditions. An addition of 1–2 g/l sodium m-nitrobenzenesulphonate is a useful palliative.

Dyes of low substantivity and rapid fixation are preferred in semi- and fully continuous dyeing processes. There are a great many variations of procedure. Some processes use only dye and alkali; for example, on cotton equal weights of dye and alkali over the range 5–30 g/l may be used, with a pick-up of 60–80%, whilst on viscose the pick-up is usually higher (90–100%) and the alkali reduced to half the quantity of dye [28]. With monochlorotriazinyl and some other dyes both salt and alkali are used – perhaps up to 30 g/l sodium chloride and 10–15 g/l alkali. A Remazol (HOE) process [28] uses sodium silicate as the main alkali, in order to alleviate problems of white selvedges that can occur when sodium hydroxide is used (caused by neutralisation of the sodium hydroxide by carbon dioxide or other acidic atmospheric agents). A wetting agent is commonly employed in semi- or fully continuous processes to aid rapid wetting at the pad stage. A hydrotrope such as urea may also be used, particularly for deep shades, to boost the solubility of less-soluble dyes and to aid fixation through its mechanism of retaining moisture, particularly in fully continuous thermofixation techniques. If a thickening agent is needed to minimise migration, sodium alginate is preferred since it does not react with dyes; electrolyte may serve the same purpose. The advantage of fully continuous procedures is that they use minimum quantities of alkali and water. Two-stage continuous processes, using two wet-on-wet paddings with the second pad applying the alkali, are also used.

The same general considerations apply in direct printing processes as in continuous dyeing. A single all-in, or a two-stage pad–steam procedure may be used. Again alginates are the preferred thickeners (other carbohydrates react with the dyes). The non-reactivity of alginates, in spite of their hydroxy groups, is thought to be due to the presence on each mannuronic unit of a carboxyl group that tends to repel the dye anions. Synthetic anionic poly(acrylic acid) thickeners are useful alternatives, giving higher colour yields than the alginates and also quicker washing-off. Emulsion thickenings, either oil-in-water or water-in-oil, including half-emulsions, may also be used. Hydrotropes and mild oxidising agents such as sodium m-nitrobenzenesulphonate are commonly employed. Choice of alkali depends on the reactivity of the dye. Sodium bicarbonate is usually preferred, being cheap and having high print paste stability with all but the most reactive dyes, but for dyes of sufficiently high stability the stronger alkalis (sodium carbonate or sodium hydroxide) may be chosen as better colour yields result under more alkaline conditions. The amount of bicarbonate may be reduced with highly reactive dyes; alternatively a pH-shift agent such as sodium trichloroacetate, a mildly acidic salt that hydrolyses to the more basic sodium acetate during steaming, may be used. In the two-stage process the dyes are first applied without alkali, using a thickening agent (such as alginate) that gels on subsequent application of alkali, possibly with electrolyte. High concentrations of sodium silicate ($Na_2O:SiO_2$ = 1:2.1, 47°Bé) or mixed alkali solutions (for example, 185 g/kg sodium carbonate + 185 g/kg potassium carbonate + 30 g/kg sodium hydroxide, 38°Bé) are often used.

Normal discharge prints are applicable on grounds dyed with reactive dyes, especially if vinyl sulphone dyes have been used, but there are difficulties with those non-azo blue and turquoise dyes that lend preference to resist processes [13]. Resists can be achieved by replacing the alkali usually required for fixation with a pre-printed non-volatile acid (tartaric or citric acid, for example) or with acidic salts such as sodium dihydrogen orthophosphate. The thickening agent used must be stable to acid; the hydroxyethylated and methylhydroxyethylated cellulose ethers, locust bean gum or tragacanth are suitable. This pre-printed and dried resist is then overprinted or padded with a solution of a highly reactive dye together with the minimum amount of sodium bicarbonate.

An especially important and critical aspect of the application of reactive dyes, whether by dyeing or printing, is the washing-off process necessary to remove unfixed and/or hydrolysed dye, as well as other products such as alkali, electrolyte and thickening agents. After rinsing to remove the more readily soluble products such as alkali and electrolyte, the goods are soaped at temperatures close to the boil to remove the unfixed/hydrolysed dye; a high temperature is necessary to remove hydrolysed dye from the interior of the fibres. Surfactants, especially non-ionic types, are often added to the soaping liquor, and a sequestering agent is added in hard water. Where thickening agents have been used, sufficient time must be allowed during the initial rinsing for the thickener to hydrate.

The stripping of cellulose dyed with reactive dyes is carried out by alkaline reduction followed by hypochlorite oxidation, preceded by a boiling treatment with EDTA if metal-containing dyes have been used. For example, a treatment with some 5 g/l sodium carbonate or sodium hydroxide and 5 g/l sodium dithionite at the boil is followed by a treatment in 0.5–1°Tw hypochlorite, an antichlor and thorough rinsing.

12.7.2 Wool

Although wool can be dyed with some of the reactive dyes produced essentially for cellulosic substrates, the widespread use of reactive dyes on wool has depended on the development of special ranges of dyes, capable of covalent bonding under slightly acidic conditions. The use of surfactant auxiliaries is essential.

The types of dyes used and the mechanisms of reaction have been discussed in section 7.10.2 and elsewhere [2,8]. These dyes are generally similar, as regards their response to dyebath pH, to the milling acid dyes, requiring an optimum pH value of 5 for controlled and adequate exhaustion/fixation. At lower pH values adsorption and fixation may be uneven, whilst at higher values exhaustion is poor. Even at pH 5 fixation may still be incomplete within normal dyeing times, particularly when dyeing dark shades. Hence the bath is adjusted to a weakly alkaline state, which ensures complete fixation as well as helping to remove hydrolysed dye. A typical procedure is to dye at the boil and pH 5, followed by cooling to 80°C and adjustment of the pH to 8.0–8.5 with ammonia, after which treatment is continued for some 20–30 minutes at 80°C.

A surfactant auxiliary is necessary to prevent tippy or skittery dyeing. Cationic and non-ionic products have been used but the most useful have been the amphoteric N-alkylbetaines and alkylamidobetaines (described in section 9.7) and ethoxylated amphoteric products of the type shown by structure 12.8 [93]. Products of this type can interact under slightly acidic conditions with both fibre and dye. The mechanisms have been investigated in detail by Cegarra and Riva [93,94]. The initial step appears to be the formation of an auxiliary–dye complex, such complexes being less soluble than the dye alone. As the concentration of auxiliary is increased to an excess over that required for complexing with the dye, surfactant micelles are formed that tend to solubilise the auxiliary–dye complex. Unlike most levelling agents these amphoteric products often increase the rate of wool dyeing, the extent being dependent on the chemistry and concentration of the auxiliary and on the dye, although they may have a retarding effect where the concentration of auxiliary is so high as to solubilise the auxiliary–dye complex completely. These auxiliaries also tend to improve dye exhaustion.

$$CH_3(CH_2)_{11} \diagdown \underset{CH_3 \diagup}{N^+} \diagup \overset{(CH_2CH_2O)_n \ SO_3^- \ \overset{+}{N}H_4}{\diagdown (CH_2CH_2O)_m \ CH_3SO_4^-} \qquad (n + m = 10\text{–}80)$$

12.8

The accepted explanation for this behaviour is that the auxiliary–dye complex is less electronegative than the dye itself; hence it exhibits more hydrophobic characteristics with increased molecular size and lower aqueous solubility. Consequently the affinity of the dye for the undamaged roots of the wool fibres is enhanced, relative to that for the more hydrophilic damaged tips. The auxiliary–dye complex is less sensitive to root–tip differences and hence gives more level dyeing. In addition, the adsorption of the auxiliary by the fibre increases the electropositive nature of the fibre, thus increasing the attraction for anionic dyes. This will tend to further enhance the rate of dyeing and is also the mechanism whereby the amount of dye absorbed is increased. On the whole, there is little evidence that these products increase migration, and indeed no migration can take place once the dye has covalently reacted with the fibre.

The levelling action of betaines increases with concentration and with increasing length of the alkyl chain [94], but their effects on rate and amount of absorption disappear with products containing a very long (about C_{16}) alkyl chain at high concentrations, although the levelling properties are maintained irrespective of the rate effects. In general, the betaines bring about a greater change in sorption characteristics than do the ethoxylated amphoteric products of similar alkyl chain length [94]. Thus greater quantities of the latter are needed to produce a similar effect; this can be an advantage, since the effects are not then so critically sensitive to the concentration of auxiliary. Furthermore, the manufacturer can vary the balance of properties of the auxiliary by varying the length of the oxyethylene chains as well as of the alkyl group.

Reactive dyes for wool can be applied by printing [13], using locust bean or guar derivatives as thickeners, either singly or in combination with cold-water-soluble British gum, together with a hydrotrope such as urea or thiourea and an auxiliary solvent such as thiodiethylene glycol or glycerol. Formic acid is used to maintain acidity. The print is washed in several baths containing 2 g/l disodium hydrogen orthophosphate, ammonia (to give pH 9) and an anionic surfactant in successive baths at temperatures increasing from 40 to 80°C.

12.8 SULPHUR DYES
Sulphur dyes are applied to cellulosic substrates by initial conversion by alkaline reduction to the substantive leuco form, followed by oxidation on the fibre to the insoluble parent form. Consequently reducing and oxidising agents are essential auxiliaries. Secondary auxiliaries include wetting agents, sequestering agents, antioxidants, electrolytes and hydrotropes. Useful reviews of developments in sulphur dyes and their application are available [28,95]. The concern here is with the essentials of the auxiliary agents used in their application, and it is convenient to deal separately with the aspects of reduction and oxidation. The discussion is confined to

application by dyeing since the use of sulphur dyes in printing is nowadays restricted mainly to blacks, which are applied by techniques similar to those used for vat dyes [13].

12.8.1 Reduction

The 'conventional' sulphur dyes and the solubilised types are reduced by the dyer as part of the application procedure. There are, however, some leuco sulphur dyes in which reduction has already been carried out by the manufacturer so that they are substantially in a form suitable for direct application. The chemistry of the reduction of sulphur dyes is clearly very complex as is also the chemistry of the dyes themselves; it has been well described by Aspland [96]. It is possible to describe the state of a reduced sulphur dye in alkaline sulphide or polysulphide solution by the general formula 12.9, but there are certain complexities. In many cases the chromophore does not itself reduce, but in others, notably red-browns, blues and navy blues based on indophenols, the chromophoric quinone–imine grouping can be reduced (Scheme 12.3). Additionally, the value of n in structure 12.9 varies, even for a given dye. It is not surprising, therefore, that the amount of reducing agent (and alkali) required varies from dye to dye, depending on the chemistry of the dye as well as on the concentration in the formulation. Hence the manufacturer's literature must always be consulted for the amounts of auxiliaries to be used with particular dyes in the various batchwise, semi-continuous and continuous processes.

$$12.9 \qquad D\!\!-\!\!\left(S_n\!-\!SX\right)_m \qquad \begin{array}{l} D = \text{chromophore} \\ n = 0\text{–}6,\ m \geq 1 \\ X = \text{H or Na depending on pH} \end{array}$$

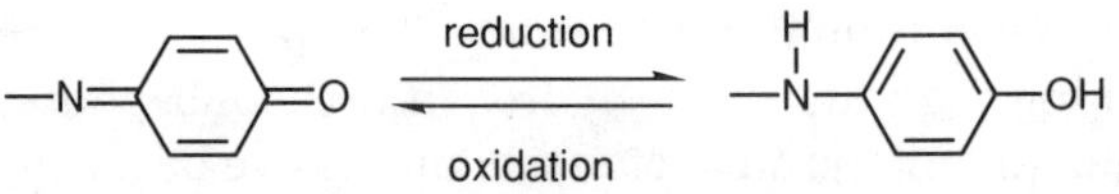

Scheme 12.3

The reduction process is invariably carried out in an alkaline medium, partly because of the instability of most reducing agents at low pH and partly because the acidic thiol groups react with alkali to give the much more soluble anionic thiolate form [96]. Traditionally the most widely used reducing agents have been sodium sulphide (Na_2S) and sodium hydrogen sulphide (NaHS). Technically these are still the most widely preferred, not only for their efficacy, but also because they are relatively inexpensive. Nowadays, however, they are increasingly subject to scrutiny on environmental grounds. At least 12 g/l sodium sulphide is required for the dissolution of the insoluble-type sulphur dyes; the quantity needed in the dyebath varies from dye to dye but is generally proportional to the amount of dye, with a minimum of 1.5–3.0 g/l [28]. When using sodium hydrogen sulphide the quantity is generally 0.6 times that of sodium sulphide, but it is also necessary to use alkali (10 g sodium hydroxide or 5 g sodium carbonate per 7 g sodium hydrogen sulphide). The pre-reduced leuco sulphur dyes usually contain a mixture of sodium sulphide and sodium hydrogen sulphide together with hydrotropic and dispersion-assisting agents such as 2-ethoxyethanol, sodium 1,3-xylene-4-sulphonate, sodium p-toluenesulphonate and sodium tetralinsulphonate [95,97]. (The quantities of sodium sulphide and sodium hydrogen sulphide referred to above relate to the full-strength concentrated products and must obviously be proportionately adjusted if weaker commercial products are used).

In some applications, particularly in jet and winch dyeing, there is a danger that the reducing agent may be prematurely oxidised by air. Antioxidants, added along with the dyes and the main reducing agent at the beginning of dyeing, can be used as palliatives. Polysulphides of general formula 12.10 [98], such as disodium tetrathionite, have been widely used for this purpose, and lead to better dyebath stability. These products can also be used with other reducing agents described below but are not compatible with dithionite. Another approach is to add some relatively more stable alkaline reducing agent such as sodium dithiodiglycolate (12.11) [99].

12.10 $S_n(SO_3X)_2$ X = Na, K, H or NH_4 ; n = 1–4

$$NaOOCCH_2-S-S-CH_2COONa \qquad 12.11$$

Several products have been suggested as environmentally more acceptable alternatives to the alkali sulphides. All are more expensive, and have other disadvantages. For example, the reduction may be more difficult to control, or a particular product may be effective only with a narrower range of dyes and, even then, may not be as effective in terms of colour yield as the alkali sulphides. The most obvious alternative is sodium dithionite (12.12) with alkali, which is widely used with vat dyes; the process is difficult to control and some dyes may be partly destroyed through over-reduction, but it is effective with the water-soluble and sulphur vat dyes. It is also possible to use a mixed reducing agent of sodium sulphide, sodium dithionite and alkali [28].

$$Na_2S_2O_4 \quad 12.12 \qquad\qquad NaHSO_2.CH_2O.2H_2O \quad 12.13$$

Products based on sodium formaldehyde–sulphoxylate (sometimes referred to as sodium hydroxymethanesulphinate) (12.13) and alkali, although more stable than dithionite, tend to have the same disadvantages. Sodium dithiodiglycolate (12.11) was mentioned above as an antioxidant. Such products may be used as the sole or main reducing agent in conjunction with alkali. Although they do not give rise to environmentally undesirable inorganic sulphides in the effluent, their high stability leads to a high chemical oxygen demand, which can cause more problems than those arising with sodium sulphide [95]. Currently the most promising alternative to sulphides, from an environmental point of view, is the use of the reducing sugar glucose with an alkali such as sodium hydroxide and/or sodium carbonate. The system does not satisfactorily reduce all dyes, however. It appears to be most effective with the water-soluble types [100], with which it may be used either as the sole reducing agent or in conjunction with sodium polysulphide, usually resulting in increased dye yields. It can be used as an additional reducing agent with the leuco dye types, thus giving a lower sulphide content in the dyebath, or together with sulphide or polysulphide in the reduction of the traditional water-insoluble types [28]. The system is pH- and temperature-dependent (hence results may be good on jet machines but poor on the more temperature-sensitive jigs). Typical quantities quoted for a batchwise dyeing method [28] at liquor ratios of 10:1 to 20:1 are 3–8 g/l glucose, 4–10 g/l sodium carbonate and 2–6 g/l sodium hydroxide, depending on depth, a minimum dyeing temperature of 90–95°C being required.

2-Mercaptoethanol (12.14) with alkali has been suggested as an alternative to sulphides [100], having the claimed advantages of not giving rise to sulphides in the effluent together with no smell in the dyebath, although the product itself can give off unpleasant and highly toxic fumes [101]. This process is relatively expensive, with a tendency to lower yields and a more restricted range of amenable dyes than the use of the traditional sulphides, and does not appear to have achieved significant commercial use.

$$HSCH_2CH_2OH \quad 12.14$$

More recently a sulphur-free reducing agent, hydroxyacetone (or acetol) (12.15), originally introduced for vat dyes, has also been found to be useful with sulphur dyes. This is used under strongly alkaline conditions, the concentrations adopted being critical, and is said to give results similar to those with dithionite [102].

$$CH_3COCH_2OH \quad 12.15$$

Klein [100] has questioned the need to eliminate the use of sulphides, pointing out that highly effective means of removing sulphides and residual dyes from effluent have been in use for many years. Consequently sulphides are likely to remain the major reducing agents at least for some time to come, but the use of the alternative agents may be of interest to smaller companies that cannot afford the cost of sulphide effluent treatment.

Secondary auxiliaries used along with the reducing agent(s) during preparation of the leuco dyebath may include wetting and sequestering agents; the disperse forms of sulphur dye may also require dispersing agents. The choice of wetting agent is not particularly critical as they do not affect the behaviour of most sulphur dyes, apart from one or two that can show an adverse reaction (lower yield or even precipitation) with certain products, notably non-ionic surfactants [28]. Suitable sequestering agents include hexametaphosphate and EDTA [28]. Electrolytes are also added to the dyebath, particularly in batchwise dyeing, to assist exhaustion.

After application of the leuco dye, a thorough rinse is essential to remove any loose dye.

12.8.2 Oxidation

Chemically simple thiols and thiolates are readily oxidised to disulphides (Scheme 12.4). The situation is more complex with the leuco sulphur dyes [96], since in addition to having two or more thiol groups, they may contain other reactive functions that are potentially susceptible to oxidative attack, examples being primary, secondary or tertiary amino groups, hydroxy groups and aryl thioether (R–S–R) groups, as well as sulphonic acid groups in some cases. Furthermore, the substantivity of the leuco dye for the substrate may inhibit free movement of the dye molecules and thus prevent complete conversion of thiol groups to disulphide crosslinks; nevertheless, it is generally assumed that disulphide or polysulphide crosslinks are formed.

$$2 \; RSH \xrightarrow{\;[O]\;} RS\text{--}SR$$

Scheme 12.4

Traditionally the most favoured, and still the most widely effective, oxidising system for sulphur dyes is sodium dichromate acidified with acetic acid. The concentration of dichromate is not critical [28], 1–2 g/l being generally recommended for batchwise processes carried out at 60–80°C, but the pH is more so and should be controlled to within the range 4.5–5.5, reliably giving good colour yields and fastness properties against which the efficacy of all other oxidising systems can be compared. Up to 1 g/l copper(II) sulphate may be added to dichromate baths to give an improvement in light fastness, at the expense of some dulling of shade and a harsher handle. The copper salt should only be added to acidified and sulphide-free liquors, otherwise it may precipitate as the hydroxide and/or sulphide. The addition of copper should not be made when oxidising sulphur blacks, however, since it promotes acid tendering with these dyes. The addition of sequestering and dispersing agents to the dichromate bath may give an improvement in rubbing fastness [28].

Dichromate oxidation does tend to give a harsher handle and a less hydrophilic fibre, which may cause handling problems in subsequent processes such as weaving, and is therefore less popular in yarn dyeing. As discussed in section 12.2.2 in connection with mordant dyes, increasing environmental concern and legislation are threatening the use of chromium compounds in textile wet processing. The threat is particularly pertinent to the oxidation of sulphur dyes, where the use of dichromate may ultimately be prohibited. Whilst considerable success has been achieved in devising environmentally acceptable dichromate systems for mordant dyes, with sulphur dyes the emphasis has been on finding alternative oxidising agents, but in spite of considerable efforts, no system hitherto developed attains the versatility, efficacy, economy and robustness of acidified dichromate [28,95,96,100,101]. Products that have shown some promise beyond laboratory trials include (a) iodates and bromates, (b) hydrogen peroxide or sodium peroxide and (c) sodium chlorite.

A concentration of 0.2–1.5 g/l iodate (potassium or sodium) [28,100] at 60°C and pH 3.5–5 (preferably 3.5–4.0) gives similar shades and fastness properties to those obtained with dichromate. The process shows good reproducibility and does not give the harsh handle associated with dichromate, but is expensive. The pH, controlled by using acetic acid, is critical; oxidation is slower at values higher than pH 4.5 and stronger acids such as formic acid lead to precipitation of iodine which, apart from being corrosive to machinery, is environmentally harmful. Higher temperatures lead to partial reduction of the iodate with consequent loss of efficacy. Bromates, under the same conditions, are less effective than iodates but perform equally well if a catalyst such as sodium metavanadate ($NaVO_3$) is added [28,103].

Peroxides have been used for some considerable time as alternatives to dichromate, especially for yarn dyeing (giving a softer handle) and for sulphur blues and blacks. About 1–2 g/l hydrogen peroxide (130 vol.) is generally used at pH 10 and 40°C [28,100]. Careful control is needed since under alkaline conditions oxidation is rapid and may go beyond the disulphide stage. In mildly acidic media oxidation is much slower but under batch conditions is adequate for most dyes except C.I. Sulphur Red 10. It may be too slow for rapid continuous methods, and there is a danger of catalytic degradation of the fibre. Nevertheless, 1 g/l hydrogen peroxide (130 vol.) with 0.8 g/l acetic acid at 50–60°C is widely used on yarns [28]. Oxidation under neutral conditions is occasionally carried out. Electronic metering and control is particularly useful with peroxide systems. The use of metal-ion catalysts with peroxide has been tried; vanadates offer some promise but iron and copper salts have not proved entirely suitable [100].

Peroxide oxidation has gained a reputation for giving somewhat lower wash fastness than that obtained with dichromate. Although this is largely true in relation to wash tests based on soap, Klein has pointed out [100] that wash tests based on the perborate-containing detergents (which are much more prevalent nowadays) do not show this problem.

Sodium chlorite is the basis of several proprietary oxidising agents for sulphur dyes. It is used at pH 10 (sodium carbonate) and 90–95°C; careful control of conditions is again needed as the reaction is rather slow. The presence of other products appears to be necessary for the successful use of chlorite as the proprietary formulations also appear to contain stabilisers, EDTA-type sequestering agents and detergents or dispersing agents.

Other oxidising agents that have been proposed include

(a) sodium m-nitrobenzenesulphonate in alkaline media
(b) sodium salt of N-chloro-p-toluenesulphonamide (chloramine T)
(c) sodium nitrite with sulphuric acid (this carries a danger of fibre degradation)
(d) potassium and ammonium salts of peroxydisulphonic acid with acetic acid.

However, at the present time, the most promising of the alternatives to dichromate appear to be acidic or alkaline peroxide or vanadate-catalysed bromate.

12.8.3 Alkylation of thiol groups

As an alternative or supplement to oxidising treatments, many leuco sulphur dyeings can be treated with alkylating agents such as those based on epichlorohydrin. This was discussed in section 10.7.4. The alkylating agent reacts with the dye thiol to yield an alkyl thioether, or with amino groups in the dye to yield substituted amines [96]. These are generally referred to as fixation treatments and give enhanced fastness to acid storage and to wet treatments although, strictly speaking, they are still oxidation mechanisms involving the removal of an electron from the dye thiolate.

A soaping treatment after oxidation or other fixation treatment is recommended.

12.8.4 Continuous dyeing

Continuous methods are far more important with sulphur dyes than is batchwise dyeing in terms of production volumes [28]. There are many methods, including pad–steam, pad–sky, pad–dry–chemical-pad–steam and pad–dry–develop; summary descriptions of these processes are available [28]. In general the auxiliaries used, and particularly the redox chemicals, are the same as those used in batchwise dyeing although they are usually used in higher concentrations, especially reducing agents which tend to be more exposed to air in continuous processes. Wetting and sequestering agents are commonly used, and some processes incorporate hydrotropes (such as urea) and migration inhibitors. Electrolytes may be used in a chemical (reducing) pad to assist fixation but are less frequently used when padding leuco dyes, since they can promote tailing effects.

12.9 VAT DYES

Vat dyes, like sulphur dyes, are applied to cellulosic fibres after initial conversion by alkaline reduction to the substantive leuco form, followed by oxidation on the fibre back to the insoluble form. Consequently the major auxiliaries are, once again, reducing and oxidising agents. Ancillary products include electrolyte, wetting, dispersing, levelling and sequestering agents; thickening agents and hydrotropes may feature in continuous dyeing and printing. An extremely important part of vat dye application is the final soaping treatment, which is essential for developing the ultimate colour and optimum fastness. Up-to-date detailed accounts of vat dye application are available [28,104]. Here the reducing and oxidising stages of the process and the soaping treatment are considered separately; the main discussion deals with batchwise dyeing, after which the requirements for continuous dyeing and printing are considered.

12.9.1 Reduction

Vat dyes are available mainly in their conventional insoluble form, although a group of solubilised dyes, the leuco vat esters, are supplied in a stabilised pre-reduced form that does not require any reduction by the dyer. The chemistry of vat dyes, and of their reduction and oxidation, is much more clearly understood than is the case with sulphur dyes. Johnson [105] has given a detailed account of the reduction and oxidation processes. In essence, the reduction process can be represented as the addition of an electron to each of the keto groups of the vat dye, with conversion to a conjugated dihydric quinol, the system being readily reversible by oxidation (i.e. the abstraction of electrons) (Scheme 12.5) [105].

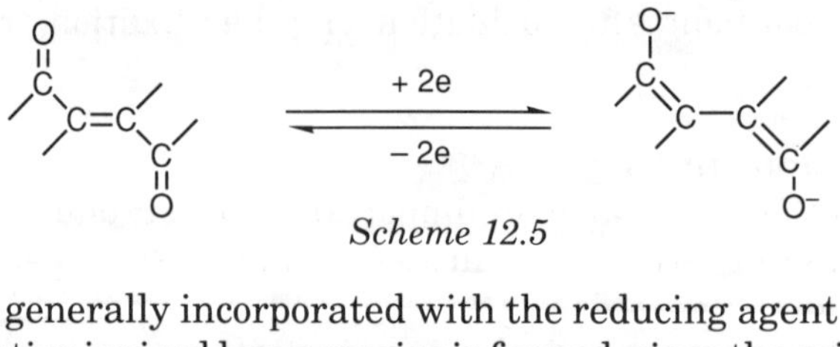

Scheme 12.5

Alkali is generally incorporated with the reducing agent to ensure that the substantive ionised leuco species is formed, since the acid leuco form is generally insoluble and has limited substantivity for cellulose. The leuco potentials of vat dyes cover a wide range [28,105] and it is generally accepted that a reducing agent, to be successful, should have a lower potential than the system it is intended to reduce. The system in practice is more complex, however, since the redox potentials have generally been measured in organic solvents, which are not typical of commercial dyeing systems. Moreover, the reduction rate is critically dependent on the physical form of the dye as characterised by its crystal form and particle size distribution (see section 3.1.4). The stability of the leuco dye in solution is also a function of the concentrations of dye and reducing agent, temperature, pH and liquor ratio. The counter-action of air oxidation, as it relates to different application systems, also has to be carefully considered. Hence even the quantities of reagents suggested by the dye manufacturers can only be used as preliminary guidelines.

By far the most important reducing system for the batchwise application of vat dyes is alkaline sodium dithionite ($Na_2S_2O_4$), the most usual alkali being sodium hydroxide. Obviously the theoretical concentrations will depend on the number of keto groups in the dye and on its relative molecular mass and concentration, but the reaction can be represented as in Scheme 12.6 for a dye with two keto groups [28]. The effect of air oxidation on alkaline dithionite must also be taken into account in practical situations and can be represented by Scheme 12.7 [28].

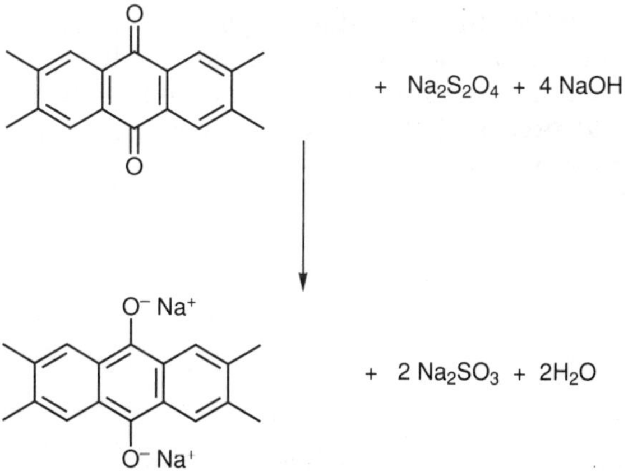

$$+ \ Na_2S_2O_4 \ + \ 4\,NaOH$$

$$+ \ 2\,Na_2SO_3 \ + \ 2H_2O$$

Scheme 12.6

$$Na_2S_2O_4 \ + \ 2\,NaOH \ + \ O_2 \ \longrightarrow \ Na_2SO_3 \ + \ Na_2SO_4 \ + \ H_2O$$

Scheme 12.7

In practice, more sulphite than sulphate tends to be formed. Clearly, this atmospheric oxidation results not only in loss of reducing agent but also of alkali, another reason why excess alkali as well as reducing agent is required. The influence of atmospheric oxidation varies enormously;

Baumgarte [28] has mentioned stability over many hours in a large vessel with relatively small surface area, compared with some 30–60 seconds in a padding system. The ideal pH value for this system is between 12 and 14; below this range there is an increasing danger that the dye will either revert to its keto form or yield the leuco acid; above it there is a danger that the dithionite may decompose to form thiosulphate, sulphite or even sulphide if the temperature is high enough.

There are some potential environmental problems associated with dithionite since in effluent it can produce some sulphite and sulphate. Although the sulphite can be oxidised quite easily to sulphate, this does not entirely obviate the problems since high concentrations of sulphate can cause damage to unprotected concrete pipes. Thus there are latent environmental reasons for alternative reducing agents to dithionite and, indeed, several are available, although at the present time they are mainly used for special purposes. In particular, their better stability to atmospheric oxidation makes them of special interest for continuous dyeing and printing processes, rather than for batchwise dyeing.

Thiourea dioxide (or formamidinesulphinic acid) (12.16) is certainly a powerful reducing agent for vat dyes. It has a lower relative molecular mass than sodium dithionite and gives lower concentrations of sulphite and sulphate in the effluent, but it has certain disadvantages. Its mode of action in hot aqueous alkali is represented in Scheme 12.8, showing first the rearrangement to sodium formamidinesulphinate, which then decomposes to yield urea and the active reducing species, normally sodium hydrogen sulphoxylate.

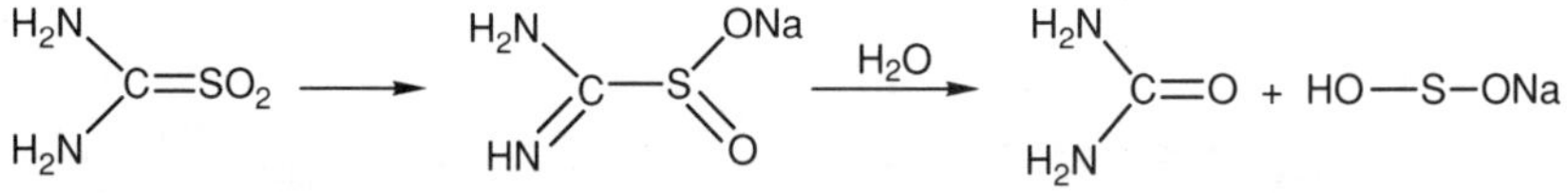

Scheme 12.8

Although thiourea dioxide is more stable than dithionic acid, the formamidinesulphinate formed in alkaline media is more readily oxidised than dithionite, thus negating any potential advantages. It can also cause over-reduction of indanthrone vats, against which inhibitors such as glucose or sodium nitrite have no palliative effect. Baumgarte [104] has mentioned two recent proposals concerning the use of thiourea dioxide in combination with other products: one of these [106] uses thiourea dioxide in combination with dithionite, formaldehyde and sodium hydroxide, whilst the other [107] uses it in combination with saturated aliphatic ketones. Their use in practice is not evident, however.

Rather greater commercial significance is attached to certain derivatives of dithionite, of which the more important is sodium formaldehyde–sulphoxylate (hydroxymethanesulphinate) (Scheme 12.9); the other is sodium acetaldehyde–sulphoxylate (hydroxyethanesulphinate) (12.17). These reducing agents have been of particular interest in printing applications, especially in the so-called flash-ageing process [108–111]. The derivation of sodium formaldehyde–sulphoxylate by reaction of dithionite with formaldehyde is shown in Scheme 12.9; the bisulphite formed can be further reduced with zinc to produce another molecule of sulphoxylate.

$$Na_2S_2O_4 + 2HCHO + H_2O \longrightarrow NaHSO_2.CH_2O + NaHSO_3.CH_2O$$

Scheme 12.9

12.17 $H_3C-CH \begin{matrix} OH \\ O-S-ONa \end{matrix}$

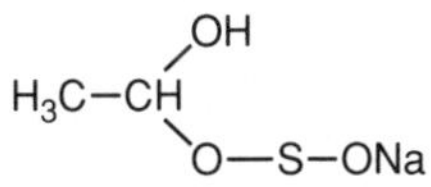

These reducing agents are much more stable than dithionite at lower temperatures; hence they can be used to prepare stable pad liquors and print pastes. At higher temperatures, as in steam fixation treatments, they are capable of bringing about rapid reduction of vat dyes. Sodium formaldehyde–sulphoxylate was used first in conventional steam fixation of vats, although the acetaldehyde analogue was initially preferred for the flash-ageing process. As vat dyes are invariably fixed under alkaline conditions, the sodium salts of the sulphoxylates are preferred to the basic salts of zinc (12.18) or calcium (12.19), which are unstable under alkaline conditions.

$HOCH_2-O-S-OZn(OH)$ 12.18 $HOCH_2-O-S-OCa(OH)$ 12.19

Sodium formaldehyde–sulphoxylate has been occasionally used in combination with sodium dithionite [104] but other two-component or two-phase systems based on the formaldehyde–sulphoxylate have generally used an accelerating or catalyst system. For example, a process that has been used to some extent in bulk practice [112,113] uses as one component a strongly alkaline solution of sodium borohydride (sodium tetrahydroborate) (12.20), together with a second component consisting of sodium formaldehyde–sulphoxylate and the catalyst sodium nickel cyanide.

$NaBH_4$ *12.20*

Various advantages have been claimed for this process, although there must be misgivings regarding the environmental acceptability of sodium nickel cyanide [114]. Other accelerators used with sodium formaldehyde–sulphoxylate include sodium dimethylglyoxime complexes, anthraquinone and aminoanthraquinonesulphonic acids. Although sodium borohydride is itself a reducing agent, it generally reacts too slowly on its own for use in vat systems; nor is there any evidence that it will act as a stabiliser for dithionite [115], as has sometimes been suggested.

Another reducing agent, which has found use not only in flash-ageing but also in batchwise high-temperature package dyeing, is sodium nitrilo-triethanesulphinate (12.21) [116]. Finally, there is the sulphur-free and biodegradable hydroxyacetone or acetol (12.15), which was mentioned in connection with sulphur dyes in section 12.8.1 [117]. This can be used in the pad–steam application of vat dyes in the presence of high concentrations of sodium hydroxide (about 3.5–4.5 g/l). It does not cause over-reduction of indanthrone type vats but does give different shades with carbazole dyes, compared with dithionite [104].

$$
12.21 \quad N
\begin{cases}
CH_2CH_2O-S-ONa \\
CH_2CH_2O-S-ONa \\
CH_2CH_2O-S-ONa
\end{cases}
$$

It is now opportune to consider additives in reduction systems. As mentioned above, the reduction process is invariably carried out in an alkaline medium, the most common alkali, particularly in batchwise dyeings, being sodium hydroxide. In printing, and in certain continuous dyeing processes, sodium hydroxide enhances the reduction potential of the reducing agent but impairs its stability, increasing the danger of pre-mature loss of reducing agent, particularly during the drying operation prior to steaming. In these processes carbonates give better stability and hence are preferred [118]. There is little difference between sodium and potassium carbonates in terms of effect on the reducing agent, but there are advantages to be gained from the use of potassium carbonate in the prep-aration of relatively concentrated print pastes and pad liquors. Not only does potassium carbonate have a higher aqueous solubility (112% wt/wt at 20°C) than sodium carbonate (21% wt/wt at 20°C), but the potassium leuco salts of vat dyes also have better solubility [13]. It is important to ensure the presence of excess alkali to counteract that consumed by the reducing agent and the substrate, as well as any lost through atmospheric oxidation of the system [28]. Electrolyte may also be used to promote the exhaustion of the leuco dye, particularly in batchwise dyeing. The use of electrolyte in the essentially 'short liquor' printing and continuous dyeing processes is not generally necessary and could be inadvisable, as it may promote tailing during padding. Electrolyte can, however, play a positive part in those continuous processes in which the unreduced dye is applied first followed by separate application of reducing agent in the so-called chemical pad. The amounts of alkali and electrolyte obviously vary widely according to the coloration process (such as the liquor ratio) and the dyes used. A qualitative summary of the amounts used with different classes of dye, together with some quantitative indications, has been given by Baumgarte [28].

Levelling agents are frequently used, since the initial strike by leuco dyes can be rapid. A non-ionic surfactant such as a cetyl poly(oxyethylene) alcohol of optimum chain length (such as structure 12.5) is particularly useful because it can also act as a wetting agent. Poly(ethylenimine) adducts are similarly used. On the other hand, certain products that act through a complexing mechanism are essentially non-surfactants; for example, one such proprietary product is said to be based on poly(vinylpyrrolidone), whilst another is said to be 'an oligomer condensation product', i.e. a polymeric hydroxy compound. Wetting and dispersing agents are further useful aids, particularly with inadequately prepared substrates. Aliphatic sulphonates are also widely used as wetting agents, particularly in combination with the non-surfactant levelling agents. Any surfactants used must be stable under the alkaline reducing conditions. For continuous pad application they should also have a low propensity to foam; phosphoric esters are preferred to aliphatic sulphonates in this respect and in regard to the amount of pad liquor absorbed [119]. Dispersing agents, sometimes referred to as protective colloids, help to maintain the particulate distribution of the unreduced dye and also inhibit aggregation/agglomeration of sparingly soluble leuco compounds; naphthalenesulphonic acid–formaldehyde condensates are especially useful. They are also essential ingredients in the application of vat dyes by the so-called pigmentation methods, using either the unreduced vat dyes themselves or, less frequently, acid leuco compounds [120].

A sequestering agent such as EDTA will prevent the formation of insoluble metal complexes, which would otherwise interfere with the reduction process and with level dyeing. An addition of pyrocatechol or tannin can help to counteract the well-known propensity of certain yellow and orange dyes to induce tendering, whilst the addition of glucose or sodium nitrite can help to prevent the over-reduction of certain dyes.

12.9.2 Oxidation

Various methods have been used for the reoxidation of vat leuco dyeings; atmospheric skying, hypochlorite, chlorite and acidified dichromate are now rarely employed, the most commonly used oxidising agents being hydrogen peroxide, sodium perborate and sodium m-nitrobenzenesulphonate [28]. Sodium nitrite acidified with sulphuric acid is also used, mainly with the solubilised vat leuco ester dyes.

Atmospheric oxidation can be difficult to control and may hence be uneven; with some dyes it is also too slow, particularly for continuous methods. Sodium hypochlorite is used only for those few black dyes that tend to become dark green when oxidised with peroxides; obviously it should be avoided with the many chlorine-sensitive dyes. Similarly sodium chlorite, acidified to below pH 5 with acetic acid, can only be used with certain dyes, although with these it certainly gives rapid oxidation. Dye selectivity is also the drawback to the use of acidified dichromate since, not surprisingly, its chelating potential can give rise to different hues, especially with sensitive blues and greens.

Thus peroxide and perborate remain the mainstay of the oxidation process; again, the amounts to be used vary widely according to the conditions of processing. Consequently even dye manufacturers' recommendations can only be used as guidelines and may need modification according to the machinery and conditions used. Many important factors have to be considered, especially the liquor ratio, the contact frequency between liquor and goods, the particular dyes and the depth of shade, as well as the efficiency with which the reduction liquor has been rinsed out. For example, in a long-liquor (30:1 to 50:1) winch-dyeing process as little as 0.5–1.0 g/l hydrogen peroxide (130 vol.) or sodium perborate at 50°C is usually adequate; this may be increased to 3–5 g/l at 50–60°C in short-liquor jig dyeing. The rate of oxidation can be controlled by addition of acetic acid to neutralise excess alkali carried over from reduction but care should be taken not to over-acidify as this would tend to convert the sodium leuco compound into the less soluble acid leuco form. Some blues are exceptionally sensitive to alkaline oxidation, however, and must therefore be rinsed thoroughly before oxidation in the presence of a small amount of acetic acid. Inadvertent over-reduction can often be corrected by again reducing the dyeing and then reoxidising under more carefully controlled conditions.

Sodium m-nitrobenzenesulphonate has been recently proposed as an oxidising agent for vat dyes. It is available as a proprietary product and is said to react with leuco compounds more quickly than does peroxide [104]. The solubilised vat leuco esters are most commonly hydrolysed and then reoxidised to the insoluble parent dye using sodium nitrite and sulphuric acid. Some more recent proposals for oxidising agents for use with vat leuco esters include hydrogen peroxide and ammonium metavanadate, persulphates and nitric acid [104].

12.9.3 Soaping

The so-called soaping of oxidised vat dyeings must be considered to be an integral part of the application sequence, rather than an optional extra, since the reproducibility of colour and fastness is dependent on it. The traditional process is to use a boiling bath containing 3–5 g/l Marseilles (olive oil) soap and 2 g/l sodium carbonate, usually for 10–15 minutes in a batchwise process. Soaping times of less than 1 minute are the norm in continuous pad–steam ranges, however, and it is then preferable to select dyes that show only a small change in colour during soaping [28,119]. Synthetic surfactants, particularly of the non-ionic type, may be used in place of soap.

12.9.4 Continuous dyeing and printing

In general, the reducing, oxidising and soaping agents for continuous dyeing are the same as those used in batchwise dyeing, although they tend to be used at higher concentrations. In some cases there may be a preference for more stable reducing agents than dithionite, such as sulphoxylates; in continuous dyeing dithionite is probably still the most widely applicable product [119], however, though sulphoxylates are undoubtedly preferred in printing. In continuous pigmentation methods the use of a migration inhibitor is essential in order to prevent tailing, two-sidedness or even general unlevelness, as well as to stabilise the pad liquor against pigment sedimentation [119]. It is important to use agents that promote the tendency of the dye particles to form larger agglomerates as this is the mechanism whereby migration is inhibited. Poly(acrylic acid) derivatives, alginates, branched polysaccharides and block copolymers of ethylene oxide and propylene oxide have proved useful.

Conversely, some printing thickeners such as locust bean gum, starch ethers, guar derivatives and carboxymethylcellulose have been less successful in preventing particulate migration in continuous dyeing, thus demonstrating that a simple increase in viscosity is not an effective mechanism [119].

In direct printing by an all-in single-stage process the most favoured reducing agent is sodium formaldehyde–sulphoxylate with potassium carbonate as alkali. A thickening agent is required; the choice can affect the rate of reduction and British gum thickenings can accelerate the decomposition of the reducing agent, but otherwise the actual choice of thickening agent does not appear to be critical. A hydrotrope helps to improve fixation in steam. A typical print paste recipe is given in Table 12.4 [13].

A reduction accelerator, such as an aminoanthraquinonesulphonic acid, may also be added. The flash-ageing method is a two-stage process in which the initial print paste contains dye and thickener only. The reducing agent and alkali are subsequently applied by padding. In this process exposure to air prior to steaming is minimal, and hence the less stable sodium dithionite can be used as the reducing agent. The thickening agent should coagulate in the presence of alkali in order to inhibit bleeding of colour; alternatively a gelling effect can be obtained by adding a borate to a thickener such as locust bean gum, as described in section 10.6.1. Mixtures of thickeners are often used in order to obtain the required degree of coagulation [13]; if this is exceeded there can be problems at the washing-off stage.

TABLE 12.4

**Typical print paste recipe for
single-stage process with vat dye**

Component	Amount/% by wt
Vat dye	x
Potassium carbonate	15
Sodium formaldehyde–sulphoxylate	8
Glycerol (hydrotrope)	5
Thickening agent	24
Water	to 100

The solubilised vat leuco esters can also be used for printing. There are two main means of oxidation. The first incorporates sodium nitrite in the print paste and this is converted to nitrous acid by a short immersion in dilute sulphuric acid after drying and steaming. The second method uses sodium chlorate, which is incorporated into the print paste together with ammonia (to maintain alkalinity in the paste) and a steam-activated acid generator such as ammonium thiocyanate; an oxidation catalyst, ammonium metavanadate (NH_4VO_3), is also used.

Vat dyes can be used as illuminant colours in discharge styles where the discharged dyes may be azoic, direct or reactive types. In such cases the quantity of reducing agent has to be increased since it is needed for discharging the other dyes as well as for reducing (but not discharging) the vat dye [13]. A further agent, known as a leucotrope, may also be needed if white discharges are required; leucotropes act as discharge (or stripping) promoters and are described below.

12.9.5 Correction of faults

Levelling and partial stripping may be carried out in a reducing bath using sodium dithionite and sodium hydroxide in combination with a suitable levelling agent such as those described earlier. Greater quantities of levelling agent can be employed to increase the stripping effect. The complexing agents are more effective than are the non-ionic levelling agents. Poly(vinylpyrrolidone), for example, rapidly forms stable leuco dye–polymer complexes in the liquor [28]. Certain quaternary ammonium compounds (such as compounds 12.22 and 12.23) similarly promote stripping by complexing with the leuco form of the dye.

These products are used in conjunction with dithionite and sodium

12.22

12.23

hydroxide to give the most effective stripping action. They are often referred to as leucotropes, although strictly speaking this word is a trade mark; for instance, compound 12.22 is Leucotrope W (BASF).

REFERENCES

1. J A Bone, J Shore and J Park, *J.S.D.C.*, **104** (1988) 12.
2. C L Bird, *The theory and practice of wool dyeing*, 4th Edn (Bradford: SDC, 1972).
3. S, BP 2 147 319 (1985).
4. J Frauenknecht, P C Hextall and A C Welham, *Textilveredlung*, **21** (1986) 331.
5. H Salathe, *Amer. Dyestuff Rep.*, **74** (6) (1985) 20.
6. W Beal, *Aust. Textiles*, **6** (6) (1986) 28; *Dyer*, **172** (2) (1987) 31.
7. CGY, EP 0 089 004 (1983).
8. D M Lewis, *Rev. Prog. Coloration*, **8** (1977) 10.
9. K R Schneider, *Dyer*, **172** (9) (1987) 13.
10. I B Angliss and J Delminico, *J.S.D.C.*, **80** (1964) 543.
11. I B Angliss, P R Brady and J Delminico, *J.S.D.C.*, **84** (1968) 262.
12. W Beal, *J.S.D.C.*, **83** (1967) 3.
13. *Textile printing*, Ed. L W C Miles (Bradford: Dyers' Company Publications Trust, 1981).
14. DuP, Notes on the dyeing of Dacron polyester fibres (1052C 15, D2846).
15. A Würz, *Melliand Textilber.*, **42** (1961) 439.
16. P Liechti, *J.S.D.C.*, **98** (1982) 284.
17. S M Doughty, *Rev. Prog. Coloration*, **16** (1986) 25.
18. A C Welham, *J.S.D.C.*, **102** (1986) 126.
19. F R Hartley, *J.S.D.C.*, **85** (1969) 66.
20. C C Cook, *Rev. Prog. Coloration*, **12** (1982) 73.
21. P A Duffield and K-H Hoppen, *Melliand Textilber.*, **68** (1987) 195.
22. G Meier, *J.S.D.C.*, **95** (1979) 252.
23. IWS dyeing technical bulletin No. 12 (1981).
24. K Schaffner and W Mosimann, *Textilveredlung*, **14** (1979) 12.
25. L Benisek, *J.S.D.C.*, **94** (1978) 101.
26. P Spinnacci and N C Gaccio, Proc. 12th IFATCC Congress, Budapest (June 1981).
27. Acna, BP 2 061 326 (1981).
28. *The dyeing of cellulosic fibres*, Ed. C Preston (Bradford: Dyers' Company Publications Trust, 1986).
29. A M Jowett and A S Cobb, *Rev. Prog. Coloration*, **3** (1972) 81.
30. W Beckmann in *The dyeing of synthetic-polymer and acetate fibres*, Ed. D M Nunn (Bradford: Dyers' Company Publications Trust, 1979) 359.
31. I Holme, *Chimia*, **34** (1980) 110.
32. I Holme, *Rev. Prog. Coloration*, **13** (1983) 10.
33. S Cohen and A S Endler, *Amer. Dyestuff Rep.*, **47** (1958) 325.
34. O Glenz and W Beckmann, *Melliand Textilber.*, **38** (1957) 296, 783, 1152.
35. W Beckmann, *J.S.D.C.*, **77** (1961) 616.
36. W Beckmann, *Z. Ges. Textilind.*, **71** (1969) 603.
37. W Beckmann and O Glenz, *Melliand Textilber.*, **49** (1968) 1463.
38. SDC Basic Dyes on Acrylic Fibres Committee, *J.S.D.C.*, **89** (1973) 292.

39. AATCC Metropolitan Section, *Text. Chem. Colorist*, **8** (1976) 165.
40. C L Zimmermann and A L Cate, *Text. Chem. Colorist*, **4** (6) (1972) 150/37.
41. D Blackburn, *Dyer*, **153** (8) (1975) 418.
42. J Park, *A practical introduction to yarn dyeing* (Bradford: SDC, 1981) 56.
43. J Park, *Dyer*, **167** (1) (1982) 16.
44. W Beckmann and K Jacobs, *Bayer Farben Rev.*, **16** (1969) 1.
45. R Rokohl, *Tenside*, **2** (1965) 76.
46. R Schiffner and B Borrmeister, *Faserforsch. u. Textiltech.*, **16** (1965) 264.
47. M E Dullaghan and A J Ultee, *Text. Research J.*, **43** (1973) 10.
48. AATCC Midwest Section, *Text. Chem. Colorist*, **8** (1976) 22/6.
49. J A Leddy, *Amer. Dyestuff Rep.*, **47** (1960) 272.
50. H P Landerl and D R Baer, *Amer. Dyestuff Rep.*, **54** (1965) 222.
51. H Kellett, *J.S.D.C.*, **84** (1968) 257.
52. W L Anderson, C J Bent and R H Ricketts, *J.S.D.C.*, **88** (1972) 250.
53. DuP, USP 2 955 009 (1960).
54. *Index to textile auxiliaries*, 10th Edn (Bradford: World Textile Publications, 1986).
55. J P Neary and R J Thomas, *Amer. Dyestuff Rep.*, **46** (1957) 625.
56. M Bonche, *Teintex*, **33** (1968) 519, 585.
57. D R Lemin and G G Simpson, *J.S.D.C.*, **87** (1971) 257.
58. U Mayer and M A Reichert, *Amer. Dyestuff Rep.*, **57** (1968) 1104.
59. P Wangelow, R Detscheva and R Betscheva, *Melliand Textilber.*, **64** (1983) 588.
60. SDC Committee on the Dyeing Properties of Direct Cotton Dyes, *J.S.D.C.*, **62** (1946) 280; **64** (1948) 145.
61. W Beal, *J.S.D.C.*, **72** (1966) 146.
62. J Cegarra, *J.S.D.C.*, **73** (1957) 375.
63. J Wegmann, *J.S.D.C.*, **71** (1955) 777.
64. C L Bird, *J.S.D.C.*, **70** (1954) 68.
65. H Braun, *Rev. Prog. Coloration*, **13** (1983) 62.
66. K Masters, *J.S.D.C.*, **104** (1988) 79.
67. S Heimann, *Rev. Prog. Coloration*, **11** (1981) 1.
68. A Murray and K Mortimer, *J.S.D.C.*, **87** (1971) 173.
69. P Dilling, *Text. Chem. Colorist*, **18** (2) (1986) 17.
70. P Dilling, *Text. Chem. Colorist*, **20** (5) (1988) 17.
71. P Dilling, Proc. AATCC Nat. Tech. Conf., (1986) 148.
72. W Biedermann, *J.S.D.C.*, **88** (1972) 329.
73. A N Derbyshire, W P Mills and J Shore, *J.S.D.C.*, **88** (1972) 389.
74. F Schlaeppi, R D Wagner and J L McNeill, *Text. Chem. Colorist*, **14** (1982) 257.
75. P Richter, *Melliand Textilber.*, **64** (1983) 347.
76. K Mortimer, *Aust. Text.*, **6** (6) (1986) 35.
77. A Murray and K Mortimer, *Rev. Prog. Coloration*, **2** (1971) 67.
78. E Waters, *J.S.D.C.*, **66** (1950) 609.
79. E S Lower, *Dyer*, **173** (4) (1988) 29.
80. R W Schumm and C J Cruz, *Text. Chem. Colorist*, **1** (1969) 389.
81. B A Evans and R W Schumm, *Text. Chem. Colorist*, **2** (1970) 262.
82. YCL, BP 1 161 475 (1969).
83. J Carbonell, T Robinson, R Hasler, M Winkler and M Urosevic, *Textil Praxis*, **27** (1972) 711.
84. J Carbonell, R Hasler and T Robinson, *Internat. Textile Bulletin*, (4) (1972) 305.
85. T M Baldwinson, *J.S.D.C.*, **91** (1975) 97.
86. W Griesser, H Jacob and H Tiefenbacher, *Melliand Textilber.*, **68** (1987) 417.
87. P Richter, Proc. AATCC Nat. Tech. Conf., (1983) 255.
88. DuP, Dyes and Chemicals Technical Bulletin No. 5 (June 1949) 82.
89. DuP, USP 2 663 612 (1953).
90. J W Gibson, P Knapp and R Andres, *Amer. Dyestuff Rep.*, **42** (1953) 1.
91. J J Iannarone and W J Wygand, *Amer. Dyestuff Rep.*, **49** (1960) 81.
92. W F Beech, *Fibre-reactive dyes* (London: Logos Press, 1970) chapter 11.

93. J Cegarra and A Riva, *J.S.D.C.*, **103** (1987) 32.
94. J Cegarra and A Riva, *J.S.D.C.*, **104** (1988) 227.
95. W E Wood, *Rev. Prog. Coloration*, **7** (1976) 80.
96. J R Aspland, *Text. Chem. Colorist*, **2** (1970) 229/29.
97. Southern Dyestuff Corpn, BP 720 440 (1952); BP 721 333 (1952).
98. Martin-Marietta Corpn, BP 1 138 325 (1965).
99. C Heid, *Z. Ges. Textilindustrie*, **70** (1968) 626.
100. R Klein, *J.S.D.C.*, **98** (1982) 110.
101. Aldrich Chemical Co., Catalogue Handbook of Fine Chemicals (1986–87).
102. C Senior, Private communication.
103. Olin Corpn, USP 3 944 382 (1974).
104 U Baumgarte, *Rev. Prog. Coloration*, **17** (1987) 29.
105. A Johnson in *The theory of coloration of textiles*, 2nd Edn, Ed. A Johnson (Bradford: SDC, 1989) 477.
106. T T Fritskaya, *Legka prom.*, (2) (1977) 32.
107. Tokai Denka Kogyo, USP 4 244 690 (1978).
108. R J Hannay, *J.S.D.C.*, **78** (1962) 593.
109. W Küppers, *J.S.D.C.*, **78** (1962) 597.
110. F R Alsberg and W F Liquorice, *J.S.D.C.*, **78** (1962) 603.
111. H Zimmerman, *J.S.D.C.*, **78** (1962) 609.
112. M M Cook, *Amer. Dyestuff Rep.*, **68** (3) (1979) 41.
113. G L Medding, *Amer. Dyestuff Rep.*, **69** (9) (1980) 30.
114. L C Ellis, Proc. AATCC Nat. Tech. Conf., (1981) 266.
115. U Baumgarte and U Keuser, *Melliand Textilber.*, **47** (1966) 286.
116. P Senner and J Schirm, *Textil Praxis*, **20** (1965) 1006.
117. BASF, German P 2 164 463 (1971).
118. F R Alsberg, W Clarke and A S Fern, *J.S.D.C.*, **75** (1959) 89.
119. U Baumgarte and H Schlüter, *Text. Chem. Colorist*, **17** (1985) 10.
120. W C Wilcoxson, *Amer. Dyestuff Rep.*, **71** (9) (1982) 34.

CHAPTER 13

Auxiliaries in the coloration of fibre blends

Terence M Baldwinson

13.1 INTRODUCTION

From a purely technical point of view, the best way to dye blends is usually to dye each fibre in a separate bath. For example, with a polyester/cellulosic blend the polyester could be dyed first at high temperature with disperse dyes followed by dyeing of the cellulose in a separate bath with, say, reactive dyes. The chances of one dye–fibre system interfering with the other are thereby minimised and the auxiliaries used are essentially the same as when dyeing the component fibres separately. In present-day practice, however, such separate processing is often unacceptable on cost grounds; wherever possible blends are dyed by 'all-in' single-stage methods. Even where this is not possible dyers often resort to two-stage, but still one-bath, processes. Such dyeing processes then bear many resemblances to the 'combined processes' discussed in section 10.3.6 and, indeed, must be regarded as such since the same types of problem arise. These processes often require the use of essentially incompatible dyes (acid and basic dyes, for instance) in the same bath, which also poses compounded difficulties in reproducibility and quality control. Furthermore, there is the question of compatibility regarding the auxiliaries required for each dye–fibre system in the blend, and it is this aspect that is the primary concern in this chapter. No attempt can be made here to describe dyeing procedures for every available blend, for which there are many sources in the literature [1–3], nor to address the all-important question of dye selection. Rather, emphasis will be given mainly to the use of auxiliaries in the coloration of the principal blends, and particularly to their compatibility towards each other and towards the various dyes in the system. The general principles outlined can often be applied to other blends and dye systems.

13.2 POLYESTER/CELLULOSIC BLENDS

These are by far the most important of the fibre blends and are dyed by both batchwise and continuous methods, as well as being printed. Only disperse dyes are used on polyester, but cellulose is open to coloration by direct, reactive, azoic, sulphur and vat dyes.

No major problems with auxiliaries are posed when using direct dyes. The electrolyte required for the direct dyes (10–15 g/l) is rarely of such a concentration that it affects the dispersion stability of the disperse dyes, although stability problems occasionally arise in short-liquor (package or beam) equipment. Similarly, neither the dispersing agents used for the disperse dyes nor any carriers used normally interfere with the direct dyes, many of which are however adversely affected by the pH generally used for disperse dyes on polyester (pH 4.5–5.5) and the high dyeing temperatures (120–130°C). The general vulnerability of direct dyes to alkaline reducing agents clearly precludes reduction clearing of the dyed polyester. The various aftertreatments for direct dyes can usually be employed, although the effect of certain resin finishes on the fastness of disperse dyes after stenter drying is variable and must be checked for each individual case.

Disperse/reactive systems, on the other hand, pose several problems. Firstly, reactive dyes generally require high concentrations (40–80 g/l) of electrolyte, which interferes with disperse dye stability in certain formulations by suppressing the essential ionising mechanism of the anionic polyelectrolyte dispersing agents through a common-ion effect, thus decreasing the charge on the dispersed particles and promoting agglomeration. The interference is variable, frequently affecting one manufacturer's version of a particular dye more than another's and even varying from batch to batch of a given manufacturer's product, since it is determined by many parameters such as batch quality of the dispersing agents used and the physical form of the dye (not just its particle size and particle size distribution but its crystal form). Manufacturers of both dyes and dispersing agents take considerable trouble to match dispersion agent quality and the crystal form of dyes so as to ensure the production of dyes in a form that offers maximum dispersion stability, in particular attempting to reduce the susceptibility to high concentrations of electrolyte. This problem is less prevalent than it was, although it still cannot be discounted in the dye selection procedure; it may be alleviated by the judicious use of additional levelling/dispersing agents, of which the ethoxylated phosphate type (12.7) described in section 12.6.3 is particularly effective.

The second problem arising in disperse/reactive systems is that of reconciling the different pH requirements of the two dye systems. The most commonly used reactive dyes require alkaline conditions (pH 10–12) for fixation; although some disperse dyes will withstand such alkalinity during the dyeing phase, many require a dyebath pH below 6.0. Nevertheless, practically all disperse dyes will withstand quite severe alkaline conditions once they have been absorbed by the fibre. If a single-stage process is to be used, the pH must be alkaline to ensure fixation of the reactive dyes; there is then no option but to choose disperse dyes stable to alkali. It is more common, however, to choose a two-stage process involving a change of pH. One such process first applies both the reactive and disperse dyes at high temperature and pH 4.5–6.0. It is helpful to add a mild oxidising agent such as sodium m-nitrobenzenesulphonate to inhibit reduction of the azo reactive dyes at high temperature. Salt, if added at this stage, will help exhaustion of the reactive dye but could then exert its maximum potential deleterious effects on the disperse dyes in the dyebath; it is therefore best added later. After exhausting the disperse dyes at high temperature, the bath is cooled to around 80°C. This is really the best point at which to add the salt since the amount of disperse dyes left in the bath is too small to be affected. After the hot-dyeing reactive dyes have been exhausted, alkali (usually sodium carbonate) is added to bring about fixation. As with direct dyes, it is not possible to adopt reduction clearing of the disperse dyes, but some clearing may take place during the alkaline fixation and subsequent soaping to remove unfixed and hydrolysed reactive dyes.

An alternative process essentially uses the reverse procedure, in which either cold- or hot-dyeing reactive dyes are applied first using salt and perhaps sodium m-nitrobenzenesulphonate under appropriate alkaline conditions. The bath is then adjusted to a slightly acidic pH followed by addition of dispersing agent and the disperse dyes, which are then exhausted on to the polyester either at the boil with a carrier or at high temperature. In this method, as the disperse dyes and electrolyte are present together, appropriate precautions should be taken as mentioned above. There are other variants on these procedures, but the general principles as regards the auxiliaries and their effects on the dyes remain essentially the same. These interactive principles also remain the same, at least qualitatively, in continuous dyeing and printing, bearing in mind that any migration inhibitor should be selected with due regard to its compatibility (i.e. non-reactivity) with reactive dyes – an alginate, for example. Recently some reactive dyes that fix under slightly acidic conditions [4] have been introduced; the application conditions required for these dyes are clearly closer to those generally required for disperse dyes, thus simplifying combined application.

It is hardly likely, given the nature of the azoic dyeing process (see section 12.3), that combined application of disperse and azoic dyes would be used, but combinations of disperse and sulphur dyes offer some practical possibilities, particularly for continuous dyeing. Most disperse dyes in the dyebath would not withstand the reducing system required for the sulphur dyes, but once they have been absorbed on to the polyester they are quite resistant. The basic method is to apply the disperse dyes together with dispersed or solubilised sulphur dyes by padding at pH 4.5–5.5 and drying, after which the disperse dyes are thermofixed at 190–210°C; padding with alkaline reducing agent, steaming and reoxidation to fix the sulphur dyes completes the process. There are no conflicting requirements regarding the auxiliaries used, which are the same as those normally employed when applying the dyes separately by continuous methods. An alternative process involves padding with disperse dye, solubilised sulphur dye and the reducing agent thiourea dioxide at pH 5–6 [5], followed by drying and thermofixation to fix both disperse and sulphur dyes; in this case, however, the thiourea dioxide restricts the choice of disperse dyes since some dyes are affected by it. Obviously in both these processes the sulphur dyes are oxidised and soaped as normal without undue effects on the fixed disperse dyes.

Vat and solubilised vat dyes can sometimes be used alone to colour both the polyester and cellulosic components, mainly where pale shades are required. For example, certain vat dyes can be applied as disperse dyes by batchwise dyeing at 130°C, or in a continuous pad–Thermosol method, followed by padding with alkaline reducing agent and steam fixation to effect dyeing of the cellulose. Solubilised vat leuco esters can be applied by padding with sodium nitrite, developing on the jig with sulphuric or formic acid and, after neutralising and soaping, thermofixing to effect penetration of the dyes into the polyester. For a wider shade range, however, the combined application with disperse dyes is much more common. The critical factor is the stability of the disperse dyes to reducing systems, once they are fixed on the polyester. Hence batchwise dyeing can be carried out with both disperse and vat dyes at pH 4.5–6.0 and 130°C, followed by cooling to the appropriate dyeing temperature (20–60°C) and adding sodium hydroxide and dithionite to reduce and apply the vat dyes. This reduction process effectively acts as a reduction clear for the disperse dyes. Similarly the disperse and vat dyes can be applied by padding; after drying and thermofixation, the fabric is padded in the alkaline reducing agent, steamed, reoxidised and soaped to fix the vat dyes. As with sulphur dyes, there is no conflict of requirements between the auxiliaries required for each dyeing stage. The solubilised vat leuco esters can also be applied in combination with disperse dyes [6,7]. These are padded at pH 5–6 with, in addition to the usual migration inhibitor, a mixture of anionic and non-ionic auxiliaries. Subsequent thermofixation for the disperse dyes initiates decomposition of the leuco esters, which are then fully developed by padding in the usual nitrite and acid.

In all the above systems for polyester/cellulosic blends the need for levelling agents is less critical than when dyeing the individual fibres. One of the main reasons is that in the earlier stages of dyeing (and during padding processes) the cellulosic component absorbs an appreciable quantity of disperse dye, which subsequently gradually migrates to the polyester as the final dyeing or fixing temperature is reached. The cellulose is thus, in a sense, acting as a complexing and retarding/levelling agent for the disperse dyes.

13.3 POLYESTER/WOOL BLENDS

This blend is most frequently, if not invariably, dyed nowadays by an all-in process using disperse dyes for the polyester and either milling acid or metal-complex dyes for the wool. Since neutral to slightly acidic conditions are required for both classes of dye there are no conflicting pH requirements. The main conflicting parameter is that of temperature, since the high temperatures (perhaps 130°C) that would allow any disperse dye to be used cause serious degradation of the wool. A compromise is therefore made, using lower temperatures (such as 95–120°C) and selecting disperse dyes that will perform well under these conditions.

The damage sustained by wool is generally within acceptable limits at temperatures up to about 107°C within reasonable dyeing times, but at higher temperatures or over longer times it is necessary to add a wool protection agent. As mentioned in section 12.2.1, these are usually formaldehyde [8] or a formaldehyde precursor such as NN'-dimethylolethyleneurea [9]. For example, the use of 5% o.w.f. formaldehyde (30% solution) at pH 3.5–5.0 gives acceptable wool quality under the following extremes [8,10]:

– 4 hours at 105°C
– 3 hours at 110°C
– 2 hours at 115°C
– 1 hour at 120°C.

The protective mechanism of formaldehyde can be attributed to several competing reactions, as shown in Scheme 13.1 [10,11]. This illustrates the initial thermal activation of functional groups in wool, followed by monofunctional and bifunctional (crosslinking) reactions with formaldehyde. The crosslinking reactions can take place within one polypeptide chain or between different chains. Formaldehyde has been widely used for this purpose since the 1950s. Its only disadvantages from a technical viewpoint are its effect on the hue of some dyes and a degree of embrittlement of the wool. Formaldehyde vapour represents a potential health hazard, however, and restrictions on its use are consequently increasing. As a wool protection agent, it can be readily replaced by a formaldehyde precursor such as NN'-dimethylolethyleneurea (13.1) [10,11], which releases the active species $(CH_2OH)^+$ only at temperatures above 70°C and at a rate that is said to correspond approximately with the rate of hydrolysis of wool. The active species is formed first from one of the methylol groups and then, at higher temperature, from the second. The rate of this decomposition, in relation to a typical dyeing curve, is shown in Figure 13.1 [10,11].

13.1

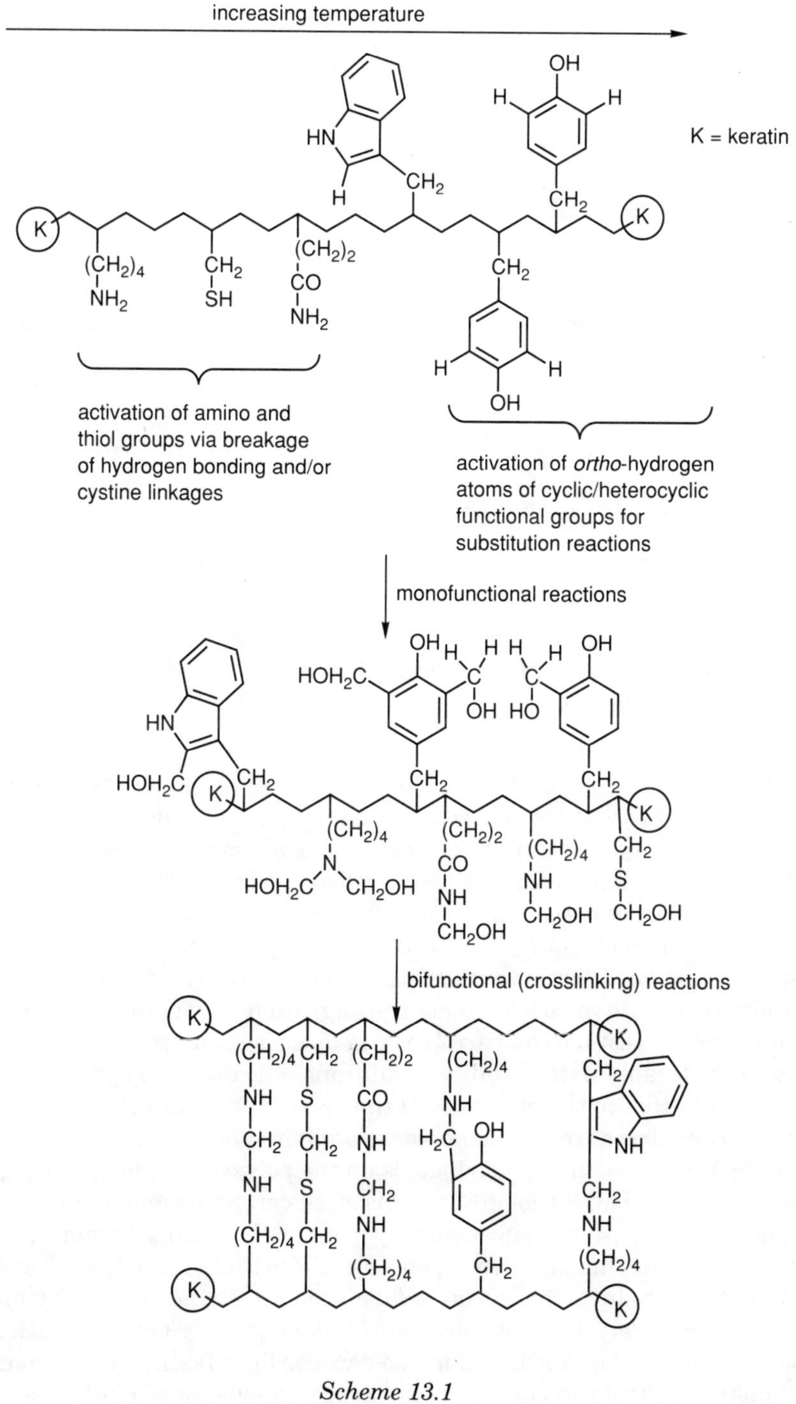
increasing temperature
K = keratin
activation of amino and thiol groups via breakage of hydrogen bonding and/or cystine linkages
activation of *ortho*-hydrogen atoms of cyclic/heterocyclic functional groups for substitution reactions
monofunctional reactions
bifunctional (crosslinking) reactions

Scheme 13.1

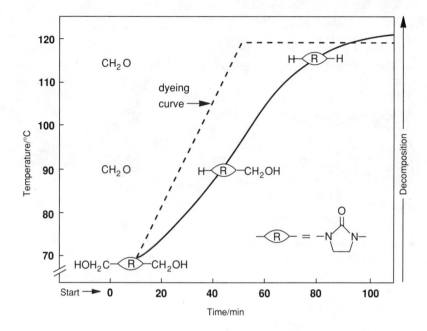

Figure 13.1 – Activation of formaldehyde from NN'-dimethylolethyleneurea as a function of time and temperature

Reactive dyes can also have a protective effect on wool. This has been reviewed by Lewis [12], who has also used the concept to develop colourless protective agents that imitate the behaviour of reactive dyes [13].

Obviously, when dyeing at temperatures below 120°C, the use of a carrier becomes of major importance, particularly when dyeing blends of polyester and wool. Since wool will absorb significant amounts of most disperse dyes, the function of the carrier is not only to increase dye uptake on the polyester but also to increase the migration of disperse dyes from the wool to the polyester. The carrier types discussed in section 12.6.4 vary quite considerably in this ability to minimise the disperse dye staining of wool. In addition to the efficiency of the carrier, its volatility and toxicity must be considered. In open machinery o-phenylphenol carriers have long been the mainstay, giving good yields on the polyester together with good reservation of wool, although light fastness can be seriously impaired if carrier residues are not subsequently completely removed from the substrate. In covered machines, as opposed to those that are completely closed and sealed, products based on either o-phenylphenol or methylnaphthalene are widely used. Methylnaphthalene gives good reservation of wool, but residual quantities can also depress light fastness. Low concentrations (2–3 g/l) of this carrier are generally satisfactory. In fully enclosed machines the toxic and volatile chlorinated benzenes, as well as methyl-naphthalene, can be used. They are particularly efficient in minimising the wool stain and do not affect the light fastness. Methyl salicylate is also an excellent carrier basis for polyester/wool. Other suitable carrier components include biphenyl and methyl cresotinate. Some proprietary carriers are mixtures, designed to give a balance of properties. When dyeing at the higher temperatures, such as 110–120°C, less carrier is needed than at temperatures of, say, 95–110°C.

The other auxiliaries used are essentially the same as when dyeing the separate fibres, although the pH will be set primarily to suit the exhaustion of the particular wool dyes used.

13.4 POLYESTER/TRIACETATE, POLYESTER/NYLON AND TRIACETATE/NYLON BLENDS

All three of these blends are often dyed with disperse dyes only, although where nylon is present the hue and depth may have to be adjusted with milling acid or metal-complex dyes; the current requirement is almost exclusively for solid shades except on items such as fancy socks.

The dyeing process for polyester/triacetate blends, from the point of view of the auxiliaries, is essentially the same as that for the fibres separately, the main requirement being the careful selection of dyes. These blends are almost always dyed at high temperature (115–130°C), although carrier dyeing is also feasible. In either case there is an overall tendency for the triacetate to be dyed preferentially (there are some exceptions) and the main means of solving this problem lies in careful selection of dyes and attention to pre-setting conditions rather than in the use of auxiliaries. Nevertheless, in high-temperature dyeing small quantities of carriers are sometimes added to shift the balance in favour of the polyester. Ester-based carriers, such as methyl salicylate or butyl benzoate, are particularly effective. Phenolic types lower light fastness and are difficult to remove without stripping the triacetate, whereas chlorinated benzenes cause some swelling of the triacetate. Polyester/triacetate blends can also be dyed by a continuous pad–Thermosol technique using a migration inhibitor and a wetting agent. Although the method is hardly ever used commercially, it is said to enable solid effects to be more easily obtained than in batchwise dyeing.

The principle of producing solid shades on polyester/nylon, using disperse dyes only, is essentially the same as for polyester/triacetate. Where acid dyes are used to adjust the colour of the nylon, pH control is obviously necessary to facilitate exhaustion of the acid dyes. If contrast effects are required, as in fancy socks, the polyester may be reserved by dyeing only the nylon with acid or metal-complex dyes and the appropriate auxiliaries. Two-colour contrast effects are usually produced by dyeing first with disperse dyes at high temperature or with carrier at the boil. The stain on the nylon is then stripped either partially with a non-ionic surfactant or destructively with a reducing agent, after which the nylon is then dyed with anionic dyes. Thus there are no conflicting requirements regarding the auxiliaries for the two dye–fibre systems.

Triacetate/nylon blends are treated similarly to polyester/triacetate blends. If problems of solidity arise due to preferential dyeing of the nylon at high temperatures, this can be improved by pretreating the blend with a suitable carrier for triacetate such as diethyl phthalate. The concentration of carrier can sometimes be adjusted to shift the balance of dyeing towards either fibre when carrier dyeing at the boil. If anionic dyes are added for the nylon pH control will be necessary too, but there is no conflict of compatibility between the auxiliaries required for the two dye classes.

13.5 ACETATE/CELLULOSIC BLENDS

These blends are generally dyed with disperse and direct dyes in the same bath. There is no conflict of compatibility between the auxiliaries required for the two dye systems. In some cases it is desired to dye only the acetate and to leave the cellulose reserved; any staining of the cellulose by the disperse dyes is then subsequently removed by clearing. Alkaline reduction with 1 g/l sodium dithionite and 1 g/l di- or tri-sodium orthophosphate is efficacious with most azo dyes, although an oxidation treatment with 1–2 ml/l sodium hypochlorite in a similarly mildly alkaline medium (followed by an antichlor) is often better with anthraquinonoid dyes. Either clearing treatment must be carried out at ambient temperature to avoid decomposition of dye on the acetate. Where mixed azo and anthraquinonoid dyes have been used it may be necessary to use both clearing treatments in sequence, the reduction process being carried out first. Potasssium permanganate, followed by treatment in acidified sodium bisulphite to remove manganese stains, has also been reported as giving a better clear than hypochlorite with some dyes, although it is doubtful if it is used nowadays. The essential mechanisms are azo fission and leuco-anthraquinonoid formation in the reduction process and destruction of the anthraquinonoid residue by oxidative attack. These clearing processes may also be used where necessary as intermediate treatments in the dyeing of high-contrast shades in which the acetate is dyed to a heavy depth. It is easier to obtain clear bright shades on the cellulose in these instances by dyeing the acetate first and then clearing the stain from the cellulose as described above, before applying the direct dyes.

13.6 NYLON/WOOL BLENDS

Like some of the blends described in section 13.4, these blends are also dyed with a single class of dye, either milling acid or metal-complex dyes. Hence there is no real conflict of requirements for the auxiliaries. Ensuring solidity of shade is the most common requirement and calls for very careful dye selection in the first instance; this is not an easy matter and the principles involved have been discussed elsewhere [2,3,14]. Partitioning of the dyes between the two fibres can also be influenced by the use of certain auxiliaries, however, including the syntan blocking agents described in section 10.7.1, a technique that is widely used. Shore [2] has pointed out that the partitioning effects of acid dyes on this blend depend on many factors, including dye structure, applied depth, pH, blend ratio and quality of the component fibres.

The problem arises because, although nylon absorbs acid dyes more readily than does wool, partition is not constant between the two fibres at all depths since the saturation concentration for nylon is less than that for wool. Thus in pale depths both the initial uptake and the ultimate exhaustion are higher on nylon; on the other hand, in heavy depths the initial strike still occurs on nylon but eventually the wool becomes more heavily dyed because it has a much higher saturation uptake. At some intermediate depth, and this varies from dye to dye as well as depending on conditions, there is a point at which both fibres are dyed to the same depth even though the nylon initially dyed more quickly. Consequently, given the widely varying quality of the individual fibres as well as the varying blend composition, it is not surprising that specific conditions cannot be laid down, only guideline starting points for initial experimentation.

The anionic blocking agents can be used to restrain this preferential uptake of dye by the nylon at depths below the critical saturation point. These products, many of which are also used as syntan aftertreating agents, comprise a chemical group of which formulae 10.30–10.34 are typical and which were described in section 10.4.1 (i.e. the condensation products of formaldehyde with phenols or naphthylaminesulphonic acids). Analogous sulphur-containing products, such as those based on thiophenols, are also used. The chemical 'tailoring' of these products to give the required properties is described in Chapter 10. Other anionic agents can also be used, such as alkylbenzenesulphonates, sulphates derived from fatty alcohols and sulphated castor oil, as well as compounds 13.2 and 13.3, which are more commonly used as insectproofing agents for wool.

13.2   13.3

The results vary with the types and concentrations of the dyes and anionic agents in the system but all the agents function by preferential absorption on the nylon, competing for sites with anionic dyes of comparable affinity for the nylon. Products of lower affinity are effective with levelling acid dyes and, for a given concentration, reach an equilibrium uptake that does not vary significantly on further boiling. Conversely, milling acid and 1:2 metal-complex dyes respond to agents of higher affinity. It is interesting that these higher-affinity products still allow levelling acid dyes to migrate, although the partition of the milling and metal-complex dyes remains the same as a result of their intrinsically low migration properties. With both the lower- and higher-affinity products, increasing the concentration of the agent favours lower dye uptake by nylon and greater uptake by wool; indeed the concentration can sometimes be increased to a level where complete reservation of the nylon may occur. Thus there is considerable scope for control of the system. If, as is most usual, solidity of shade is the aim, it clearly does not make sense to use these products above the critical distribution point for the dyes on the two fibres. Conversely, below this point the amount of agent needed tends to increase with decreasing depth of shade.

It is not normally necessary to employ these blocking agents on the few occasions when chrome dyes are used, since these dyes at the heavy depths normally adopted give quite good solidity.

13.7 NYLON/CELLULOSIC BLENDS
There are various possibilities regarding the choice of dye types for these blends [2]:
(a) 1:2 metal-complex/direct dyes
(b) 1:2 metal-complex/reactive dyes
(c) disperse/direct dyes
(d) direct dyes alone to give either solid or reserve effects
(e) vat dyes alone
(f) reactive dyes alone
(g) sulphur dyes either alone or with acid or metal-complex dyes.

Apart from fastness considerations, the choice of dye system will be very much influenced by blend construction. Choices (a) and (b) are of the greatest importance where both fibres play a significant part in the appearance of the fabric. Choice (c) is limited by the fastness properties of the dyes, especially the disperse dyes. The remaining methods are mainly used where the nylon is a minor component, that is, where only the cellulosic fibre plays a significant part in the surface appearance of the blended fabric, the nylon occupying the interior or the reverse side of the construction.

When using 1:2 metal-complex or milling acid dyes in combination with direct dyes there is no significant conflict regarding the use of auxiliaries, but it is often useful to include a syntan to inhibit staining of nylon by the direct dyes. Thus the bath is set at 40°C with the acid dyes (at the appropriate pH for their exhaustion, i.e. pH 7–8 for pale depths and pH 5–6 for medium–heavy depths), the minimum amount of syntan (0.5–2% o.w.f. depending on the direct dyes and the depth) and a levelling agent if necessary. The direct dyes are added when the temperature reaches about 60°C; the dyebath is then raised to the boil and appropriate aliquots of salt are added to exhaust the direct dyes. If a cationic-based levelling agent is used care should be taken to ensure that sufficient of an effective non-ionic component or other anti-precipitant (see section 13.8) is also added to guard against precipitation with the anionic dyes.

A similar technique can be used for blends of polyurethane and cellulosic fibres; for minimum staining of the polyurethane by the direct dyes a pH of 8–8.5 may be required.

When using 1:2 metal-complex or milling acid dyes with reactive dyes it is best to apply the reactive dyes first followed by the acid dyes, in which case the choice of auxiliaries follows the traditional lines for each dye class. A one-bath/two-stage method can be used, however, in which the dyes are first applied under alkaline conditions to fix the reactive dyes and acid is then added to give pH 7 before raising to the boil to dye the nylon component with the acid dyes. During washing-off the pH should be kept slightly alkaline to minimise uptake of hydrolysed reactive dye by the nylon.

The use of disperse and direct dyes in the same bath presents no difficulties with the auxiliaries. Again a syntan can be used to inhibit staining of the nylon by the direct dyes.

Direct dyes alone can be used to produce reserve effects by dyeing at 80–90°C in the presence of a syntan to inhibit the dyeing of the nylon, using electrolyte in the usual way to exhaust the direct dyes on to the cellulose. Solid effects can also be produced by careful selection of appropriate dyes; slightly acidic conditions (for example, 1% o.w.f. sodium dihydrogen phosphate) are required to give exhaustion on to the nylon, and solidity can be further controlled by restricting the amount of salt added.

Vat dyes, when used alone to produce solid shades, are best applied by the pigmentation method at ambient temperature. Vatting is then carried out with alkaline reducing agent and the temperature is raised to the optimum level, this being the most critical factor for solidity [2].

Despite many difficulties in regard to dye–fibre selectivity [2], reactive dyes can be applied alone to give solid effects, using a two- or three-stage (one-bath) procedure. In the former case dyes having good neutral-dyeing properties are applied from neutral electrolyte solution, followed by addition of alkali to bring about fixation, this differing little from the traditional cellulose dyeing process. The three-stage process is used for those dyes that do not have good neutral-dyeing properties. These are first applied under slightly acidic conditions; electrolyte is then added to promote exhaustion on to the cellulose, and lastly alkali is added to effect fixation. Solidity is dependent on depth, pH, temperature and electrolyte concentration [2]. As with acid dyes on nylon/wool blends, the nylon tends to be dyed preferentially in paler depths and there is an equilibrium/saturation point beyond which the distribution is towards the cellulose.

Carefully selected sulphur dyes can be used to produce solid depths [2]. As with vat dyes temperature is a critical factor, and higher temperatures favour greater uptake by nylon. In some cases virtual reservation of the cellulose allows subsequent overdyeing with dyes of low affinity for nylon. Precise temperature control within the range 50–70°C generally favours solidity. Conversely lower temperatures (say 45–55°C) and appropriate selection of dyes can be used to reserve the nylon, which may subsequently be dyed with appropriate acid dyes in a separate bath. In none of these cases is there any conflict in the use of auxiliaries, which are substantially the same as for 100% cellulose.

13.8 ACRYLIC/WOOL AND ACRYLIC/CELLULOSIC BLENDS

These two blends present a common problem, as the acrylic fibre is invariably dyed with cationic dyes and the natural fibres with anionic dyes. There is thus a high tendency for the dyes to interact. This often leads to precipitation of the complex, but even where this does not occur the interaction seriously interferes with reproducibility and causes increased cross-staining. The best and most reliable method of dealing with these blends is therefore to dye each of the fibre components separately and in some cases, as with vat and reactive dyes, this is the only viable method. When dyeing the components separately, the auxiliaries used are the same as for the appropriate dyes on their respective fibres and will not be considered further here. It has, however, been possible to develop viable combined methods of applying basic/acid and basic/direct combinations, and these are of particular interest since they involve the use of auxiliaries, generally termed anti-precipitants, to overcome the problems of dye interaction.

Many proprietary products are marketed specifically as anti-precipitants for use in these processes, but some levelling agents used for acid dyes on wool will also function effectively in this role, either alone or with an addition of an appropriate surfactant. Non-ionic agents are by far the most common anti-precipitants, and their general solubilising power is well known. Judicious use of other types is also practicable, but in many systems of interacting anionic and cationic surfactants an excess of one or other may have a solubilising effect on the complex primarily by a disaggregating mechanism. Particularly useful in this respect are the hybrid surfactants generally characterised as weakly anionic or weakly cationic polyethoxylates, since the ethoxylate chain both advantageously inhibits ionisation (without completely neutralising it) and acts as a stabilising/solubilising force on both the cationic and anionic entities in the system. Pratt [15] has described the main chemical types, which are listed in Table 13.1.

TABLE 13.1

Chemical types of anti-precipitant

Type	Composition	Number of oxyethylene units per molecule
Non-ionic	Non-ionic fatty alcohol or alkylphenol ethoxylates	20 or more
Weakly cationic	Coco (tallow, oleyl or soya) fatty amine ethoxylates	20 or more
Non-ionic	Copolymers of ethylene oxide and propylene oxide	40 or more
Weakly anionic	Fatty alcohol or alkylphenol oxyethylene phosphate esters	4–12
Weakly anionic	Fatty alcohol or alkylphenol oxyethylene sulphate esters	3 or more
Weakly anionic	Alkali metal (amine or alkanolamine) salt of an alcohol or alkylphenol ethoxylated acetate (e.g. carboxymethylates)	5 or more
Cationic/amphoteric	Alkyl chloride or dialkyl sulphate salt of an *NN'*-ethoxylated quaternary amine (e.g. quaternaries of ethoxylated fatty amines with ethoxylated fatty amine sulphates and phosphate esters)	15 or more

A wide range of non-ionic surfactants, with 20 or more oxyethylene units per molecule, give varying degrees of efficacy; suitable hydrophobes include fatty alcohols, alkylphenols, alkylamines and alkanolamines as well as block copolymers of ethylene oxide with propylene oxide. The weakly anionic oxyethylene phosphates and sulphates, containing fewer (perhaps 9) oxyethylene units per molecule than the non-ionic types, are widely used. Mixtures often function better than single products, and this is why many proprietary products are carefully but empirically balanced mixtures. For example, in dye liquors containing significant proportions of cationic and anionic dyes, purely non-ionic agents are often found to be inadequate in effecting complete solubilisation of the complex. On the other hand, if an anionic surfactant is added, this may disrupt the dye–dye complex by preferentially complexing with the basic dye, and addition of a non-ionic agent will then effectively solubilise this. Pratt [15] has pointed out that in this type of system strongly anionic surfactants function effectively, presumably because high anionicity is necessary to dissociate the dye–dye complex. Thus many proprietary products are mixtures of a strongly anionic surfactant with an excess of non-ionic agent. Other mixtures, which are said to be more reliable and of wider use, include (a) mixed ethoxylated fatty amines and (b) combinations of sulphated or phosphated ethoxylates with ethoxylated fatty amines. These mixtures are particularly useful for minimising the cross-staining of fibres, a property that can be further improved, at additional expense, by adding an amphoteric product such as a quaternised fatty amine ethoxylate.

Used in appropriate quantities anti-precipitants generally inhibit cross-staining of fibres, but excessive amounts can increase it by promoting migration between the different fibre types, thus resulting in lower fastness. In particular, care should be taken to rinse off all traces of anti-precipitant thoroughly so as to avoid any potential problems in subsequent processes – for example, residual anti-precipitants can interfere with the absorption of syntan agents by nylon.

It is now opportune to return to the dyeing of acrylic/wool blends. Whilst acid dyes do not tend to stain acrylic fibres, basic dyes are quite readily absorbed by wool, particularly in the earlier stages of dyeing, but have a tendency to migrate to the acrylic fibres as dyeing proceeds. This migration, and hence the final distribution of the basic dyes between the fibres, is influenced by many factors [16], including the presence of surfactants (anti-precipitants and levelling or retarding agents), electrolyte, time, temperature and pH. Since wool initially absorbs a significant proportion of the basic dye and then slowly releases it to the acrylic fibre, the wool is in effect acting as a retarding agent. It is therefore often unnecessary to use the traditional cationic retarder for basic dyes, which in any case would add complications through its potential to interact with the anionic dyes and any anionic levelling agent used for the wool dyes. Consequently, if it is necessary to use a levelling agent for the basic dyes, this is one instance where the anionic type (see section 12.4) has some advantages. If such a retarder is indeed used, the extent to which it will also act as a levelling agent for the wool dyes should be considered, in order to keep additions to a minimum. Conversely, if an anionic agent is being employed as a levelling agent for the wool dyes, it may be possible to extend its use to that of an anti-precipitant by adding an appropriate non-ionic or an ethoxylated ester (sulphate or phosphate) as described above. Obviously quantities will have to be adjusted according to the results of careful laboratory trials for each combination of dyes. A slightly acidic pH generally suits both the basic and the acid dyes.

It is also possible to use 1:1 metal-complex dyes for the wool. These require a pH of 2–2.5, which is obtained with sulphuric acid. In fact, the zwitterionic character of these dyes at such pH values renders them more compatible than the neutral-dyeing acid dyes with basic dyes [2], but an anti-precipitant will still be required.

The above principles also apply when using basic/reactive dye systems on acrylic/wool and also basic dyes on acrylic/nylon blends. In the former case the influence of the amphoteric levelling agents commonly adopted with reactive wool dyes should be carefully considered; at appropriate concentrations, either alone or supported by other surfactants, they may also act as effective anti-precipitants.

A useful critical review of the dyeing of acrylic/cellulose blends has recently been published [17]. They can be dyed with combinations of basic and direct dyes using an effective anti-precipitant in addition to electrolyte and reagents to give the slightly acidic pH required for basic dyes (the direct dyes need to be chosen for their suitability at this pH). This method, however, is best reserved for pale–medium shades; better reliability is obtained by using two-stage or even two-bath methods for medium–heavy shades. In addition it is possible to obtain reserve effects; for example, acrylic or modacrylic fibres can be reserved by pretreating with a syntan at 60–70°C followed by dyeing of the cellulose at 70°C and pH 7–8 with direct dyes. Alternatively the blend can be dyed with basic dyes and the stain subsequently removed from the cellulose by treatment with alkaline dithionite and non-ionic surfactant at 60°C [2].

REFERENCES

1. R C Cheetham, *Dyeing fibre blends* (London: Van Nostrand, 1966).
2. J Shore in *The dyeing of synthetic-polymer and acetate fibres*, Ed. D M Nunn (Bradford: Dyers' Company Publications Trust, 1979).
3. *The dyeing of cellulosic fibres*, Ed. C Preston (Bradford: Dyers' Company Publications Trust, 1986).
4. N Morimura and M Ojima, *Amer. Dyestuff Rep.*, **74** (1985) 28.
5. JR, BP 1 321 453 (1973).
6. H Schlüter, *Textil Praxis*, **26** (1971) 684.
7. R T Norris and A Ward, *J.S.D.C.*, **89** (1973) 197.
8. A Würtz, *Melliand Textilber.*, **42** (1961) 439.
9. P Liechti, *J.S.D.C.*, **98** (1982) 284.
10. S M Doughty, *Rev. Prog. Coloration*, **16** (1986) 25.

11.   G Römer, H U Berendt, J B Feron, H Fierz and A Lauton, *Textilveredlung*, **15** (1980) 465.
12.   D M Lewis, *Rev. Prog. Coloration*, **19** (1989) 49.
13.   D M Lewis and Wool Development International, EP Application 85 306 256 000 (1985).
14.   J Park, *Dyer*, **173** (3) (1988) 27.
15.   H D Pratt, *Amer. Dyestuff Rep.*, **68** (9) (1979) 39.
16.   H Flosbach, W Walter and H B Müller, *Textilveredlung*, **11** (1976) 254.
17.   A Laepple and R Jenny, *Textilveredlung*, **23** (1988) 248.

Auxiliaries index

The numbers in square brackets are the structure numbers as used in the text.

Subject index

This index refers to both Volumes 1 and 2 of this book.

rate of dyeing 110
replacement of halogen in halogeno-
hydroxyazo chromogens 219
structure and aggregation 113
structure and substantivity 95, 122
structure and wet fastness on cellulosic
fibres 136
time of 'half-dyeing' on viscose yarn 110
uses 20
Disazo dyes, from aminonaphtholsulphonic
acids 159
Disazo pigments, from benzidine
derivatives 46, 191
Disperse dyes
aftertreatments for use on ester fibres
451
agglomeration 90
alkylation and substantivity 108
aqueous solubility 91, 107
aqueous solubility of mixtures 108
build-up in mixtures on cellulose acetate
108
chemical classes 21
coplanarity and substantivity 106
crystal form 90
definition 20
degree of penetration into polyester
fibres 119
diffusion coefficient in cellulose acetate
115
diffusion coefficient in nylon 115
diffusion coefficient in polyester 115, 120
dispersion stability 90, 427
dyeing rate constant on nylon 118
fibre saturation 90, 106, 116, 128
for automotive use 453
for ester fibres 2, 105, 242
formation of mixed crystals 108
formulation 90, 428
from anthraquinones 241, 243
from NN-dialkylamines 156, 180
from heterocyclic anthraquinones 244
from heterocyclic coupling components
179
from heterocyclic diazo components 181
gas-fume fading 243, 451
in dyeing of fibre blends 569, 572, 575
in transfer printing of polyester 139
Ionamine range of ω-methane-
sulphonates 178
light fastness on hydrophobic fibres 133
melting-point curves of mixtures 108
particle size 89, 427
partition coefficient between cellulose
acetate and ethanol 128

partition coefficient between cellulose
acetate and water 106
phototropism 160
saturated solution 90
saturation solubility in cellulose acetate
107, 116
sensitivity to reduction at high pH and
temperature 533
solubility in mixtures on cellulose
acetate 108
solubility in organic solvents 107
solubility parameter and substantivity
for polyester 109
structure and diffusion in ester fibres
114, 138, 179
structure and heat fastness on polyester
139, 242
structure and levelling properties on
polyester 130
structure and light fastness on ester
fibres 133, 180
structure and light fastness on nylon
135
structure and rate of dyeing 116
structure and sublimation in transfer
printing 139
structure and vapour pressure 138
structure and wet fastness on
hydrophobic fibres 136
thermal decomposition on hydrophobic
fibres 138
time of 'half-dyeing' on cellulose acetate
116
uses 21
with hydrolysable ester groups 182
Dispersing agents
cloud point 536
enol–formaldehyde condensate type
424
for disperse dye formulation 533
for naphtholate solutions in azoic dyeing
520
in solutions of diazo components 522
lignosulphonate type 425
polyelectrolyte types 424, 426
reducing effect of lignosulphonates on
disperse dyes 534
uses 423
Dyeing auxiliaries
classification 375, 398
definition 375
primary functions 374
uses 373
Dyes
aggregation 76, 78